PROGRESS IN CLINICAL AND BIOLOGICAL RESEARCH

RECENT TITLES

Please contact the publisher for information about previous titles in this series.

PROGRESS IN DEVELOPMENTAL BIOLOGY
Part B

ME: International Society of Developmental Biologists. International Congress (10th : 1985 : Los Angeles, Calif.)

PROGRESS IN DEVELOPMENTAL BIOLOGY
Part B

Proceedings of the Tenth International Congress of the International Society of Developmental Biologists, held in Los Angeles, CA, August 4–9, 1985

Editor

Harold C. Slavkin
Laboratory for Developmental Biology
School of Dentistry
University of Southern California
Los Angeles, California

ALAN R. LISS, INC. • NEW YORK

Address all Inquiries to the Publisher
Alan R. Liss, Inc., 41 East 11th Street, New York, NY 10003

Copyright © 1986 Alan R. Liss, Inc.

Printed in the United States of America

Library of Congress Cataloging-in-Publication Data

International Society of Developmental Biologists.

    International Congress (10th : 1985 : Los Angeles, Calif.)
    Progress in developmental biology.

    (Progress in clinical and biological research ; 217B)
    Includes index.
    1. Developmental biology—Congresses. I. Slavkin, Harold C.   II. Title.   III. Series.
QH491.I48   1985a   591.3   86-7485
ISBN 0-8451-0193-5 (v. 2)
ISBN 0-8451-5067-7 (set)

Contents

OOPLASMIC DETERMINANTS

EPITHELIAL-MESENCHYMAL INTERACTIONS

Contributors

Shonan Amemiya, Misaki Marine Biological Station, University of Tokyo, Tokyo, Japan [187]

Fred Anderson, School of Dental Medicine, Washington University, St. Louis, MO [409]

Ann Andrew, Department of Anatomy, Medical School, University of the Witwatersrand, Johannesburg, South Africa [441]

Katsuhiko Arai, Department of Tissue Physiology, Medical Research Institute, Tokyo Medical and Dental Institute, Tokyo, Japan [381]

Margaret T. Armstrong, Department of Zoology, University of California, Davis, CA [177]

Peter B. Armstrong, Department of Zoology, University of California, Davis, CA [177]

S. Ashrafi, Department of Histology, College of Dentistry, University of Illinois at Chicago, Chicago, IL [215]

Christiane Ayer-Le Lievre, Institut d'Embryologie du CNRS et du Collège de France, Nogent-sur-Marne, France; present address: Department of Histology, Karolinska Institute, Stockholm, Sweden [255]

William R. Bates, Center for Developmental Biology and Department of Zoology, University of Texas, Austin, TX [341]

Ennio Becchetti, Institute of Histology and General Embryology, University of Ferrara, Ferrara, Italy [385]

Spencer J. Berry, Department of Biology, Wesleyan University, Middletown, CT [99]

M.K. Bhondeley, Neuroanatomy Laboratory, Department of Anatomy, All-India Institute of Medical Sciences, New Delhi, India [141]

Veena Bijlani, Neuroanatomy Laboratory, Department of Anatomy, All-India Institute of Medical Sciences, New Delhi, India [141,149]

A. Blankenau, Department of Biology, Tulane University, New Orleans, LA [133]

Jacqueline L. Brailey, Department of Anatomy, College of Medicine, University of Arizona, Tucson, AZ [207]

Connie S. Bricker, Department of Zoology, University of Vermont, Burlington, VT [325]

Jonathan A. Brier, Department of Anatomy, New York Medical College, Valhalla, NY [433]

Marianne Bronner-Fraser, Developmental Biology Center, University of California, Irvine, CA [229]

Marcello G. Cacace, Institute of Protein Biochemistry and Enzymology, National Council of Research, Naples, Italy [79]

The number in brackets is the opening page number of the contributor's article.

W. Zacheus Cande, Department of Botany, University of California, Berkeley, CA **[345]**

Arnold I. Caplan, Biology Department, Case Western Reserve University, Cleveland, OH **[307]**

Paolo Carinci, Institute of Histology and General Embryology, University of Ferrara, Ferrara, Italy **[385]**

Gianna Casazza, Zoological Station, Naples, Italy **[57]**

Qin-Xue Chen, Institute of Developmental Biology, Academia Sinica, Beijing, China **[47]**

Gary Ciment, Department of Biology, University of Oregon, Eugene, OR **[259]**

Kees de Jong, Zoological Laboratory and Department of Molecular Cell Biology, University of Utrecht, Utrecht, The Netherlands **[353]**

Rosaria De Santis, Zoological Station, Naples, Italy **[57]**

M. Rene Dohmen, Zoological Laboratory, University of Utrecht, Utrecht, The Netherlands **[353]**

Takeshi Doi, Department of Regulation Biology, Saitama University, Urawa, Japan **[211]**

B. Downing, Department of Obstetrics and Gynaecology, Monash University, Queen Victoria Medical Centre, Melbourne, Victoria, Australia **[289]**

Jean-Loup Duband, Institut d'Embryologie du CNRS et du Collège de France, Nogent-sur-Marne, France **[155]**

D. Eisenmann, Department of Histology, College of Dentistry, University of Illinois at Chicago, Chicago, IL **[215]**

Hans H. Epperlein, Anatomisches Institut, Universität Freiburg, Freiburg, Federal Republic of Germany **[191]**

Carol A. Erickson, Department of Zoology, University of California, Davis, CA **[225]**

Rita Evangelisti, Institute of Histology and General Embryology, University of Ferrara, Ferrara, Italy **[385]**

C. Fiori, Biomedical Engineering and Instrumentation Branch, National Institutes of Health, Bethesda, MD **[215]**

Joanna Floros, Department of Pediatrics, Harvard Medical School, Boston, MA **[333]**

Scott E. Fraser, Developmental Biology Center and Department of Physiology and Biophysics, University of California, Irvine, CA **[113]**

Dorothy A. Frenz, Department of Anatomy, New York Medical College, Valhalla, NY **[199]**

Hajime Fujisawa, Department of Anatomy, Kyoto Prefectural University of Medicine, Kyoto, Japan **[109]**

Jelena Gavrilovic, Department of Cell Physiology, Strangeways Research Laboratory, Cambridge, England **[203]**

Kurt R. Gehlsen, Department of Anatomy, College of Medicine, University of Arizona, Tucson, AZ **[207]**

John C. Gerhart, Department of Molecular Biology and Group in Biophysics, University of California, Berkeley, CA **[349]**

Dorothy A. Gibralter, Department of Biochemistry, State University of New York Upstate Medical Center, Syracuse, NY **[43]**

Bengt Glimelius, Department of Oncology, Akademiska Sjukhuset, Uppsala, Sweden **[259]**

Suresh C. Goel, Department of Zoology, University of Poona, Poona, India **[301]**

Robert M. Greene, Daniel Baugh Institute, Thomas Jefferson University, Philadelphia, PA **[319]**

Karin A. Grimnes, Department of Zoology, University of Vermont, Burlington, VT **[325]**

Brian K. Hall, Department of Biology, Dalhousie University, Halifax, Nova Scotia, Canada **[263]**

G.M. Happ, Department of Zoology, University of Vermont, Burlington, VT **[325]**

Fernand Harrisson, Department of Anatomy and Embryology, State University Center of Antwerp, Antwerpen, Belgium **[377]**

Ryu-ichiro Hata, Department of Tissue Physiology, Medical Research Institute, Tokyo Medical and Dental University, Tokyo, Japan **[381]**

Kohei Hatta, Department of Biophysics, Faculty of Science, Kyoto University, Kyoto, Japan **[17]**

Mary J.C. Hendrix, Department of Anatomy, College of Medicine, University of Arizona, Tucson, AZ **[207]**

Akiya Hino, Department of Biochemistry, University of Washington, Seattle, WA; present address: Department of Biology, Nagoya University, Nagoya, Japan **[69]**

Jill G. Hobbs, Department of Physiology and Pharmacology, University of Queensland, Brisbane, Australia **[103]**

Thomas G. Honegger, Zoological Institute, University of Zürich, Zürich, Switzerland **[85]**

Marthe J. Howard, Division of Pharmacology, University of California, San Diego, La Jolla, CA **[267]**

C.F. Ide, Department of Biology, Tulane University, New Orleans, LA **[133]**

Y. Inoue, Department of Anatomy, Hokkaido University, Sapporo, Japan **[137]**

Olena Jacenko, Department of Biology, University of Pennsylvania, Philadelphia, PA **[401]**

Laurinda A. Jaffe, Department of Physiology, University of Connecticut Health Center, Farmington, CT **[75]**

Jutta Janeczek, Institut für Molekularbiologie und Biochemie, Freie Universität Berlin, Berlin, Federal Republic of Germany **[357]**

Bruce M. Jarnot, Department of Biology, Wesleyan University, Middletown, CT **[99]**

William R. Jeffery, Center for Developmental Biology and Department of Zoology, University of Texas, Austin, TX **[341]**

Karen L. Jensen, Department of Biology, University of Iowa, Iowa City, IA **[429]**

Susan M. Jerian, Department of Biology, Occidental College, Los Angeles, CA **[219]**

Howard W. Jones, Jr., Institute for Reproductive Medicine, Department of Obstetrics and Gynecology, Eastern Virginia Medical School, Norfolk, VA **[275]**

Raymond T. Kado, Laboratoire de Neurobiologie Cellulaire, CNRS, Gif-sur-Yvette, France **[75]**

Klaus Kalthoff, Center for Developmental Biology, Department of Zoology, University of Texas at Austin, Austin, TX **[365]**

Haruo Kanatani*, National Institute for Basic Biology, Okazaki, Japan, *(deceased) **[95]**

Robert M. Kay, Genetics Institute, Cambridge, MA **[333]**

Peter L. Kaye, Department of Physiology and Pharmacology, University of Queensland, Brisbane, Australia **[103]**

Hironori Kitamura, Department of Oral Histology, Kanagawa Dental College, Kanagawa, Japan **[329]**

Douglas Kline, Department of Physiology, University of Connecticut Health Center, Farmington, CT **[75]**

Samuel S. Koide, Population Council, New York, NY and Marine Biological Laboratory, Woods Hole, MA **[95]**

Hiroshi Konomi, Department of Biochemistry, University of Medicine and Dentistry of New Jersey–Rutgers Medical School, Piscataway, NJ **[169]**

Beverley Kramer, Department of General Anatomy, School of Dentistry, University of the Witwatersrand, Johannesburg, South Africa **[441]**

Danuta M. Krotoski, Developmental Biology Center, University of California, Irvine, CA **[229]**

Edward L. Krug, Department of Anatomy and Cell Biology, Medical College of Wisconsin, Milwaukee, WI **[195]**

Monique LaCorbiere, The Salk Institute for Biological Studies, San Diego, CA **[3]**

Robert M. Langille, Department of Biology, Dalhousie University, Halifax, Nova Scotia, Canada **[263]**

R. Leapman, Biomedical Engineering and Instrumentation Branch, National Institutes of Health, Bethesda, MD **[215]**

Nicole Le Douarin, Institut d'Embryologie du CNRS et du Collège de France, Nogent-sur-Marne, France **[255]**

J. Leeton, Department of Obstetrics and Gynaecology, Monash University, Queen Victoria Medical Centre, Melbourne, Victoria, Australia **[289]**

Jedd F. Levine, Department of Medicine, Stanford University School of Medicine, Stanford, CA **[417]**

Marya B. Lieberman, Department of Zoology, University of California, Berkeley, CA **[345]**

Hardy Limeback, Faculty of Dentistry, University of Toronto, Toronto, Canada **[405]**

Diana Card Linden, Department of Biology, Occidental College, Los Angeles, CA **[219]**

Wilbert A.M. Linnemans, Department of Molecular Cell Biology, University of Utrecht, Utrecht, The Netherlands **[353]**

Charles D. Little, Cell and Molecular Biology Program and Department of Anatomy, University of Virginia, Charlottesville, VA **[173]**

Martha R. Lloyd, Daniel Baugh Institute, Thomas Jefferson University, Philadelphia, PA **[319]**

Jan Löfberg, Department of Zoology, Uppsala University, Uppsala, Sweden **[191]**

Guillermina Lozano, Department of Biochemistry, University of Medicine and Dentistry of New Jersey–Rutgers Medical School, Piscataway, NJ [397]

Mary MacKinnon, Faculty of Dentistry, University of Toronto, Toronto, Canada [405]

Max Maizels, Division of Urology, Children's Memorial Hospital, Chicago, IL [445]

Roger R. Markwald, Department of Anatomy and Cell Biology, Medical College of Wisconsin, Milwaukee, WI [195]

Michael F. Marusich, Department of Biology, University of Oregon, Eugene, OR [249]

Kohji A. Matsui, Department of Anatomy, Hiroshima University School of Medicine, Hiroshima, Japan [145]

Raj D. Mehra, Neuroanatomy Laboratory, Department of Anatomy, All-India Institute of Medical Sciences, New Delhi, India [141,149]

K. Mikoshiba, Division of Regulation of Macromolecular Function, Institute for Protein Research, Osaka University, Osaka, Japan [137]

Nadine C. Milos, Department of Anatomy, University of Alberta, Edmonton, Alberta, Canada [239]

Alberto Monroy, Zoological Station, Naples, Italy [57]

J. Morrow, Department of Biology, Tulane University, New Orleans, LA [133]

A.A. Moscona, Department of Molecular Genetics and Cell Biology, University of Chicago, Chicago, IL [29]

Gillian Murphy, Department of Cell Physiology, Strangeways Research Laboratory, Cambridge, England [203]

Yutaka Nagai, Department of Tissue Physiology, Medical Research Institute, Tokyo Medical and Dental University, Tokyo, Japan [381]

Harukazu Nakamura, Department of Anatomy, Hiroshima University School of Medicine, Hiroshima, Japan [145, 255, 437]

Diane M. Nelson, Department of Biology, University of Oregon, Eugene, OR [259]

Stuart A. Newman, Department of Anatomy, New York Medical College, Valhalla, NY [199]

Yoshifumi Ninomiya, Department of Biochemistry, University of Medicine and Dentistry of New Jersey–Rutgers Medical School, Piscataway, NJ [169,397]

Sumio Nishikawa, Department of Oral Histology, Kanagawa Dental College, Kanagawa, Japan [329]

Y. Nishimura, Department of Anatomy, School of Medicine, Keio University, Tokyo, Japan [137]

T. Nomura, Central Institute for Experimental Animals, Kanagawa, Japan [137]

Akinao Nose, Department of Biophysics, Faculty of Science, Kyoto University, Kyoto, Japan [17]

Roy C. Ogle, Cell and Molecular Biology Program and Department of Anatomy, University of Virginia, Charlottesville, VA [173]

H. Okano, Division of Regulation of Macromolecular Function, Institute for Protein Research, Osaka University, Osaka, Japan [137]

Bjorn R. Olsen, Department of Biochemistry, University of Medicine and Dentistry of New Jersey–Rutgers Medical School, Piscataway, NJ **[169,397]**

Nancy A. O'Rourke, Developmental Biology Center and Department of Physiology and Biophysics, University of California, Irvine, CA **[113]**

Philip Osdoby, School of Dental Medicine, Washington University, St. Louis, MO **[409]**

Merry Jo Oursler, School of Dental Medicine, Washington University, St. Louis, MO **[409]**

Amedeo Pagliarini, Institute of Histology and General Embryology, University of Ferrara, Ferrara, Italy **[385]**

Sanjiv R. Patel, Department of Cell Biology and Anatomy, The Johns Hopkins University School of Medicine, Baltimore, MD **[243]**

Douglas F. Paulsen, Morehouse School of Medicine, Atlanta, GA **[199]**

Lucia B. Pemble, Department of Physiology and Pharmacology, University of Queensland, Brisbane, Australia **[103]**

Roberto Perris, Department of Zoology, Uppsala University, Uppsala, Sweden **[191]**

Roger G. Phillips, Center for Developmental Biology, Department of Zoology, University of Texas at Austin, Austin, TX **[365]**

Maria Rosaria Pinto, CNR Institute of Molecular Embryology, Naples, Italy **[57]**

Dominique M. Piguet, Cell and Molecular Biology Program and Department of Anatomy, University of Virginia, Charlottesville, VA **[173]**

Thomas J. Poole, Department of Anatomy and Cell Biology, State University of New York Upstate Medical Center, Syracuse, NY **[235]**

Martin Post, Department of Pediatrics, Harvard Medical School, Boston, MA **[333]**

Keyvan Pourmehr, Department of Biology, University of Oregon, Eugene, OR **[249]**

B.B. Rawdon, Department of General Anatomy, School of Dentistry, University of the Witwatersrand, Johannesburg, South Africa **[441]**

Abdul Razak-Datu, Department of Anatomy, Hiroshima University School of Medicine, Hiroshima, Japan **[437]**

Rebecca S. Reiter, Department of Biology, University of Iowa, Iowa City, IA **[429]**

Sylvie Rocher, Institut d'Embryologie du CNRS et du Collège de France, Nogent-sur-Marne, France **[155]**

Floriana Rosati, Zoological Institute, University of Siena, Siena, Italy **[57]**

Alfonso Sada, Institute of Protein Biochemistry and Enzymology, National Council of Research, Naples, Italy **[79]**

Kiyoshi Sano, Kitasato University School of Medicine, Sagamihara, Japan **[95]**

Robert W. Schackmann, Department of Biochemistry, University of Washington, Seattle, WA **[69]**

Stanley R. Scharf, Department of Zoology, University of California, Berkeley, CA **[345]**

Gerald Schatten, Department of Biological Science, Florida State University, Tallahassee, FL **[91]**

Heide Schatten, Department of Biological Science, Florida State University, Tallahassee, FL [91]

David Schubert, The Salk Institute for Biological Studies, San Diego, CA [3]

Bennett M. Shapiro, Department of Biochemistry, University of Washington, Seattle, WA [69]

Ying-Hsien Shih, Institute of Developmental Biology, Academia Sinica, Beijing, China [47]

S.L. Shinde, Department of Zoology, University of Poona, Poona, India [301]

Yasuaki Shirayoshi, Department of Biophysics, Faculty of Science, Kyoto University, Kyoto, Japan [17]

Maya Sieber-Blum, Department of Cell Biology and Anatomy, The Johns Hopkins University School of Medicine, Baltimore, MD; present address: Department of Anatomy and Cellular Biology, Medical College of Wisconsin, Milwaukee, WI [243]

Sidney B. Simpson, Department of Biochemistry, Molecular and Cell Biology, Northwestern University, Evanston, IL [445]

Barry T. Smith, Department of Pediatrics, Harvard Medical School, Boston, MA [333]

Jaro Sodek, Faculty of Dentistry, University of Toronto, Toronto, Canada [405]

Michael Solursh, Department of Biology, University of Iowa, Iowa City, IA [429]

Johanna E. Speksnijder, Zoological Laboratory, University of Utrecht, Utrecht, The Netherlands [353]

Giordano Stabellini, Institute of Histology and General Embryology, University of Ferrara, Ferrara, Italy [385]

Nigel Stephens, Anatomy Department, Kings College, London, England [129]

Frank E. Stockdale, Department of Medicine, Stanford University School of Medicine, Stanford, CA [417]

Hironobu Sunada, Department of Tissue Physiology, Medical Research Institute, Tokyo Medical and Dental University, Tokyo, Japan [381]

Takashi Suzuki, Department of Regulation Biology, Saitama University, Urawa, Japan [211]

Shin Takagi, Department of Anatomy, Kyoto Prefectural University of Medicine, Kyoto, Japan [109]

K. Takamatsu, Department of Physiology, School of Medicine, Keio University, Tokyo, Japan [137]

Masatoshi Takeichi, Department of Biophysics, Faculty of Science, Kyoto University, Kyoto, Japan [17]

J.M. Talbot, Department of Obstetrics and Gynaecology, Monash University, Queen Victoria Medical Centre, Melbourne, Victoria, Australia [289]

H. Terashima, Department of Anatomy, Hokkaido University, Sapporo, Japan [137]

Jean Paul Thiery, Institut d'Embryologie du CNRS et du Collège de France, Nogent-sur-Marne, France [155,235]

Heinz Tiedemann, Institut für Molekularbiologie und Biochemie, Freie Universität Berlin, Berlin, Federal Republic of Germany [357]

Hildegard Tiedemann, Institut für Molekularbiologie und Biochemie, Freie Universität Berlin, Berlin, Federal Republic of Germany [357]

James J. Tomasek, Department of Anatomy, New York Medical College, Valhalla, NY **[199,433]**

R. Tompkins, Department of Biology, Tulane University, New Orleans, LA **[133]**

Yasuto Tonegawa, Department of Regulation Biology, Saitama University, Urawa, Japan **[211]**

John Torday, Department of Pediatrics, Harvard Medical School, Boston, MA **[425]**

Robert L. Trelstad, Department of Pathology, Rutgers Medical School, University of Medicine and Dentistry of New Jersey, Piscataway, NJ **[371]**

A. Trounson, Department of Obstetrics and Gynaecology, Monash University, Queen Victoria Medical Centre, Melbourne, Victoria, Australia **[289]**

Y. Tsukada, Department of Physiology, School of Medicine, Keio University, Tokyo, Japan **[137]**

Rocky S. Tuan, Department of Biology, University of Pennsylvania, Philadelphia, PA **[401]**

Richard P. Tucker, Department of Zoology, University of California, Davis, CA **[225]**

Pierre S. Tung, Faculty of Dentistry, University of Toronto, Toronto, Canada **[405]**

David C. Turner, Department of Biochemistry, State University of New York Upstate Medical Center, Syracuse, NY **[43]**

Jean-Paul Vincent, Department of Molecular Biology and Group in Biophysics, University of California, Berkeley, CA **[349]**

Richard Warn, School of Biology, University of East Anglia, Norwich, England **[361]**

Kenji Watanabe, Department of Anatomy, Fukui Medical School, Fukui, Japan **[255]**

James A. Weston, Department of Biology, University of Oregon, Eugene, OR **[249,259]**

Darrell J. Wiens, Department of Medicine, Stanford University School of Medicine, Stanford, CA **[417]**

H. Christopher Wilson, Department of Anatomy, University of Alberta, Edmonton, Alberta, Canada **[239]**

C. Wood, Department of Obstetrics and Gynaecology, Monash University, Queen Victoria Medical Centre, Melbourne, Victoria, Australia **[289]**

Kenneth M. Yamada, Laboratory of Molecular Biology, National Cancer Institute, Bethesda, MD **[155]**

Marcia S. Yaross, Department of Developmental and Cell Biology and Developmental Biology Center, University of California, Irvine, CA **[51]**

Mineo Yasuda, Department of Anatomy, Hiroshima University School of Medicine, Hiroshima, Japan **[145,437]**

M. Yokoyama, Central Institute for Experimental Animals, Kanagawa, Japan **[137]**

A. Zaki, Department of Histology, College of Dentistry, University of Illinois at Chicago, Chicago, IL **[215]**

Contents of Part A

Foreword

I am so pleased to be a part of the Tenth Congress of the International Society of Developmental Biologists (ISDB), held in the unique city of Los Angeles, California, during the week of August 4–9th, 1985. Our Society, ISDB, is proud of sustaining the tradition to present the International Congress for these many years. The Congress, which is held every four years, is a highlight of the many activities sponsored by our Society. The Congress has long been appreciated as the major occasion for international communication between research scientists and teachers in the field of developmental biology. At every Congress we have not only enjoyed the true cosmopolitan atmosphere of each country, but have also learned and evaluated the "cutting edge" of the science of developmental biology.

Thanks to the tremendous effort of the Organizing Committee, chaired by the able hands of Professor Harold Slavkin, we met together in Los Angeles, perhaps the most cosmopolitan metropolis in the world; a creative environment in Southern California to complement our scientific experiences.

The theme of the Tenth Congress is "New Discoveries and Technologies," which clearly describes the present situation of rapid advances in the sciences of developmental biology. The scope and technologies in our field are dramatically expanding and changing in modern times. For instance, it is now very evident that Recombinant DNA Technology, immunochemistry and developmental biology studies are together unraveling the problem of gene structure and how genes may regulate major events in formation of an organism. Developmental Biology is expanding and impacting on many different areas of so-called biotechnology—the applications to improve the human condition.

At the same time, we also continue to advance scientific progress in the classical problems of developmental biology. I firmly believe that the scientific programme of the Tenth Congress, which consisted of 6 major symposia, 16 minisymposia, and 19 different topics for poster presentations, clearly was comprehensive to attract all colleagues with interests in developmental biology, ranging from molecular to classical approaches. On the other hand, the programme was exciting enough not only for expert researchers, but also for students, young scientists and educators. It is our tradition, indeed, to stimulate, nurture, and encourage young generations throughout the world to meet the challenges of developmental biology.

Tokindo S. Okada
President
International Society of Developmental Biologists

Preface

The Tenth Congress of the International Society of Developmental Biologists (ISDB) met in Los Angeles from August 4–9th, 1985 at The Westin Bonaventure Hotel. The Organizing Committee of the Tenth Congress, Board Members of ISDB and an international group of cellular, molecular and developmental biologists attempted to bring together the broad international community of scientists interested in problems of developmental biology. This publication, in part, transmits the content and texture of scientific contributions related to development in the 1980s. The theme of the Congress "New Discoveries and Technologies" suggests that developmental biology continues to represent hybridizations and rearrangements of many complementary scientific disciplines. The Congress, therefore, provided a forum to celebrate the achievements of contemporary developmental biology, to explore new and old questions of development, and to advance an outreach program to improve the teaching of developmental biologists to the future scientists of the 21st Century.

To facilitate optimal communication, the Organizing Committee for the Tenth Congress formed invaluable collaborations with private industry, public education and government. Through these collaborations and the vision of many people it was possible to provide Special Travel Fellowship Awards, to hold an International Science Film Competition, sponsor a High School Student Science Competition, sponsor a Youth Symposium for gifted high school students from the Los Angeles geographic area, sponsor a Breakfast Briefing for corporate and university executives, sponsor a Math/Science Teacher Fellowship Program, and to produce a film with National Public Broadcasting System called "A Lifetime of Change." ISDB collaborations with private and public interest groups clearly defined our deep commitment to nurture the scientists and citizenry of today and tomorrow.

Of course, the success of the Congress is the reflection of the untiring efforts of my colleagues who served on the Organizing Committee. The scientific contributions found in this publication, in part, represent the state-of-the-art of international investigators involved with developmental biology. It is our hope that these published proceedings will further foster renewed interests in the challenges of developmental biology.

As Editor, I am extremely grateful to those contributors who faithfully cooperated with the deadlines and preparatory requirements of this camera-ready publication. I am deeply indebted to Ms. Gwen Airkens who served as our very competent Congress Coordinator throughout the four years of pre-planning and now has served to assemble the manuscripts for publication. Finally, I wish to acknowledge the professional and thoughtful efforts of Alan R. Liss and his associates for their logistical support and rapid publication.

Harold C. Slavkin
Los Angeles

Cell Surface Interactions During Development

Progress in Developmental Biology, Part B, pages 3–16
© 1986 Alan R. Liss, Inc.

ROLE OF PURPURIN IN NEURAL RETINA HISTOGENESIS

David Schubert and Monique LaCorbiere

The Salk Institute for Biological Studies, P.
O. Box 85800, San Diego, CA 92138-9216

Several macromolecules which are thought to be involved in the adhesive interactions of chick neural
retina have been purified to homogeneity. These include
cognin (Hausman and Moscona, 1976), N-CAM (Thiery, et
al., 1977), ligatin (Merrell, et al., 1975), a heparan
sulfate proteoglycan (Schubert and LaCorbiere, 1985b) and
a 170,000 MW heparin binding protein (Cole and Glaser,
1984a,b). We have recently isolated an additional protein from the growth conditioned medium of cultured
10 day embryonic chick neural retina which appears to
play a role in cellular adhesion. This protein, named
purpurin because of its silver staining characteristics
on acrylamide gels, was purified on the basis of its
ability to stimulate the rate of cell-substratum adhesion
of neural retina cells (Schubert and LaCorbiere, 1985a).
Purpurin is a major constituent of neural retina adherons. Adherons are extracellular glycoprotein complexes
which contain essentially all of the adhesion promoting
activities found in growth conditioned media. The
following paragraphs briefly outline the structure and
function of adherons and the characterization of one protein, purpurin, within these particles. An additional
protein has been isolated from chick neural retina
adherons which has cell binding characteristics similar
to purpurin (Cole and Glazer, 1984a,b,c; Cole, et al.,
1985). It will also be shown that monovalent antibodies
against purpurin and its cell surface receptor disrupt
the normal pattern of histogenesis in cultured chick
retina.

The Adheron Concept

The basis for a great deal of work on cellular adhesion is the observation of Lilien and Moscona (1967) that cultured cells release molecules into their growth medium which promote cell-cell adhesions in a cell type specific manner. This observation has led to the purification of many adhesion proteins from the growth conditioned media of a variety of cell types. During the course of studying a clonal rat myoblast cell line, it was shown that extracellular molecules cause cell-cell and cell-substratum adhesion. When the nature of this adhesion promoting material was examined, it was found that all of the biological activity could be sedimented (pelleted) by centrifugation at 100,000 xg for 3 hrs. The 100,000 xg supernatant is completely devoid of adhesion promoting activity. When the pelleted material is centrifuged into a calcium free 5 to 20% sucrose gradient, the adhesion activity sediments as a symmetrical 16S peak which consists of glycoprotein particles 20 nm in diameter (Schubert and LaCorbiere, 1982; Schubert, et al., 1983b). In the presence of calcium the particles aggregate. These adherons consist of 3 moles of collagen α chains, 2 moles of fibronectin monomer, and 3 moles of proteoglycans. Adhesion deficient variants of L6 myoblasts have been selected, and their adherons lack fibronectin and have a correspondingly reduced adheron size and biological activity (Schubert and LaCorbiere, 1982; Schubert, et al., 1983b). To date about 15 cell lines and primary culture systems have been examined for both adhesion promoting activity and adheron particles in their growth conditioned medium. In most of the cells which we have examined, all of the adhesion promoting activity is pelleted by centrifugation at 100,000 xg for 3 hrs. The only cell types where these extracellular particles have not been detected are those of lymphoid origin, which grow in suspension culture, and 2 neuroblastoma cell lines, which grow loosely attached to the substratum.

When 10 day embryonic neural retina cells are dissociated, placed in culture, and the growth conditioned medium examined for adhesion promoting activities using cell-substratum adhesion assays and a modification of a kinetic aggregation assay (Hausman and Moscona, 1976), all of the adhesion activity is contained within adherons 15 nm in diameter. These particles sediment at 12S on

sucrose gradients (Schubert, et al., 1983a). Monovalent
Fab' fragments of an antiserum against adherons completely inhibit spontaneous neural retina aggregation, as
do antisera against cognin and N-CAM. Adheron antiserum
also inhibits the binding of isotopically labeled adherons to intact cells. Since it is most likely that either
cognin or N-CAM (or both) are involved in the cell-cell
adhesions of this tissue, we concentrated our efforts on
the interaction of cells with adherons adsorbed to an adhesion inert Petri dish surface. Because adherons are
selectively incorporated into extracellular matrix
(Schubert, et al., 1983b), the use of a substrate coated
with adherons may provide a simple experimental paradigm
for cell-matrix interactions. Although there is not a
large amount of basement membrane in the CNS, there is
extracellular matrix associated with essentially all CNS
cell types; its exact role is not known. To identify the
possible role of extracellular matrix in neurogenesis,
adherons from embryonic chick neural retina were used as
a simplified experimental preparation. The ability of
adherons to increase the rate of cell-substratum adhesion
was determined, and antibodies to purified adheron components were shown to block cell-matrix adhesion and alter
the histotypic organization of explanted embryonic neural
retina.

The major "raison d'etre" for adherons is probably
to keep several biological functions together within a
defined structure or tissue. Cell type specific adhesion
molecules, survival factors, and mitogenic molecules have
all been found in adheron-like particles. Their mutual
association with this matrix material may prevent diffusion and help maintain tissue structure and function.
The close apposition of molecules within a multicomponent
adhesion system may also be required for the most effi-
cient type of adhesive interactions to take place (see
later).

Properties of Chick Neural Retina Adherons and Their Receptor

When adherons are adsorbed to a plastic surface and
the rate of cell adhesion measured, adherons cause the
adhesion of the whole neural retina population. Three
molecules involved in this interaction have been purified

to apparent homogeneity and characterized. Adheron-cell adhesions of cultured retina cells are selectively inhibited by heparin and heparan sulfate glycosaminoglycans, but not by chondroitin sulfate or hyaluronic acid. A heparan sulfate proteoglycan was isolated from the growth conditioned medium of neural retina cells, and an antiserum was prepared against it. Monovalent Fab' fragments of these antibodies completely inhibit cell-adheron adhesion. They also partially block spontaneous cell-cell aggregation (Schubert and LaCorbiere, 1985a; Cole, et al., 1985). An antigenically similar heparan-sulfate proteoglycan was isolated from the cell surface. This proteoglycan binds directly to adherons, and the binding is inhibited by heparin and heparan sulfate, but not by other GAGs. These data suggest that a heparan sulfate proteoglycan on the surface of chick neural retina cells acts as a receptor for adhesion mediating glycoprotein complexes (adherons). A structurally distinct heparan sulfate proteoglycan has been isolated from neural retina adherons. If this proteoglycan is able to interact with the cell surface, then there is reciprocal binding between cell and adheron.

Two proteins have been isolated from chick neural retina adherons which bind to the cell surface heparan sulfate proteoglycan and promote cellular adhesion. One is a 170,000 MW protein which was isolated on the basis of a monoclonal antibody's ability to block adhesion (Cole and Glaser, 1984a,b). This protein is found throughout the CNS and is involved in the adhesion of brain cells in addition to the neural retina population. The second protein is of lower molecular weight and was isolated in our laboratory on the basis of its ability to stimulate adhesion. It has been purified to homogeneity and antisera prepared against it. It stimulates cell-substratum adhesion at nanogram levels and binds specifically to the heparan sulfate proteoglycan cell surface receptor (Schubert and LaCorbiere, 1985a). This protein, called purpurin, is the subject of the remainder of this manuscript.

Neural Retina Purpurin

Neural retina adherons are composed of many proteins and at least two proteoglycans. The protein heterogeneity of neural retina adherons relative to those of clonal muscle cell cultures presumably reflects the fact that the neural retina contains over 50 distinct cell types (Brecha, 1983). To isolate the material within the particles which binds to cell-surface heparan sulfate proteoglycan, the particles are dissociated with 4 M guanidine HCl and the biological activity followed during purification by adsorbing each fraction to plastic Petri dishes and assaying its ability to promote cell-substratum adhesion. The use of isotopically labeled neural retina adherons assures that all of each fraction is adsorbed to the Petri dish before the adhesion assays are performed. Chromatography on Sephadex G100 in guanidine, SDS acrylamide gel electrophoresis, and chromatography on carboxymethylcellulose yields a single heparan sulfate binding protein as defined by acrylamide gel electrophoresis (Schubert and LaCorbiere, 1985a). Because it stains bright purple on acrylamide gels with the silver stain, it was named purpurin. Purpurin stimulates cell-substratum adhesion with a half maximal response of about 70 ng per 35 mm culture dish and has an apparent MW of about 20,000 daltons. Purpurin-cell binding is inhibited by heparan sulfate but not by chondroitin sulfate or hyaluronic acid. Antibodies against the cell surface heparan sulfate proteoglycan also inhibit purpurin-cell adhesion. The ability of purpurin to bind heparan sulfate was demonstrated directly by electrophoresing adheron protein on SDS acrylamide gels, transferring the protein to nitrocellulose, and then reacting the nitrocellulose containing the adheron proteins with ^{35}S-heparan sulfate proteoglycan isolated from the cell surface. Only the 20,000 MW protein binds the proteoglycan. Binding is inhibited by the GAGs heparin and heparan sulfate, but not by chondroitin. These data show that the individual 20,000 MW protein has all of the cell binding characteristics of the complete adheron.

An antiserum was prepared against purpurin. Monovalent Fab' fragments of this antiserum block cell-adheron adhesion. The antigens recognized by this antiserum are localized to specific tissues. Western blot analysis and immune precipitation of isotopically labeled protein showed that purpurin is synthesized in embryonic chick neural retina, but not in heart, skeletal muscle, liver, brain, or optic lobe. The antiserum did not, however, react with any component of newborn rat or cow neural retina. Anti-purpurin was also used to demonstrate that purpurin is involved in the histogenesis of the embryonic retina.

Disruption of Histogenesis by Antibodies to Purpurin and Heparan Sulfate Proteoglycan

The central plexiform layers of the chick neural retina are formed between embryonic days 6 and 9 (Kahn, 1974). Since neural retina isolated from 6 day embryos can continue to develop when placed in organ culture (Moscona and Moscona, 1979), these cultures were used to examine the effects of anti-purpurin and anti-heparan sulfate antibodies on tissue histogenesis. If antibodies alter the developmental sequence in a manner distinct from the pre-immune sera, it can be argued that the 2 macromolecules play a significant role in the development of the retina.

Pieces of neural retina from embryonic day 6 were dissected from the area near the choroid fissure and the pigment epithelium was removed. The fragments were cultured vitreous side down on 26 mm Millipore filters, 0.8 μm pore size, in organ culture dishes containing modified Eagle's medium, 10% fetal calf serum, 2% chicken serum, and 1% chicken extract. Monovalent Fab' fragments of rabbit antisera prepared against purpurin, cell surface heparan sulfate proteoglycan (HSPG, the cell surface receptor for purpurin), or preimmune sera were included at the beginning of the incubation period at 1 mg per ml. After 2 days incubation, the retina were fixed with 2% cold gluteraldehyde, dehydrated, embedded in Historesin, cut into 8 μ sections, and stained with toluidine blue. Figure 1 shows that tissue cultured under all three conditions contained some vaculated areas, but that both anti-purpurin and anti-HSPG caused an additional alteration in the normal pattern of histogenesis. Anti-purpurin grossly disrupted the orientation of the cells, while anti-HSPG increased the amount of extracellular space between cells. The control cultures developed in vitro for 2 days in a manner similar to the in vivo neural retina, although at a slightly slower rate (Moscona and Moscona, 1979). These results extend previous observations and show that purpurin and the neural retina adheron cell surface receptor HSPG are

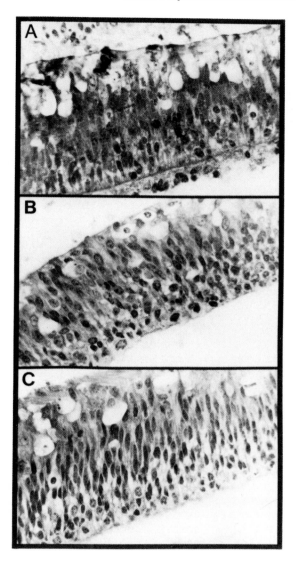

Figure 1. Effect of monovalent Fab' fragments on chick neural retina histogenesis. Organ cultures from 6 day chick embryos were exposed to Fab' fragments of antisera against (B) purpurin, (C) heparan sulfate proteoglycan, or (A), preimmune serum for 2 days. The tissue was then fixed and stained as described in text.

involved in the development of the neural retina. Similar results have been obtained with anti-cognin and anti-N-CAM (Ophir, et al., 1984; Buskirk, et al., 1980). However, a control lacking in all of these studies, including our own, is an antibody against a single high density surface protein which is unambiguously not involved in cell-cell interactions. There are, in fact, many problems with using strictly immunological criteria to define putative adhesion mediating macromolecules. These are outlined in the next section.

Alternatives for Serological Intervention in the Adhesion Process

There are a number of models that can be used to describe adhesion (Fig. 2). The simplest class involves the interaction between two "receptors," R_1-R_2 (a situation analogous to antigen-antibody binding; if $R_1 = R_2$, then the process is homophilic), or the bridging of similar receptors by a ligand, R_1-L-R_1 (two antibodies and a multivalent antigen). In principle a single molecule could explain the complex cell sorting in a tissue such as neural retina, for Steinberg, as a corollary to his differential adhesion hypothesis, stated that quantitative changes in either the cell surface density or distribution of a single adhesion molecule could lead to selective adhesion between different cell types (Steinberg, 1970). However, in the neural retina and probably most other systems, neither alternative appears to be sufficient, for specific antibodies against several different antigens block adhesion. This could be explained by alternative mechanisms. First, only one determinant is directly involved in adhesion, but a large number of others are clustered around it such that antibodies against these neighboring determinants are sufficient to sterically inhibit ligand binding to the receptor and thus inhibit cellular adhesion. The inhibition of ligand binding by antibodies bound to different abundant surface antigens has been well-documented in the immune system (Dorf, 1981). Extended monovalent Fab' fragments are large (6 x 4 nm; Valentine and Green, 1967) relative to neural retina adherons (15 nm in diameter).

Fig. 2. Adhesion Alternatives

BINARY R_1-R_2 $(R_1 = R_2)$

                          R_1-L-R_1

MULTISITE $R_1-R_2-R_3$
                          $\downarrow$ $\downarrow$ $\downarrow$
                          L_1 L_2 L_3

MULTISTEP $L-R\rightarrow A\rightarrow B\rightarrow C$

INHIBITORY $R_1-I_{(1,2)}-R_2$

    A second alternative is that adhesion is a multistep
process involving the sequential intervention of multiple
surface components in addition to the ligand (L) binding
to the receptor (R), $(L-R\rightarrow A\rightarrow B\rightarrow C)$. In this case, the L-R
interaction is sufficient to initiate adhesion, but anti-
bodies against A, B, or C may block adhesion even though
these molecules are not involved in the initial binding
event.   Inhibition of adhesion of a subpopulation of
neural retina cells could be explained if the inhibiting
antibody were against a unique receptor or against a component of any one of the subsequent steps found only
within that subpopulation. This model is compatible with
the observation that adhesion is a relatively slow,
energy-dependent process. The mechanism may be either an
allosteric change within one complex or a series of
sequential changes analogous to a biosynthetic pathway.
An example of a sequential process is the requirement of
cell surface receptors to migrate in the membrane to the
sites of adhesive contact (Grinnell, 1980).   Another
example is that fibronectin requires "activation" through
ligation with collagen and/or proteoglycans before it is
maximally effective in adhesion (Johannson and Hook,
1984).   Adherons may be such an activated complex of
macromolecules.

    The third possibility is that adhesion is a multi-
site process involving the sequential or simultaneous interaction of multiple surface receptors with different
ligands. If all of the reactions are required for effective adhesion, the antisera against any one component of
the system may block adhesion. For example, fibronectin

contains multiple sites for binding to the cell, collagen, and proteoglycans, all of which may be involved in
adhesion (Akiyama, et al., 1981). Lastly, some molecules
may act as haptens and block cellular adhesion. Examples
in the neural retina are soluble heparan sulfate proteoglycans and the inhibitory protein ligatin.

All of the above alternatives are compatible with
the observations that while antibodies against several
molecules (cognin, a 170,000 MW adheron protein, purpurin, and a proteoglycan, Cole and Glaser, 1984; Hausman
and Moscona, 1979; Schubert and LaCorbiere, 1985a,b)
block adhesion and the molecules themselves directly
stimulate cell adhesion, some molecules do not directly
stimulate cellular adhesion, but antibodies against them
block adhesion. It follows that the observation that an
antibody blocks adhesion does not prove that its antigen
is the unique "adhesion molecule." Necessary and sufficient criteria should be that the molecule either stimulates (if multivalent or on a neutral substratum) or inhibits (if in excess in solution) adhesion, and that
polyclonal antibodies against it block adhesion.

Relationship Between Purpurin and Heparin Binding Growth Factors

In addition to the stimulation of cellular adhesion,
retinal purpurin promotes cell survival (Schubert and
LaCorbiere, 1985a). A large number of mitogenic (growth
factor) activities have recently been associated with
16,000 to 20,000 dalton proteins which are able to bind
heparin (Bohlen, et al., 1984; Conn and Hatcher, 1984;
D'Amore and Klagsburn, 1984). Although retinal purpurin
does not cause the division of the postmitotic neural
retina cells used here, it does support the survival of a
subpopulation of these cells cultured from 10 day
embryonic chicks. An activity has also been isolated
from the eye which supports the survival of cultured
chick ciliary ganglion cells (Barbin, et al., 1984; Nishi
and Berg, 1981; Collins, 1985). This activity apparently
resides in a 20,000 dalton protein. Although there is no
published data showing that it is a heparan sulfate binding molecule, it is possible that this ciliary ganglion
"trophic factor" and purpurin are the same. In addition,
the heparin binding domain of laminin promotes the survi-

val of cultured chick sympathetic neurons (Edgar, et al., 1984). The shared features between the various mitogens and purpurin (similar molecular weights and heparan sulfate binding activities), suggest that they may be a related group of molecules with similar biological functions. Protein sequence data will be required to define the relationship between this group of molecules. It is, however, necessary to establish the biological specificity of these mitogenic molecules, for many appear to stimulate the growth of a variety of cell types, and they are found in many tissues.

The mechanism by which purpurin and the other heparin binding growth factors promote cell survival is not clear. Since many cell types require an adhesive surface on which to attach in order to survive in culture (see, for example, Folkman and Moscona, 1978), and since many nonbiological surfaces such as tissue culture plastic and polylysine can fulfill these requirements, it follows that simply an increase in cell-substratum adhesion can be of survival value for cultured cells. In addition to survival per se, cell-substratum adhesion can have profound effects on cellular metabolism (see, for example, Otsuka and Moskowitz, 1975).

In contrast to survival "factors", molecules which stimulate cell division may function by the perturbation of cell-substratum adhesion. For example, mild trypsinization of cultured fibroblasts induces mitosis (Carney and Cunningham, 1977) and some growth factors, such as glial growth factor, have proteolytic activity (Brockes, et al., 1980). Perhaps any weakening of cell-substratum adhesion can induce mitosis. If cells are tightly associated with a layer of matrix via a heparan sulfate proteoglycan, heparin binding proteins may act as haptens and block the matrix bound heparin-cell surface interaction. This interaction could lead to a weakening of cell attachment and induce mitosis. The commonly held alternative is that the heparin binding growth factors interact with specific cell surface receptors, such as that described for EGF, and that this interaction leads to the initiation of mitosis. If adhesion, survival, and growth promoting activities are all contained within the same heparin binding molecule, then its biological effects must be dependent upon its extracellular concentration and solubility. If the protein is tightly associated with matrix, then it would promote cell-matrix adhesion and survival; the soluble form of the protein may be mitogenic.

Acknowledgements

We wish to thank Drs. William Stallcup, Jean LeBeau, and Joe Henry Steinbach for their thoughtful comments on this manuscript. The work was supported by the Muscular Dystrophy Association of America and the National Institutes of Health.

References

Akiyama SK, Yamada KM, Hayashi M (1981). The structure of fibronectin and its role in cellular adhesion. J. Supramol. Struct. 16:345-358.

Barbin G, Manthrope M, Varon S (1984). Purification of the eye ciliary neuronotrophic factor. J. Neurochem. 43:1468-1478.

Bohlen P, Baird A, Esch F, Ling N, Gospodarowiez D (1984). Isolation and partial molecular characterization of pituitary fibroblast growth factor. Proc. Natl. Acad. Sci. USA 81:5364-5368.

Brecha N (1983). Retinal neurotransmitters: histochemical and biochemical studies. In Emson PC (ed): "Chemical Neuroanatomy," New York: Raven Press, pp 85-129.

Brockes J, Lemke G, Balzer DR (1980). Purification and preliminary characterization of a glial growth factor from bovine pituitary. J. Biol. Chem. 255:8374-8377.

Buskirk DR, Thiery JP, Rutishauser U, Edelman JM (1980). Antibodies to a neural cell adhesion molecule disrupt histogenesis in cultured chick retinae. Nature 285:488-489.

Carney DH, Cunningham DD (1977). Initiation of chick cell division by trypsin action at the cell surface. Nature 268:602-605.

Cole GJ, Glaser L (1984a). Inhibition of embryonic neural retinal cell-substratum adhesion with a monoclonal antibody. J. Biol. Chem. 259:4031-4034.

Cole GJ, Glaser L (1984b). Cell-substratum adhesion is mediated by a 170,000-dalton neural-specific peptide. J. Cell Biol. 99:1605-1612.

Cole GJ, Glaser L (1984c). Identification of novel

neural and neural retina-specific antigens with a monoclonal antibody. Proc. Natl. Acad. Sci. USA 81:2260-
2264.

Cole GJ, Schubert D, Glaser L (1985). Cell-substratum
adhesion in chick neural retina is dependent upon
heparan sulfate interactions. J. Cell Biol. 100:1192-
1199.

Collins F (1985). Electrophoretic similarity of the ciliary ganglion survival factors from different tissues
and species. Dev. Biol. 109:255-258.

Conn G, Hatcher V (1984). The isolation and purification
of two anionic endothelial cell growth factors from human brain. Biochem. Biophys. Res. Comm. 124:262-268.

D'Amore PA, Klagsbrun M (1984). Endothelial cell mitogens derived from retina and hypothalamus: Biochemical
and biological similarities. J. Cell Biol. 99:1545-
1549.

Dorf ME (1981). "The role of the major histocompatibil-
ity complex in immunology." New York: Garland Publishing, Inc., 356 pp.

Edgar D, Timpl R, Thoenen H (1984). The heparin-binding
domain of laminin is responsible for its effects on
neurite outgrowth and neuronal survival. The EMBO
Journal 3:1463-1468.

Folkman J, Moscona A (1978). Role of cell shape in
growth control. Nature 273:345-349.

Grinnell F (1980). Fibroblast receptor for cell-
substratum adhesion: studies on the interaction of BHK
cells with latex beads coated by cold insoluble
globulin. J. Cell Biol. 86:104-112.

Hausman RE, Moscona, AA (1976). Isolation of retina-
specific cell-aggregating factor from membranes of
embryonic neural retina tissue. Proc. Natl. Acad. Sci.
73:3594-3598.

Hausman RE, Moscona AA (1979). Immunologic detection of
retina cognin on the surface of embryonic cells. Exp.
Cell Res. 119:191-204.

Johannson J, Hook M (1984). Substrate adhesion of rat
hepatocytes: on the mechanism of attachment of fibronectin. J. Cell Biol. 98:810-817.

Kahn AJ (1974). An autographic analysis of the time of
appearance of neurons in the developing chick neural
retina. Dev. Biol. 38:30-40.

Lilien JE, Moscona AA (1967). Cell aggregation: its enhancement by a supernatant from cultures of homologous
cells. Science 157:70-72.

Maciag T, Mehlman T, Friesel R, Schreiber AB (1984). Heparin binds endothelial cell growth factor, the principal endothelial cell mitogen in bovine brain. Science 225:932-934.

Merrell R, Gottlieb DI, Glaser I (1975). Embryonal cell surface recognition. Extraction of an active plasma membrane component. J. Biol. Chem. 250:5655-5562.

Moscona M, Moscona AA (1979). The development of inducibility for glutamine synthesis in embryonic neural retina: inhibition by BrdU. Differentiation 13:165-172.

Nishi R, Berg D (1981). Two components from eye tissue that differentially stimulate the growth and development of ciliary ganglion neurons in culture. J. Neurosci. 1:505-513.

Ophir I, Moscona AA, Ben-Shaul Y (1984). Cell disorganization and malformation in neural retina caused by antibodies to R-cognin: ultrastructural study. Cell Differentiation 15:53-60.

Otsuka H, Moskowitz M (1975). Difference in transport of leucine in attached and suspended 3T3 cells. J. Cell Physiol. 85:665-674.

Schubert D, LaCorbiere M (1982). Properties of extracellular adhesion-mediating particles in myoblast clone and its adhesion-deficient variant. J. Cell Biol. 94:108-115.

Schubert D, LaCorbiere M, Klier FG, Birdwell C (1983a). A role for adherons in neural retina cell adhesion. J. Cell Biol. 96:990-999.

Schubert D, LaCorbiere M, Klier FG, Birdwell G (1983b). The structure and function of myoblast adherons. Cold Spring Harbor Symp. Quant. Biol. 48:539-549.

Schubert D, LaCorbiere M (1985a). Isolation of an adhesion mediating protein from chick neural retina adherons. J. Cell Biol., Sept. issue.

Schubert D, LaCorbiere M (1985b). Isolation of a cell surface receptor for chick neural retina adherons. J. Cell Biol. 100:56-63.

Steinberg MS (1970). Does differential adhesion govern self-assembly processes in histogenesis? Equilibrium configurations and the emergence of a hierarchy among populations of embryonic cells. J. Exp. Zool. 173:395-433.

Thiery J, Brackenbury R, Rutishauser U, Edelman, G (1977). Adhesion among neural cells of chick retina. J. Biol. Chem. 252:6841-6845.

Valentine RC, Green NM (1967). Electron microscopy of an antibody-antigen complex. J. Mol. Biol. 27:615-617.

Progress in Developmental Biology, Part B, pages 17–27
© **1986 Alan R. Liss, Inc.**

CADHERINS: THEIR MORPHOGENETIC ROLE IN ANIMAL DEVELOPMENT

Masatoshi Takeichi, Yasuaki Shirayoshi, Kohei
Hatta, and Akinao Nose

Department of Biophysics, Faculty of Science,
Kyoto University, Kyoto 606, Japan

INTRODUCTION

An essential step in animal morphogenesis is
segregation of the cell layers entering into different
differentiation pathways. Townes and Holtfreter (1955)
proposed that the selective adhesiveness of cells might
play a role in the segregation of different cell types, and
this idea seems to be widely accepted. The molecular basis
of the selective adhesion, however, remains to be solved.

Recent studies succeeded in identifying various
classes of cell-to-cell adhesion molecules, and showed that
many of these molecules are cell-type-specific (see Damsky
et al., 1984 for review). One molecular class is
"cadherins", which were defined as the functional components of the calcium-dependent cell-cell adhesion systems
(Takeichi, 1977; Yoshida-Noro et al., 1984; Hatta et al.,
1985). The cadherins were detected in many kinds of
tissues, probably in all kinds of solid tissues. Immunological studies indicated that cadherins should be divided
into multiple types with different specificities (Takeichi
et al., 1985). In this review, we will discuss the
possible implication of cadherins in tissue segregation in
animal morphogenesis.

DEFINITION OF THE CALCIUM-DEPENDENT CELL ADHESION SYSTEM

The Ca^{2+}-dependent cell adhesion system (CADS) shows a
unique Ca^{2+}- and protease-sensitivity (Takeichi, 1977). It

is very sensitive to protease such as trypsin in the absence of Ca^{2+}. Tissues treated with trypsin in the presence of EGTA, therefore, lose this adhesion system, being disaggregated. However, if tissues are treated with trypsin in the presence of Ca^{2+}, the CADS is not removed from cell surfaces so that their cell-cell connections are not disrupted. The tissues treated with the trypsin-Ca^{2+} can be disaggregated into single cells or small cell clusters by rinsing with a Ca^{2+}-free medium. These cells can restore cell-cell connections if Ca^{2+} is added, since CADS is left intact. If this type of adhesion property was detected in a given cell, we defined it as CADS.

MONOCLONAL ANTIBODIES RECOGNIZING CADHERINS

Monoclonal antibodies recognizing cadherins were obtained by the following methods. Cells with cadherin activity were injected into animals, and spleens of these animals were fused with myeloma to produce hybridoma. Culture supernatant of the hybridoma was screened for detection of antibodies reacting with cadherins by either of the following ways: (1) Culture supernatant of the hybridoma growing in wells of microtiter plates was added to monolayer cultures of cells used as the antigen. After incubation for a few hours, effect of the addition of the hybridoma supernatant on the morphology of cell layers was examined by an inverted microscope, and, if any disrupting activity of cell-cell contact was observed, the hybridoma were saved for further tests. (2) Antibodies in the hybridoma culture supernatant were screened for activity in the selective binding to components which are present in cells treated with trypsin-Ca^{2+} but not in cells with trypsin-EGTA. If antibodies with such a binding property were found, they were subjected to further tests.

Monoclonal antibodies selected by either of the above methods were tested for activity of the specific inhibition of Ca^{2+}-dependent aggregation of cells dissociated with trypsin-Ca^{2+}. If an antibody specifically inhibited such Ca^{2+}-dependent cell aggregation but not Ca^{2+}-independent aggregation, it was subjected to immunoblot analysis for detection of antigens. After confirming that the antigens are detected in cells treated with trypsin-Ca^{2+} but not in cells treated with trypsin-EGTA, we defined these antigens as cadherins.

TWO DISTINCT CADHERINS

E-cadherin

The monoclonal antibody ECCD-1 was obtained as an antibody blocking Ca^{2+}-dependent aggregation of mouse teratocarcinoma cells (Yoshida-Noro et al., 1984). ECCD-1 recognized a 124,000 dalton glycoprotein (Fig. 1). This

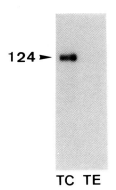

124 ➤

TC TE

Figure 1. Immunoblot detection of E-cadherin by a monoclonal antibody recognizing CADS in teratocarcinoma F9 cells. TC, cells treated with trypsin-Ca^{2+}; TE, cells treated with trypsin-EGTA.

protein is expressed in early mouse embryos, playing an essential role in compaction of the morula. It is also expressed by the inner cell mass of blastocysts, and, at the egg cylinder stage, expressed by all the ectodermal and endodermal layers except the parietal endoderm. Mesodermal cells do not express this molecule. At the later developmental stage, most epithelial layers derived from the ectoderm and endoderm continue to express this molecule, but cells derived from the mesoderm do not express it with the except of kidney tubules. Cells belonging to the nervous system also do not have this molecule although they originally derived from the ectoderm.

We termed this 124kd glycoprotein E-cadherin. Some molecules identified by other laboratories, such as uvomorulin (Peyrieras et al., 1983; Vestweber and Kemler, 1984) and cell-CAM 120/80 (Damsky et al., 1983), seem to be the same molecule as E-cadherin since their molecular weight and tissue distribution pattern are very similar. L-CAM identified in chicken tissues (Gallin et al., 1983) was assumed to be the chicken equivalent of E-cadherin (Ogou et al., 1983).

N-cadherin

The monoclonal antibody NCD-1 was obtained as an antibody blocking the Ca^{2+}-dependent aggregation of mouse brain cells (Hatta et al., 1985). The target molecules of this antibody, however, have not been identified. The tissue distribution of the hypothetical antigens was determined by a complement-dependent cytotoxicity assay. The results showed that the NCD-1 targets are present in nervous systems, cardiac and skeletal muscle cells, lens and so on. Most of these tissues do not have E-cadherin. Therefore, it was suggested that NCD-1 recognizes a Ca^{2+}-dependent cell adhesion molecule different from E-cadherin. We termed this hypothetical adhesion molecule N-cadherin.

The monoclonal antibody NCD-2 was isolated from antibodies raised against chicken neural retina and brain (Hatta and Takeichi, manuscript submitted). This antibody inhibited the Ca^{2+}-dependent aggregation of cells of these tissues and recognized a 127,000 dalton protein. The tissue distribution of this molecule was identical to that of N-cadherin, so that we called this 127kd protein the chicken N-cadherin.

SPECIFICITY OF CADHERINS

E- and N-cadherins are distinct in molecular weight and tissue distribution, as described above. They are also distinct in immunological and functional specificity. ECCD-1 does not cross-react with N-cadherin, nor does NCD-1 or NCD-2 with E-cadherin. Cells expressing E-cadherin such as F9 cells do not cross-adhere with cells expressing N-cadherin such as G26-20 cells (Takeichi et al., 1985). These observations suggested that cadherins may have an active role in the sorting-out of different cell types in embryonic development. To verify this idea we attempted by immunohistochemical studies to determine whether there was any correlation between the expression of cadherins and various morphogenetic events (Hatta and Takeichi, manuscript submitted).

DIFFERENTIAL EXPRESSION OF CADHERINS

At gastrulation

As mentioned above, E-cadherin is expressed in the
ectoderm and visceral endoderm, but not in the mesoderm in
mouse embryos at the gastrula stage. Thiery et al. (1984)
found a similar expression pattern with L-CAM, the chicken
equivalent of E-cadherin. L-CAM is expressed in the
epiblast and hypoblast layers but not in the cells
migrating into the lower layer through the primitive
streak.

When the expression pattern of N-cadherin was examined
in chicken embryos using NCD-2 (an antibody which does not
react with mouse), we found that this cadherin is not
expressed in the blastula stage. N-cadherin is first
expressed at the primitive streak stage in the cells
migrating into the lower layer of blastoderm, whereas it is
not expressed in the epiblast at the same stage (Fig. 2).

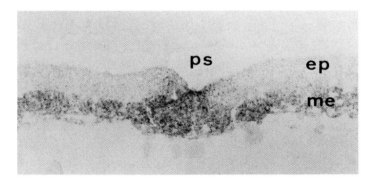

Figure 2. Expression of N-cadherin in a chicken embryo at
the primitive streak stage. The section was stained with
NCD-2 by a peroxidase method. ps, primitive streak; ep,
epiblast; me, mesoderm and endoderm.

Therefore, the expression pattern of L-CAM and N-cadherin
is complementary. Thus, switch in expression of cadherin
from E to N type occurs in the cells segregating from the
epiblast.

At neural tube formation

In the process of neural tube formation, we found a similar transition in expression of cadherins from E to N-type. In embryos at the head-process stage, the ectoderm including the neural plate expresses E-cadherin/L-CAM. However, when the neural folding begins, E-cadherin/L-CAM disppears from the neural plate, although the ectoderm on the body surface continuously expresses this adhesion molecule. Simultaneously, expression of N-cadherin begins at the bottom of the neural groove and gradually spreads to the top of the folding neural plate. When the neural tube forms after separation from the overlying ectoderm, the entire region of the tube expresses N-cadherin (Fig. 3). Thus, switch in expression of cadherins from E- to N-type occurred coincidentally with separation of the neural tube (Fig. 4).

At lens formation

Lens is formed by invagination of the ectoderm as in the case of neural tube formation. During this process, a switch in the expression of cadherins again occurs. When the lens placode forms, this thickened part of the ectoderm begins to acquire N-cadherin. As the lens vesicle forms and separates from the overlying ectoderm, the expression of N-cadherin becomes stronger (Fig. 5). The matured lens continues the expression of this adhesion molecule, while the ectoderm differentiating into the cornea epithelium only weakly and transiently expresses N-cadherin.

Thiery et al. (1984) showed that L-CAM is expressed in the ectoderm including the lens placode but it disappears from the invaginating lens vesicle. In the case of mouse, our preliminary experiments suggested that E-cadherin does not disappear during the lens vesicle formation but, instead, a third type of cadherin (P-type) expressed by the ectoderm disappears during this process (Nose and Takeichi, unpublished). Thus, in either species, replacement of cadherin types during separation of the lens vesicle occurs.

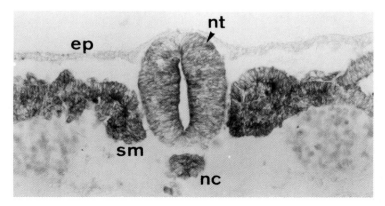

Figure 3. Expression of N-cadherin in a chicken embryo at the 18-somite stage. Stained by a peroxidase method. nt, neural tube; ep, epidermis; sm, somite; nc, notochord.

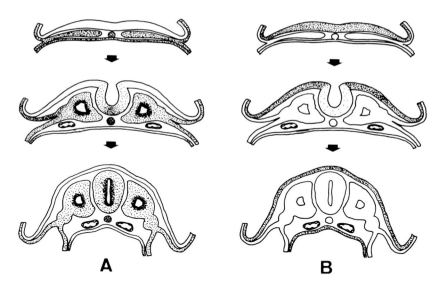

Figure 4. Schematic drawings of the expression of N-cadherin (A) and L-CAM (B) during the neural tube formation in chick embryos. The dotted area represent expression of these adhesion molecules. Data on L-CAM were taken from the paper by Thiery et al. (1984). The expression pattern of E-cadherin in mouse is not the same as that of L-CAM in chicken; E-cadherin is expressed in the endoderm layer in mouse at the corresponding developmental stages.

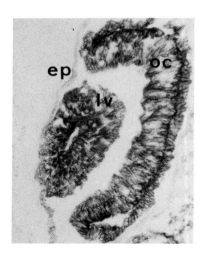

Figure 5. Expression of N-cadherin in the eye primordium in a chicken embryo at the 28-somite stage. Stained by a peroxidase method. lv, lens vesicle; oc, optic cup; ep, epidermis.

CONTROL OF MORPHOGENESIS BY CADHERINS

Mechanisms of the sorting out or selective adhesion of cells have been a point of debate for a long period. Since recent studies succeeded in identification of various cell adhesion molecules, we are now able to discuss this issue in terms of molecules.

All classes of cell-cell adhesion molecules so far identified have shown unique tissue distribution patterns; that is, they are distributed in limited cell types or tissues. For example, E-cadherin is present in a variety of tissues but only in their epithelial components (Takeichi et al., 1985). N-cadherin is detected in the nervous system, heart, lens and so on, but not in most epithelial tissues (Hatta and Takeichi, 1985). In our unpublished work, we identified a third type of cadherin termed P-cadherin (Nose and Takeichi, unpublished). The tissue distribution of this cadherin is again unique. There must be more unidentified cadherins since none of the monoclonal antibodies recognizing cadherins so far obtained reacted with certain cell types such as endothelial cells.

In these cadherin distributions, we see a tendency such that when cell layers with different phenotypes are located contiguous to each other with a distinct boundary, these layers express different types of cadherins; for example, the epidermis expresses E-cadherin but the dermis does not.

Expression of cadherins is thus regulated spatially, while it is also regulated temporally. As described in the previous sections, expression of each type of cadherin is transient in many tissues, and switch in the expression of cadherins from one type to another does occur. Such change in the cadherin expression was closely correlated with the onset of separation of cell layers, as mentioned.

Our previous studies showed that cells expressing different types of cadherins tend to segregate from each other when mixed in an experimental condition. Therefore, the observed correlation between the differential cadherin expression and the tissue segregation pattern strongly suggests that cadherins actively play a role in the segregation of cell layers in vivo.

Another important observation is that expression of the three E-, N-, and P-cadherins are overlapped in many kinds of cells in varying combinations. Such combinations of different types of cadherins must create a variety of adhesive specificity for cells. Since Ca^{2+}-independent adhesion molecules such as N-CAM are co-expressed with cadherins (Takeichi et al., 1979; Urushihara et al., 1979; Brackenbury et al., 1981), the combination of all these adhesion molecules should provide cells with a greater variety of adhesive specificity. We would then be able to account for the adhesive specificity of a given cell by assuming a particular combination of multiple types of cell adhesion molecules, without assuming the presence of a "tissue-specific" cell adhesion molecule.

These findings on the expression of cadherins provide a novel clue in elucidating the mechanisms of selective cell adhesion essential for morphogenetic processes.

ACKNOWLEDGMENTS

We thank Prof. T.S. Okada for his encouragement during the work described in this paper. This work was supported by research grants from the Ministry of Education, Science and Culture of Japan.

REFERENCES

Brachenbury R, Rutishauser U, Edelman GM (1981) Distinct calcium-independent and calcium-dependent adhesion systems of chick embryos. Proc Natl Acad Sci USA 78: 387-391.
Damsky CH, Richa C, Solter D, Knudsen K, Buck CA (1983). Identification and purification of a cell surface glycoprotein mediating intercellular adhesion in embryonic and adult tissues. Cell 34: 455-466.
Damsky CH, Knudsen KA, Buck CA (1984). Integral membrane glycoprotein in cell-cell and cell-substratum adhesion. In Ivatt RJ (ed): "The Biology of Glycoproteins," Plenum Publishing Corporation, p 1.
Gallin WJ, Edelman GM, Cunningham BA (1983). Characterization of L-CAM, a major cell adhesion molecule from embryonic liver cells. Proc Natl Acad Sci USA 80: 1038-1042.
Hatta K, Okada TS, Takeichi, M (1985). A monoclonal antibody disrupting calcium-dependent cell-cell adhesion of brain tissues: Possible role of its target antigen in animal pattern formation. Proc Natl Acad Sci USA 82: 2789-2793.
Ogou S, Yoshida-Noro C, Takeichi M (1983). Calcium-dependnt cell-cell adhesion molecules common to hepatocytes and teratocarcinoma stem cells. J Cell Biol 97: 944-948.
Peyrieras N, Hyafil F, Louvard D, Ploegh HL, Jacob F (1983). Uvomorulin: A nonintegral membrane protein of early mouse embryo. Proc Natl Acad Sci USA 80: 6274-6277.
Takeichi M (1977) Functional correlation between cell adhesive properties and some cell surface proteins. J Cell Biol 75: 464-474.
Takeichi M, Ozaki HS, Tokunaga K, Okada TS (1979). Experimental manipulation of cell surface to affect cellular recognition mechanisms. Develop Biol 70: 195-205.
Takeichi M, Hatta K, Nagafuchi, A (1985). Selective cell adhesion mechanisms: Role of the calcium-dependent cell adhesion system. In "Molecular Determinants of Animal Form, UCLA Symposia on Molecular and Cellular Biology, New Series, vol 31, ed Edelman GM", Alan R Liss, Inc, New York, in press.
Thiery JP, Delouvee A, Gallin WJ, Cunningham BA, Edelman GM (1984). Ontogenetic expression of cell

adhesion molecules: L-CAM is found in epithelia derived from the three primary germ layers. Develop Biol 102: 61-78.

Townes PL, Holtfreter J (1955). Directed movements and selective adhesion of embryonic amphibian cells. J Exp Zool 128: 53-120.

Urushihara H, Ozaki HS, Takeichi M (1979) Immunological detection of cell surface components related with aggregation of Chinese hamster and chick embryonic cells. Develop Biol 70: 206-216.

Vestweber D, Kemler R (1984). Rabbit antiserum against a purified surface glycoprotein decompacts mouse preimplantation embryos and react with specific adult tissues. Exptl Cell Res 152: 169-178.

Yoshida-Noro C, Suzuki N, Takeichi M (1984). Molecular nature of the calcium-dependent cell-cell adhesion system in mouse teratocarcinoma and embryonic cells studied with a monoclonal antibody. Develop Biol 101: 19-27.

Progress in Developmental Biology, Part B, pages 29–41

AFFINITY-RECOGNITION, ADHESION AND CONTACT-INTERACTIONS OF
EMBRYONIC CELLS

A. A. Moscona

Department of Molecular Genetics & Cell Biology,
University of Chicago, Chicago, Illinois 60637,
U.S.A.

INTRODUCTION AND BACKGROUND

Early in the course of evolution cells discovered the
benefits of societal organization. They evolved mechanisms
for adhering into multicellular structures, for functional
specialization, and for communication by contact. In the
longer run, contact-communication among cells became crucial
for the governance of morphogenesis and differentiation
during embryonic development. To form an embryo cells must,
of course, cohere; but, in order to give rise to tissues and
organs, the diverse cells in the embryo must be able to
identify one another, sort out and assemble into various
groupings, adhere selectively and interact. For this, there
exist on the cell surface mechanisms for contact-communication
which enable cells to: 1) identify and recognize one another,
2) adhere selectively with functionally matching types; 3)
engage in contact-dependent interactions which influence
cell differentiation and function. These processes are
closely interrelated: selective cell contact and adhesion
involve, on one hand, recognition and choices; on the other,
contact is a means for further intercellular communication
and cooperation. Having established matching contact, cells
may form junctions or synapses, engage in metabolic exchanges
or transmission of signals.

Recognition-adhesion mechanisms evolve on embryonic
cells progressively, coordinately with cell differentiation
and become increasingly selective. In general terms, there
exist three categories of cell recognition (1). 1) Germ
layer cell recognition is conducive to selective association

of cells belonging to each of the three primary germ layers
in the early embryo (as originally described by Holtfreter
(2). 2) *Tissue-specific cell recognition* enables cells
that belong in the same tissue to recognize their histo-
genetic relatedness, segregate from the rest and adhere
preferentially to each other (3). 3) *Cell type recognition*
enables the various cells that make up a given tissue to
establish contact-relationships necessary for organization
of tissue architecture; an example is selective association
and organization of the various cell types in the neural
retina (4).

Cell type recognition presents an extraordinarily
complex problem in that it can be *isotypic* (resulting in
contact between same type cells); *allotypic* (between similar,
but not identical cells, e.g., neuron A and neuron B);
heterotypic (between diverse cell types, e.g., neuron and
muscle). Indeed, a cell can express allotypic recognition
on one part of its surface and heterotypic on another and be
simultaneously in contact with two different cells.

The problem of tissue-specific cell affinities is somewhat less complex and our past work concentrated mainly on
this issue. This article describes, in outline, three
experimental systems which have been developed and used in
our laboratory for investigating selective affinities and
contact-communication among embryonic cells.

CELL ADHESION THEORIES

Several models have been proposed to explain selective
cell adhesion. Some have suggested that the surface of each
cell, or cell type in the embryo is specified by a unique
affinity mechanism. This view was proposed, more than
40 years ago by Roger Sperry (5) in his "chemoaffinity
theory" to explain selective contacts between various
neurons. However, at that time the prevailing opinion was
that membrane composition was similar in all cells, and that
cells could not generate the very large spectrum of unique
surface differences corresponding to the equally large
number of cell types and sub-types. Other models postulate
only a single, basic cell adhesion mechanism and invoke
various kinds of modulations (6), thermodynamic equilibria
(7), and electrostatic (surface charge) forces (8) to account
for adhesion selectivities. Modulation and chemoaffinity

theories are not mutually exclusive. Assumptions that the specificity of cell adhesion is dictated primarily by surface charges or other weak forces and thermodynamic equilibria not identified with particular cell surface components are no longer considered tenable (9, 10, 11).

Our studies on aggregation of embryonic (chick and mouse) cells (12) and sponge cells (13) led us to conclude that cell recognition and selective adhesion are mediated by gene products located on the cell surface that function both as recognition-determinants and cell-cell ligands. We proposed that cells display positive recognition and establish lasting contact if their ligands match and hook up; and that this depends not only on the molecular characteristics of ligands, but also on their topological organization on the cell surface, both being subject to changes (modulations) in the course of development (4). Thus, matching and interactions of complementary ligand patterns are considered to be the basis for cell recognition-selective adhesion and, hence, the key to further contact-communication of cells. The hypothesis does not require a very large spectrum of qualitatively distinct ligand species, since variations in ligand topologies and amounts would generate abundant information for cell recognition and selective affinities (14). We postulated that different tissues have qualitatively different cell ligands; i.e., that ligands which are characteristic for a given tissue determine the mutual tissue-affinity of all the cells belonging to this tissue (4, 15). Tissue-specific cell ligands have been demonstrated (see below); this and other evidence validated the heuristic value of the above hypothesis and led others to adopt similar concepts and research directions (9) (see also papers by D. Schubert and M. Takeichi in this volume).

CELL LIGAND MOLECULES: COGNINS

Having found that cells in different tissues express tissue-characteristic surface antigens (16, 17), we obtained from embryonic retina and brain cells (chick and mouse) surface proteins that can link and aggregate cells of the corresponding tissue, consistent with functions predicted for tissue-specific cell ligands. Such cell-aggregating proteins were detected, at first, in media from cell cultures into which they are released from the cell membrane (12, 18, 19, 20). Later, we focussed on the retina and

*purified the cell aggregating protein directly from cell
membranes isolated from embryonic retina tissue (21).*

*The bioassay is of a direct kind and is based on cell
aggregation. Briefly, when an embryonic tissue (e.g.,retina)
is exposed to trypsin, cell-linking surface components are
degraded and the cells separate. If the dissociated cells
are incubated on a rotary shaker, they regenerate lost
surface components and adhere into progressively larger
aggregates; the cells restore histological relationships and
reconstruct their tissue pattern (12, 22). This system
closely approximates normal cell associations; it can be
used to study surface molecules which function as cell
ligands, and it lends itself well to direct functional testing of isolated candidate cell-ligands. The latter are
added to dissociated cells to determine if they can link
cells into tissue-forming aggregates at a faster rate than
that dependent on autonomous regeneration of ligands.*

*When the membrane protein isolated from retina cells
(see above) is added to suspensions of dissociated embryonic
retina cells, it binds to (or inserts itself into) the cell
membrane and restores mutual cell adhesiveness; in effect,
it supplies dissociated cells with "instant" ligands. Such
cells aggregate much faster than the controls and form much
larger aggregates (21). It is important that this protein
exerts these effects only on retina cells; and that cells
aggregated by it undergo histological retinotypic organization. The amino acid composition and other characteristics
of this retina cell-aggregating protein have been examined
(23); it is glycosylated and has, in solution, a unit
molecular weight in the range of 50K daltons; its activity
is calcium dependent.*

*There is convincing evidence that this cell-aggregating
protein is a component of the natural cell-ligand mechanism
of retina cells. Antibodies directed against the protein
(as well as FAB fragments) detect the antigen as it is spontaneously regenerated on the surface of self-aggregating
retina cells, bind to it and prevent normal cell reaggregation (24). If intact retina tissue is treated with these
antibodies, cell contacts become disrupted and the tissue
partially disintegrates (25). Antigen regeneration on
spontaneously aggregating retina cells was further demonstrated by scanning electron microscopy, using as a*

visualization probe micro-beads coated with the specific
antibody (26, 27). The beads do not bind to freshly dissociated cells; they start to bind as the cells begin to
aggregate; binding increases correlatedly with antigen
regeneration on the cell surface and restoration of mutual
cell adhesiveness. The studies also revealed that, (a) all
the cell types of the retina express this antigen, starting
with very early stages of development; (b) the antigen is
not found on cells of other tissues. These results are
consistent with the conclusion that this antigen is a tissue
(retina)-specific cell affinity determinant.

Tissue-specific cell-aggregating proteins have been
obtained also from embryonic brain and spinal cord (19, 28)
and they too display functional properties expected of
tissue-specific cell ligands.

Taken as a whole, our findings and results from other
laboratories point to the existence of cell-surface proteins
that function in cell recognition as components of cell-cell
ligands. We refer to such molecules as cognins (29) to
emphasize their role in cell recognition (a prerequisite for
selective cell adhesion). Various candidate cognins have
been reported from several laboratories (9). The search for
such molecules is accelerating and new insights into their
function can be expected. With respect to the retina cognin
described by us, this may not be the only component of
retina cell-ligands; possibly, the neural cell adhesion
molecule (N-CAM) described by Edelman (9) also is involved.
It has been proposed that cell-ligand mechanisms may be
multicomponent (23) (see article by Dr. Schubert in this
volume); in this case, their mechanism of function may be
much more interesting than envisaged by current "cartoons" of
cell adhesion.

SEPARATING TISSUE AFFINITY FROM CELL TYPE RECOGNITION

The relationship of cell type recognition to tissue
affinities of cells is of obvious interest. Examination of
this problem would be greatly facilitated if these two
aspects could be functionally separated; if it were possible
to have cells that express tissue affinity, but not type-
recognition, i.e., cells capable of selectively associating
with others that belong in the same tissue, but unable to
type-identify one another and to organize tissue architec-

ture. In fact, there already exists a promising lead in this direction.

Our guideline in this work was that, cell recognition specificities evolve progressively with cell differentiation, and acquisition of type recognition follows that of tissue affinity. Accordingly, we arrested differentiation in the retina at an early stage and thereby prevented cell specification for type recognition without abolishing pre-existing tissue affinity.

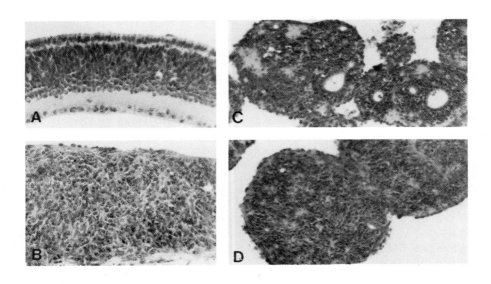

Figure 1. A, B. Retina of 5-1/2-day chick embryo organcultured for 5 days. A) Untreated; normal development. B) Treated with BrdU for 12 hrs at 5-1/2 days; cells misorganized. C) Aggregates of cells dissociated from normal retina; cells organized in retinotypic rosettes. D) Aggregates of cells dissociated from BrdU-treated retina; no retinotypic cell organization. X250. Modified from (31).

Cell differentiation was arrested by BrdU (5'-bromodeo-xyuridine; analog of thymidine). It was supplied for 12 hrs to retina from 5-day chick embryos (30). BrdU is incorporated into DNA and permanently stops certain aspects of further cell differentiation. The cells continue to multiply, are motile, but are unable to organize normal retina tissue architecture (31); instead, they adhere indiscriminately and give rise to a chaotic cell mass (32). If such cells are dissociated and reaggregated, they do not reconstruct retinotypic architecture, in contrast to normal cells (Fig. 1).

Such BrdU-modified retina cells continue to express their tissue affinity. This has been definitively demonstrated by dissociating the cells and co-aggregating them with cells from a different tissue, with cartilage-forming cells. It is well-known that normal cells in such binary combinations segregate spatially and assemble in accordance with their tissue identity, thereby displaying their characteristic tissue affinities (4, 7, 12, 33). We found that, also BrdU-modified retina cells segregate from normal cartilage cells and assemble separately; they express tissue-affinity even though they are unable to sort and organize retina tissue architecture. Furthermore, when BrdU-modified retina cells are co-aggregated with BrdU-modified cartilage cells, both express their characteristic histological affinities and segregate in different regions of the aggregate (work in progress).

The finding that tissue affinity can be functionally uncoupled from cell type recognition represents a breakthrough which makes it possible to investigate much more directly than before biochemical, temporal and regulatory aspects of these specificities. We have already determined that BrdU-modified retina cells express retina cognin; this is consistent with their display of retina tissue affinity and is further evidence of the role of retina cognin in determination of this affinity. The possibility arises that cell type recognition requires determinants which are either not expressed on BrdU-modified cells, or expressed ineffectively. Testable assumptions are that treatment with BrdU at an early stage of cell differentiation deprives cells of type-specific recognition determinants, or prevents their organization on the cell surface by altering the function of genes which encode for these processes (31). Other possibilities can presently be envisaged and are being examined.

CELL CONTACT AND PHENOTYPE REGULATION

The relation of cell contact to cell function is being investigated in the neural retina of 13-day chick embryos. At this age the retina is already post-mitotic; the phenotypes of both neurons and glia (Müller glia cells) are definitive and are undergoing functional maturation. In this study we are concerned with control of phenotypic characteristics of Müller cells.

A biochemical marker of Müller glia cells is the enzyme glutamine synthetase (GS). In these cells, GS is an inducible enzyme; the inducer is cortisol. The hormone rapidly elicits accumulation of GS mRNA and synthesis of the enzyme. However, in addition to the hormone, GS induction also requires contact between the glia cells and neurons (34). In dissociated glia cells, not in contact with neurons, GS is not inducible either in suspension cultures or in monolayer cultures. But, if the dissociated cells are reaggregated and they restore normal glia-neuron contacts, GS can again be induced (35, 36, 37). Direct evidence for the need for cell contact in this induction came from retina cell cultures which were set up so that neurons became clustered on top of patches of glia cells; GS was found to be inducible only in those glia cells that were in direct contact with neurons (Fig. 2) (38).

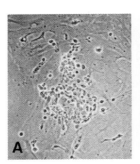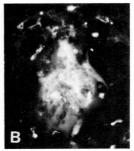

Figure 2. A) Culture of chick embryo neural retina cells: group of small neuronal cells attached to underlying flattened gliocytes. Medium contained cortisol to induce GS. B) The same culture immunostained with antiserum to GS. GS is induced only in glia cells that are in contact with neurons. Original figure. (For details see 38).

These and related findings suggest that contact with neurons generates signals in glia cells which capacitate them for GS induction by the hormone. As to the nature of such signals, they are not provided by some substance that freely diffuses out of neurons; and they are apparently not transmitted by gap junctions, since such junctions have not been demonstrated between glia and neurons in retina at this age. Our view is that the signals derive from the glia cell membrane and are elicited there by interactions of ligands which connect neurons and glia cells (Fig. 3). Cell separation voids these interactions, abrogates the signals, and renders glia cells non-inducible.

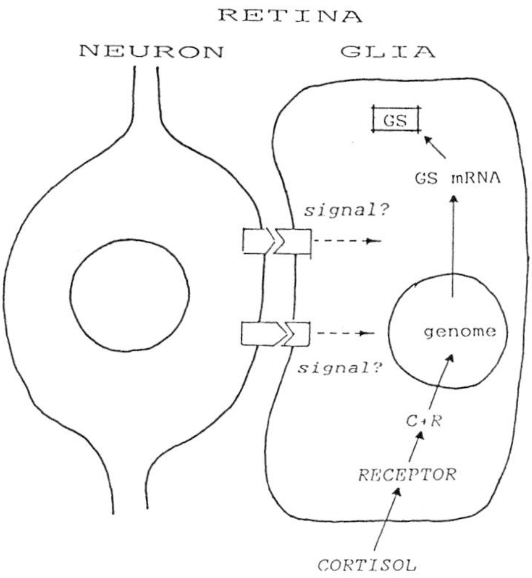

Figure 3. Diagram summarizing cortisol-mediated GS induction in glia cells and its dependence on contact-interactions with neurons.

Still other changes take place in retina glia cells if they are detached from neurons and are maintained mono-dispersed in monolayer culture for several days. They assume the shape of large epithelioid gliocytes and start to divide, although in 13-day retina glia cells are already post-mitotic. After 3 days in monolayer culture, retina cognin is no longer immunologically detectable on separated gliocytes, while neurons continue to express it (39). Indeed, such gliocytes no longer can adhere to retina

neurons; instead, they become adhesive to each other. This
striking change in cell affinity can be readily demonstrated
by aggregating retina cells after 5 to 7 days in monolayer
culture: in the aggregates, the gliocytes segregate from
neurons and strongly adhere into compact spherical bodies;
neuronal cells are loosely attached externally (Fig. 4).
As discussed earlier in this article, such cell segregation
occurs typically with cells that belong to different tissues.
However, in this case all the cells originated from the
retina.

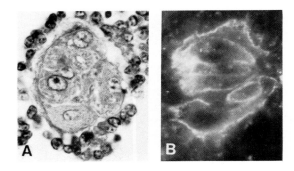

Figure 4. A) Aggregate of retina cells monolayer-cultured
for 5 days before aggregation (see text); glia-derived cells
segregate from neurons and adhere in the center (original
figure). B) Similar aggregate immunostained for MP26, a
lens cell-membrane antigen; its expression on these gliocytes symptomizes their conversion into lens-like cell type
(modified from 41).

The explanation is that separated retina gliocytes,
cultured in monolayer (thus, continuously deprived of normal
contact with neurons) convert into non-retina cell type;
hence, they stop expressing retina cognin, the tissue
affinity determinant of retina cells, and no longer recognize
neurons as histological partners. Such gliocytes acquire
characteristics of lens cells (40, 41): they accumulate lens

cytoplasmic antigens (crystallins) and newly express MP26, a lens cell-membrane antigen (Fig. 4).

These findings suggest the following working hypothesis concerning the role of cell contact in phenotype regulation of retina glia cells (42): 1) Contact-interactions of glia cells with neurons, mediated by retina cognin-containing cell ligands, play a crucial role in controlling phenotypic characteristics of the glia cells. 2) Detachment of the glia cells from neurons and their continued separation de-control the glial phenotype, elicit changes in cell surface properties and in gene expression, resulting in glia conversion into lens-like cell type.

These suggestions are consistent with the general concept of contact-communication of cells discussed at the beginning of this article. They are supported by findings in other systems indicating the importance of contact-interactions between cells for regulation of gene expression and phenotype characteristic (for example: 43-46).

Cell contact and its role in morphogenesis and differentiation are currently being intensively investigated in many laboratories. In this article I have briefly reviewed some of the background and progress of this work and described experimental systems for further clarification of these fundamental issues.

REFERENCES

1. Moscona AA (1980). In Cohen EP, Köhler H (eds): "Membranes, Receptors, and the Immune Response," Vol 42, p 171, Progress in Clinical and Biological Research, New York: Alan R. Liss.
2. Holtfreter J (1939). Arch exp Zellforsch 23:169.
3. Moscona AA, Moscona H (1952). J Anat 86:287.
4. Moscona AA (1974). In Moscona AA (ed): "The Cell Surface in Development," p 67, New York: John Wiley.
5. Sperry R (1943). J Comp Neurol 79:33.
6. Edelman G (1976). Science 192:218.
7. Steinberg M (1970). J exp Zool 173:395.
8. Curtis ASG (1966). Sci Progress 54:61.
9. Edelman G (1983). Science 219:450.
10. Antonelli PL, Rogers TD, Willard MA (1973). J Theoret Biol 41:1.

11. *Spiegel M, Spiegel ES (1975). Am Zool 15:583.*
12. *Moscona AA (1962). J Cell Comp Physiol 60:65.*
13. *Moscona AA (1968). Develop Biol.18:250.*
14. *Moscona AA (1976). In Barondes SH (ed): "Neuronal Recognition," p 205, New York: Plenum Press.*
15. *Moscona AA (1976). In Marois M (ed): "From Theoretical Physics to Biology," p 151, Amsterdam: North-Holland Publishing.*
16. *Moscona AA, Moscona H (1962). Anat Rec 142:319.*
17. *Goldschneider I, Moscona AA (1972). J Cell Biol 53:435.*
18. *Lilien JE, Moscona AA (1967). Science 157:70.*
19. *Garber BB, Moscona AA (1972). Develop Biol 27:235.*
20. *McClay DR, Moscona AA (1974). Exptl Cell Res 87:438.*
21. *Hausman RE, Moscona AA (1976). Proc Natl Acad Sci USA 73:3594.*
22. *Moscona AA (1961). Exptl Cell Res 22:455.*
23. *Hausman RE, Moscona AA (1975). Proc Natl Acad Sci USA 72:916.*
24. *Hausman RE, Moscona AA (1979). Exptl Cell Res 119:191.*
25. *Ophir I, Moscona AA, Ben-Shaul Y (1984). Cell Differentiation 15:53.*
26. *Ben-Shaul Y, Hausman RE, Moscona AA (1979). Develop Biol 72:89.*
27. *Ben-Shaul Y, Hausman RE, Moscona AA (1980). Dev Neuro 3:66.*
28. *Hausman RE, Knapp LW, Moscona AA (1976). J Exptl Zool 198:417.*
29. *Moscona AA, Hausman RE, Moscona M (1975). In Raoul Y (ed): "Proceedings 10th FEBS Meeting," Vol 38, p 245, Amsterdam: North-Holland Publishing.*
30. *Moscona M, Moscona AA (1979). Differentiation 13:165.*
31. *Moscona M, Degenstein L, Byun KY, Moscona AA (1981). Cell Differentiation 10:317.*
32. *Mayerson PL, Moscona AA (1979). Differentiation 13:173.*
33. *Monroy A, Moscona AA (1979). "Introductory Concepts in Developmental Biology," Chicago: University of Chicago Press.*
34. *Moscona AA, Linser P (1983). Curr Topics Develop Biol 18:155.*
35. *Morris JE, Moscona AA (1970). Science 167:1736.*
36. *Morris JE, Moscona AA (1971). Develop Biol 25:420.*
37. *Linser P, Moscona AA (1979). Proc Natl Acad Sci USA 76:6476.*
38. *Linser P, Moscona AA (1983). Develop Biol 96:529.*
39. *Ophir I, Moscona AA, Loya N, Ben-Shaul Y (1985). Cell Differentiation: In Press.*

40. *Moscona AA, Degenstein L (1982). In Clayton RM, Truman DES (eds): "Stability and Switching in Cellular Differentiation," p 187, New York: Plenum Press.*
41. *Moscona AA, Brown M, Degenstein L, Fox L, Soh BM (1983). Proc Natl Acad Sci USA 80:7239.*
42. *Linser P, Moscona AA (1984). In Lauder JM, Nelson PG (eds): "Gene Expression and Cell-Cell Interactions in the Developing Nervous System," p 185, New York: Plenum Press.*
43. *Weinberg H, Spencer P (1975). J Neurocytol 4:395.*
44. *Agnayo AJ, Epps J, Charron L, Bray GM (1976). Brain Res 104:1.*
45. *Holton B, Weston JA (1982). Develop Biol 89:72.*
46. *Fisher M (1984). Proc Natl Acad Sci USA 81:4414.*

ACKNOWLEDGMENTS

The work described here has been supported by research grants: HD01253 from the National Institute of Child Health and Human Development; PCM8408585 from the National Science Foundation; and 1-983 from the March of Dimes-Birth Defects Foundation. The author gratefully acknowledges the dedicated technical assistance of Linda Degenstein and Lyle Fox.

Progress in Developmental Biology, Part B, pages 43–46
© 1986 Alan R. Liss, Inc.

EVIDENCE THAT ONE OF TWO CELL-CELL ADHESION SYSTEMS OF
CHICK MYOBLASTS IS REQUIRED FOR MYOBLAST FUSION

Dorothy A. Gibralter and David C. Turner
Department of Biochemistry, State University
of New York Upstate Medical Center,
Syracuse, New York 13210

INTRODUCTION

Myoblast (Mb) adhesion is of special interest
because specific Mb-Mb adhesion event is thought to be
necessary as a prelude to Mb fusion (Bischoff, 1978). We
earlier found (Gibralter and Turner, 1985) that Mb
harvested by different procedures show different
aggregation behavior. The aggregation of cells
dissociated with high trypsin/Ca^{2+}(TC-Mb) is Ca^{2+}
-dependent (CD). Cells dissociated with EDTA (E-Mb) or
with low trypsin/EDTA (LTE-Mb) aggregate with or without
Ca^{2+}(Ca^{2+}-independent,CI), though E-Mb aggregation is enhanced with Ca^{2+}. When the treatments are
performed in sequence the cells behave like TE-Mb (Mb
treated directly with high trypsin/EDTA), aggregating
neither with nor without Ca^{2+}. Both TC-Mb and LTE-Mb
adhere more readily to homologous cells than to cells
subjected to the other treatment. We concluded that (1)
alternative treatments will produce Mb on which only one
of two adhesion systems is functional; (2) the treatments
selectively remove essential elements of one of the
systems; (3) the systems are independent; (4) the systems
are non-complementing (Gibralter and Turner, 1985).

We have adopted the univalent antibody (Ab) approach
to identify cell adhesion molecules (CAMs) that participate in the dual adhesion systems of Mb. Two antisera
(anti-TC cell; for which a rabbit was immunized with TC-
Mb and anti-E supe; with an EDTA extract of Mb) yielded
univalent Ab (Fab´) that selectively inhibit CD and CI
aggregation, respectively; the inhibitory effects of both

Fab´s can be neutralized by E supe (Turner and Gibralter, 1985). We have begun to use the inhibitory Fab´s in an effort to determine which adhesion system is required for fusion. Initial findings are presented here.

METHODS

Cell culture and harvesting, measurement of aggregation and adhesive specificity in labeled and unlabeled cell aggregates were as described in Gibralter and Turner (1985). Fab´s were prepared as described in Turner and Gibralter (1985). To assess the extent of fusion, cells were fixed, stained with mithramycin and examined with a fluorescence microscope (Puri et al., 1979).

RESULTS AND DISCUSSION

Suspended Mb cultured in serum-free medium (LH-Mb) fuse, forming "myoballs" (Puri and Turner, 1978). LH-Mb aggregate randomly with TC-Mb and E-Mb, indicating that they possess both CI and CD adhesion systems (Fig. 1).

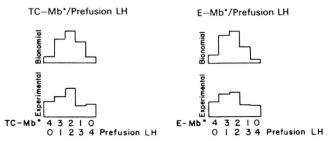

Fig. 1. Random association of LH-Mb with TC-Mb and E-Mb. LH-Mb cultured for 2 d (prefusion LH) were tested for adhesive specificity in 4-cell aggregates (Gibralter and Turner, 1985). The combinations tested were: labeled TC-Mb and unlabeled LH-Mb (left) and labeled E-Mb and unlabeled LH-Mb (right). In each case 46 aggregates were scored. Statistical analysis indicated no deviation from a random distribution in either case: left - χ^2 = 77, p = .002; right - χ^2 = 78, p = .002.

Our quantitative assay (Puri et al., 1979) involves culture of LH-Mb in medium containing a high-M_r fraction of embryo extract; maximal fusion occurs after several days. In addition to LH-Mb we wanted to use TC-Mb and LTE-Mb. Our aggregation assays had been carried out in 2 h (or less) in a simple medium and there had been no detectable restoration of the system destroyed by selective dissociation (Gibralter and Turner, 1985). However, assay times of 1 d or more were needed to detect changes in fusion and cells were not healthy for that long in a simple aggregation medium. Using a richer medium over longer times, and therefore expecting restoration to be a problem, we supplemented some cultures with the protein synthesis inhibitor, cycloheximide (Cx).

Effects of the Fab's on fusion are shown in Table 1.

TABLE 1. EFFECT OF UNIVALENT ANTIBODIES ON Mb FUSION

Cells	Additions	Concentration	Nuclei/cell at 48 h	
			with Cx (5 ug/ml)	without Cx
LH-Mb	EGTA	1.66 mM	1.1	1.1
TC-Mb	EGTA	1.66 mM	N.D.	1.1
LTE-Mb	EGTA	1.66 mM	1.2	1.1
LH-Mb	None	-	2.3	2.5
TC-Mb	None	-	2.3	5.2
LTE-Mb	None	-	2.0	3.0
LH-Mb	Anti-E supe Fab'	400 ug/ml	3.9	1.9
TC-Mb	Anti-E supe Fab'	400 ug/ml	2.4	5.5
LTE-Mb	Anti-E supe Fab'	400 ug/ml	1.8	4.2
LH-Mb	Anti-TC cell Fab'	400 ug/ml	1.0	1.1
TC-Mb	Anti-TC cell Fab'	400 ug/ml	1.2	4.8
LTE-Mb	Anti-TC cell Fab'	400 ug/ml	1.9	3.7

For LH-Mb in the presence of Cx the number of nuclei/cell increased 2.3-fold compared to fusion-blocked EGTA controls; without Cx the increase was similar. In Cx (but not in its absence) anti-E supe Fab' greatly enhanced LH-Mb fusion. Anti-TC cell Fab' blocked LH-Mb fusion with or without Cx. This suggests that the CD system is required for fusion and that the CI system is not only not required but - if allowed to function - may reduce the extent of fusion. The results with TC-Mb are consistent with those for LH-Mb. TC-Mb fuse very well in the absence of Cx and even with Cx fuse as well as LH-Mb. Anti-E supe Fab' has no effect on TC-Mb, as expected since TC-Mb lack a CI system. Anti-TC cell Fab' blocks TC-Mb fusion in Cx-treated cultures only. Finally, LTE-Mb fuse less well than TC-Mb in the same media and their fusion is little affected by either Fab'. We are unable to explain why LTE-Mb in Cx (which presumably lack a CD system) are

nonetheless able to fuse to some extent; further
experiments are needed.

The finding that Mb with the CD adhesion system
selectively removed fuse less well than cells with an
intact CD system is strong evidence for the CD system to
be necessary and sufficient for fusion. Our data also
show that we can measure effects of Fab´ on fusion. The
preliminary indications with polyspecific Fab´ are that
one Fab´ inhibits fusion of LH-Mb and TC-Mb whereas the
other promotes fusion. However, because our Ab are
polyspecific, Ab of unknown specificity may interfere in
our assays. We have yet to show that the cell extracts
that neutralize the inhibition of CD adhesion similarly
neutralize the inhibition of fusion by anti-TC cell Fab´.
Conclusive demonstration that the CD system is required
for fusion will be possible only when we obtain
monospecific inhibitory Ab. Work is underway to identify
and purify CD CAM(s) and to obtain monospecific Ab. As
yet we have no evidence that the same Ab(s) that inhibit
CI adhesion also promote fusion. Although monospecific
Ab will again be needed for definitive conclusions, the
possibility that one adhesion system can modulate the
functioning of another deserves further attention.
This research was supported by grants from the NIH (HD
17060) and from the Muscular Dystrophy Association.

REFERENCES

Bischoff R (1978). Myoblast fusion. In Poste G,
  Nicholson GL (eds): "Membrane fusion," Amsterdam:
  Elsevier/North-Holland, pp 127-179.
Puri EC, Turner DC (1978). Serum-free medium
  allows chicken myogenic cells to be cultivated in
  suspension and separated from attached fibroblasts.
  Exp Cell Res 115: 159-173.
Puri EC, Chiquet M, Turner DC (1979).
  Fibronectin-independent myoblast fusion in
  suspension cultures. Biochem Biophys Res Commun
  90: 883-889.
Gibralter D, Turner DC (1985). Dual adhesion
  systems of chick myoblasts. Dev Biol, in press.
Turner DC, Gibralter D (1985). Regulation of
  cell interactions during skeletal muscle
  development. Curr Top Cell Regul, in press.

Progress in Developmental Biology, Part B, pages 47–50
© 1986 Alan R. Liss, Inc.

THE SPECIFICITY OF CHICKEN LACTOSE LECTIN

Ying-Hsien Shih and Qin-Xue Chen

Institute of Developmental Biology,
Academia Sinica, Beijing, China

INTRODUCTION

Cell adhesion plays an important role in the generation of form during development. Various types of cells exhibit different degrees of adhesion both to their own cell type (homotypic adhesion) and to different cell types (heterotypic adhesion). These differences are presumed to reflect differences in their cell surface properties. Differential patterns of cell adhesion are observed from the earliest cleavage stages through the final precise patterning of cells into complex structures.

Cell to cell adhesion has been studied experimentally by dissociating tissues or entire organisms into single cells which subsequently form aggregates. The strength of adhesion was evaluated by measuring the size of aggregates; cells forming large aggregates were assumed to be strongly adhesive, whereas few, small aggregates were indicative of weak adhesion.

In a previous paper(1,2) we used the lactose urea method to isolate the lactose binding protein (lectin) from various tissues. Large amounts of this lectin is found in liver, kidney and skeletal muscle. The reagglucinating activity of the lactose lectins of chick embryo kidney and intestine was differentially expressed during chick embryogene-

sis(1). In this paper we analyze the tissue specificity of the lactose lectin. We address mostly
the problem of the tissue origin of the lectin
with respect to their ability to agglutinate different embryonic and adult tissue.

METHODS

The lectin was pruified with DEAE cellulose
and Dextran Blue-Sepharose 4B chromatography and
the radioactive lictin receptors on the surface
of differint cells were observed with scanning e-
lectron microscope autoradiography(SEM-ARG) according to the Suzuki and Mizuhira method(3).

RESULTS

Embryonic chicken liver which was lactose—
urea extracted and fractionated on DEAE cellulose
gave rise to a single peak of homoglutinating activity eluting at 0.25 M NaCl. Further purification of these fractions on dextran blue-sepharose
4B led to the isolation of a single peak with a
constant hemoagglutinating activity-protein concentration ratio. A single band with an apparent
molecular weight of 1.1 Kd was detected after SDS
polyacrylamide gel electrophoresis. Gel filtration
on sephadex G-75 showed
that the lectin had a na-
tive apparent molecular
weight of 2.2 Kd consis-
tent with the existence
of a dimer. A similar le-
ctin had a native apparent
molecular weight of 2.2
Kd consistent with the
existence of a dimer. A
similar lectin was puri-
fied from adult liver carrying the same specifici-
ty for lactose. This lec-
tin was able to induce
agglutination of embryo-
nic and adult liver and
kidney cells. Kidney tis-
sues from the chicken

Table I. The specificity
of the chicken lectin
(Lactose binding protein)

Lectin Cells	Adult Liver	Adult Kidney	Embryo Liver	Embryo Kidney
Adult Liver	+++	+	++	+
Adult Kidney	+	+++	++	++
Embryo Liver	++	+	+++	++
Embryo Kidney	+	++	++	+++

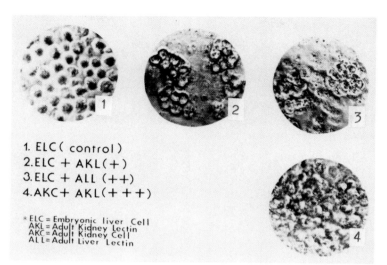

Fig. I. The comparison of lectin agglutination

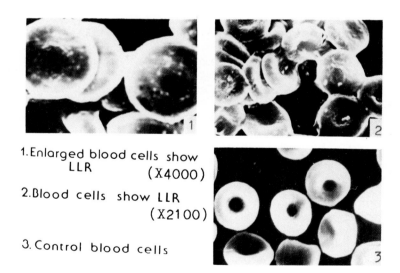

Fig. 2. Liver lectin receptor (LLR)

also contained a lactose lectin which agglutinated
very efficiently embryonic and adult kidney cells.
The kidney lectin also agglutinated chick embryonic and adult liver cells(Fig.I). Table I summari-

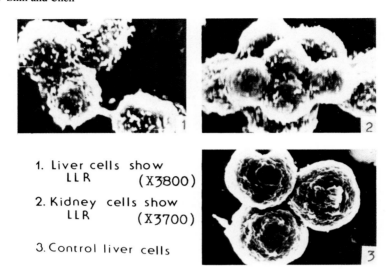

1. Liver cells show
        LL R   (X3800)

2. Kidney cells show
        LL R   (X3700)

3. Control liver cells

Fig. 3. Liver lectin receptor (LLR)

zes the results obtained with lactose lectins obtained from both embryonic and adult liver and kidney tissues. Each of lactose lectins agglutinated
much better the cells from which the lectin was extracted. Scanning electron micrographs of the agglutinated cells showed that adult liver cells
form large compact aggregates as compared to embryonic cells. In contrast, adult kidney cells col-
lect into small aggregates in the presence of the
exogenous lectin. Lactose lectin receptors can be
detected on the surface of rabbit erythrocytes
(Fig.2) and on the chicken liver and kidney cells
(Fig.3) with SEM—ARG.

REFERENCES

(1). Ying-Hsien Shih(Shi Yingxian) and Rongti
Liang (1983) Acta Zoologica Sinica Vol.29 No.1.
(2). Rongti Liang and Ying-Hsien Shih (1984)
Scientia Sinica Vol.XXVII.
(3). Hidenori Suzuki and Vinci Mizuhira (1982)
Acta Histochem Cytochem Vol.15 No.4.

Progress in Developmental Biology, Part B, pages 51–54
© 1986 Alan R. Liss, Inc.

ANALYSIS OF HYDRA INTERSTITIAL CELL POTENTIAL USING VIABLE
CELL SORTING

Marcia S. Yaross

Department of Developmental and Cell Biology and
Developmental Biology Center, University of California, Irvine, CA 92717.

INTRODUCTION

The interstitial cells of hydra constitute a multipotent stem cell population. This stem cell system maintains
its number in the adult animal while continuing to produce a
variety of differentiated cell types, including nerve cells
and nematocytes (cf. Bode and David, 1978). The diverse
array of product cells has often been assumed to derive from
a uniform pool of multipotent stem cells. Recent evidence,
however, has suggested that the interstitial cell population
may be heterogeneous with respect to proliferation and differentiation potentials (Littlefield, 1985; Heimfeld and
Bode, 1985).

To explore the extent to which interstitial cells may
be restricted in their ability to form product cells, methods have been developed to isolate viable interstitial
cells by means of flow cytometry. These cells can then be
grown in an _in vivo_ culture system to analyze their differentiation potential.

RESULTS

Hydra were dissociated into viable cell suspensions
(Gierer et al., 1972). Suspensions of normal and of interstitial cell free animals, prepared by treatment with nitrogen mustard (Diehl and Burnett, 1964), were then analyzed by
flow cytometry. Figure 1 illustrates the light scatter properties of suspensions of normal hydra (Fig. 1A) and of

interstitial cell free animals (Fig. 1B). Using an argon laser tuned to 488 nm to measure forward angle light scatter (FALS) and ninty degree light scatter (I90LS), a peak can be detected in normal animals that is missing in interstitial cell free hydra. Upon sorting, this region was confirmed to be highly enriched for interstitial cells.

Dead cells were detected using propidium iodide (PI) which binds the DNA of damaged cells and is excluded by live cells (Dangl et al., 1982). Dissociated H. oligactis cells were incubated in 2.5 ug/ml PI. Log integrated red fluorescence (>590 nm) of the interstitial cell containing population was measured by gating on FALS and I90LS. Live cells demonstrate dim autofluorescence which can be easily discriminated from the specific PI fluorescence of dead cells. By sorting on the basis of FALS, I90LS and red fluorescence, live interstitial cells were highly enriched and isolated for further analysis.

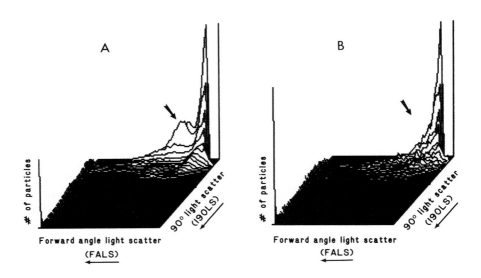

Figure 1. Light scatter characteristics of dissociated H. attenuata cells. Cells were analyzed using an EPICS V (Coulter Electronics) equipped with a 5 watt argon laser tuned to 488 nm. (A) Normal cell suspension. (B) Interstitial cell free suspension, prepared from animals treated 4 days previously with nitrogen mustard (NM).

H. oligactis cells sorted on these parameters were cultured in aggregates of NM treated H. attenuata cells. Such aggregates reestablish normal tissue architecture (David and Murphy, 1977) and provide an interstitial cell free environment for the growth and differentiation of the added, sorter purified cells. Aggregates were scored for the presence of interstitial cells and their differentiation products 6–10 days later. Interstitial cells, nerve cells and nematoblasts, all derived from the input, sorted cells, were detected. Interstital cells and nematoblasts (differentiating nematocyte precursors), which are completely absent in the host NM tissue, were identified by staining with toluidine blue (Diehl and Burnett, 1964) or by the binding of the monoclonal antibody TS23 (Heimfeld and Yaross, unpub. obser.). Nerve cells produced by the donor interstitial cells were discriminated from residual nerve cells in the NM hosts by staining with another monoclonal antibody, RC9, which binds nerve cells of H. oligactis but not H. attenuata origin (Yaross et al., 1985; unpub. obser.). Control NM aggregates (without added H. oligactis cells) were devoid of interstitial cells and their derivatives in these assays.

DISCUSSION

The results demonstrate that live interstitial cells can be recognized on the basis of their distinct light scattering properties. Such live cells can be isolated and cultured in NM aggregates where they undergo normal proliferation and differentiation, forming both nerve cells and nematocytes.

Thus, these experiments form the basis for a systematic examination of the developmental potential of interstitial cell subsets and, ultimately, of individual stem cells. Monoclonal antibodies have been generated that recognize subsets of the interstitial cell population (Littlefield et al., 1985, Yaross et al., 1985). Some antibodies also bind specific product cell types and/or intermediates, suggesting possible lineage relationships. Using these antibodies to isolate antibody-positive and -negative subpopulations of the interstitial cells, analysis of the differentiative capacities of such subsets is now in progress. The results should help to clarify the nature of the heterogeneity of the stem cell pool in hydra.

ACKNOWLEDGMENTS

I wish to thank Lorette C. Javois and Shelly Heimfeld for providing the antibodies used in these experiments and Hans R. Bode for providing laboratory facilities and equipment. This research was supported by grant PCM–83–02581 from the National Science Foundation to MSY and by grants HD 08086 and HD16440 from the National Institutes of Health to HRB.

REFERENCES

Bode HR, David CN (1978). Regulation of a multipotent stem cell, the interstitial cell of Hydra. Prog Biophys Molec Biol 33:189–206.
Dangl JL, Parks DR, Oi VT, Herzenberg LA (1982). Rapid isolation of cloned isotype switch variants using fluorescence activated cell sorting. Cytometry 2:395–401.
David CN, Murphy S (1977). Characterization of interstitial stem cells in hydra by cloning. Dev Biol 57:372–383.
Diehl FA, Burnett AL (1964). The role of interstitial cells in the maintenance of hydra. I. Specific destruction of interstitial cells in normal, asexual, non–budding animals. J Exp Zool 155:253–260.
Gierer A, Berking S, Bode H, David CN, Flick K, Hansmann G, Schaller H, Trenkner E (1972). Regeneration of hydra from reaggregated cells. Nature 239:98–101.
Heimfeld S, Bode HR (1985). Growth regulation of the interstitial cell population in hydra. III. Interstitial cell density does not control stem cell proliferation (submitted).
Littlefield CL (1985). Germ cells in Hydra oligactis males: I. Isolation of a subpopulation that is developmentally restricted to sperm production. Dev Biol 110:308–320.
Littlefield CL, Dunne JF, Bode HR (1985). Spermatogenesis in Hydra oligactis: morphological description and characterization using a monoclonal antibody specific for cells of the spermatogenic pathway. Dev Biol 110:308–320.
Yaross MS, Westerfield J, Javois LC, Bode HR (1985). Nerve cells in hydra: monoclonal antibodies identify two lineages with distinct mechanisms for their incorporation into head tissue. (submitted).

Fertilization

Progress in Developmental Biology, Part B, pages 57–68
© 1986 Alan R. Liss, Inc.

SPERM–EGG INTERACTION AND FUSION IN FERTILIZATION

Alberto Monroy[°], Gianna Casazza[°], Rosaria
De Santis[°], Maria Rosaria Pinto[+] and Floriana
Rosati[°][x]
[°]Zoological Station, Naples; [+]CNR Institute of
Molecular Embryology, Naples; [x]Zoological
Institute, University of Siena, Italy.

1. Sperm Binding to the egg: the sperm receptors

The first condition for fertilization to occur, as it
was stated by Boveri back in 1902, is that sperm and egg
"must be able to find each other". Recognition, which is
followed by the attachment of the spermatozoon to the egg,
is an exquisitely species-specific event and depends on the
presence of "receptors" at the surface of both gametes. In
the vast majority of animals the egg is covered by an
extracellular glycoprotein envelope designated as the
Vitelline Coat (V.C.)(and zona pellucida in mammals) which
is the site of the receptors for the spermatozoa (sperm
receptors). In all the animals studied so far the V.C. has
proved to be a product of the oocyte, although participation of the follicle cells, in particular in the establishment of its supramolecular organization, cannot be ruled
out (reviewed by Monroy and Rosati, 1983). In the
Ascidians, which is the material used in our Laboratory,
the main role in the function of the receptors is played
by the sugar L-Fucose (Rosati and De Santis, 1980). The
fucosyl-glycoprotein components of the receptors are synthesized by the oocyte during the vitellogenic stages of
oogenesis (Rosati et al., 1982). This shows that the
receptors, on which the fine tuning and in fact the success
of fertilization depends, are synthesized under the control
of the oocyte genome.

These findings have prompted us to use Fucose as a
marker of the receptors, in particular in attempts at
isolating them as molecular entities. The V.C. of the

Ascidians is very difficult to bring into solution. When
this is achieved, a large number of components are identified by SDS-PAGE. However, only five of them with an
average Molecular Weight from 200.000 to 80.000 daltons are
labelled either with radioactive Fucose (injected into the
ovary, Rosati et al., 1982) or in vitro with ^{125}I-labelled
Fucose Binding Protein (FBP) (Pinto et al., 1981).
Extraction of V.C. at low ionic strength brings the
Fucosyl-glycoproteins into solution while leaving behind
the bulk of the V.C. components. When spermatozoa are
challenged with this extract, they (1) lose the ability to
bind to the egg, and exhibit the morphological signs of
sperm activation (displacement of the mitochondrion,
Lambert and Epel, 1979) which in a certain percentage of
cases culminates in the acrosome reaction (De Santis et al.,
1983). We conclude that this fraction contains the material of the sperm receptors. The question then arose
whether the five fucosyl-glycoproteins identified by SDS-
PAGE are independent entities each endowed with a specific
function, e.g. one involved in sperm recognition, another
in triggering the acrosome reaction, etc.; or whether they
are subunits of a large complex that breaks down either
during the preparation or as a result of electrophoresis,
the receptor activity being in fact a property of the
complex as a whole. As a matter of fact previous electron
microscopic studies of V.C. stained with ferritin-conju-
gated FBP had shown tufts of fibrils emerging from its
outer surface to which the spermatozoa attached (Pinto et
al., 1981). This observation favoured the hypothesis that
the receptor is a very large molecular entity.

Our primary aim was then to obtain the receptors in as
native a condition as possible.

We had shown previously (Rosati et al., 1982) that the
same five fucosyl-containing components could be obtained
from ovaries injected with ^{3}H-Fucose. Also the low-ionic
strength extract from the ovaries has the same biological
activity as the low-ionic strength extract from the V.C.
of the mature eggs.

Hence, as a starting material for the purification of
the receptors the low-ionic strength extract of ovaries
injected with 40 μC/ovary of ^{3}H-L-Fucose (Spec.act.84 μC/m
Mole) was used (Fig. 1).18 hours after injection, the
ovaries were homogenized and the homogenate was first

submitted to sonication and then centrifuged at 100.000 x
g for 3 hours. The supernatant (FG) was fractionated by

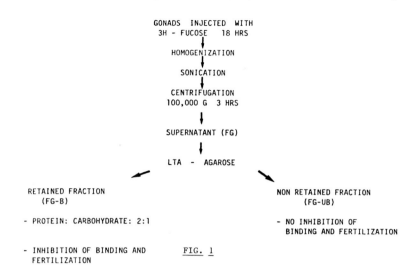

GONADS INJECTED WITH
3H - FUCOSE   18 HRS
↓
HOMOGENIZATION
↓
SONICATION
↓
CENTRIFUGATION
100,000 G 3 HRS
↓
SUPERNATANT (FG)
↓
LTA - AGAROSE

RETAINED FRACTION
(FG-B)

- PROTEIN: CARBOHYDRATE: 2:1

NON RETAINED FRACTION
(FG-UB)

- NO INHIBITION OF
  BINDING AND FERTILIZATION

- INHIBITION OF BINDING AND
  FERTILIZATION

FIG. 1

affinity chromatography on LTA (Lotus tetranoglobus
agglutinin). The fraction that was retained on the column,
comprising 30% of the fucosyl-containing components of the
extract (FG-B), inhibited binding of the spermatozoa to
the V.C. and fertilization at a concentration of 14 µg/ml
(determined as proteins). The estimated molecular weight
of FG-B is greater than 1.5×10^6 daltons, since it elutes
in the void volume of a BioGel A1.5 column. It has a
protein: carbohydrate ratio of 2:1. Negative staining of
spermatozoa treated with this fraction shows bead-like
structures attached to the tip of the unreacted spermatozoa.

The unbound fraction of FG (FG-UB) when tested under
the same conditions proved to be ineffective in inhibiting
binding of the spermatozoa to the V.C. even at a ten times
higher concentration.

Glycopeptides were obtained by exhaustive pronase
digestion of FGB-B. Two peaks were separated on BioGel
P-10: one eluted in the void volume (FG-Bp1) and the other
was included in the fractionation range (FG-Bp2). FG-Bp1
inhibited binding of spermatozoa to the V.C. at a concentration of 36 µg/ml but failed to trigger the acrosome

reaction. Similarly to FG-B from which it derives, FG-Bpl
binds to the tip of unreacted spermatozoa. Only 45% of
FG-Bpl is retained on LTA columns (Fig. 2).

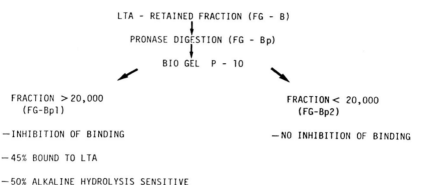

LTA - RETAINED FRACTION (FG - B)

PRONASE DIGESTION (FG - Bp)

BIO GEL P - 10

FRACTION > 20,000
(FG-Bp1)

—INHIBITION OF BINDING

—45% BOUND TO LTA

—50% ALKALINE HYDROLYSIS SENSITIVE

FRACTION < 20,000
(FG-Bp2)

—NO INHIBITION OF BINDING

FIG. 2

These observations suggest that the sperm receptor of
the V.C. of Ciona is a very high molecular weight fucosyl
glycoprotein. They further suggest that binding to the
sperm surface is mediated by its carbohydrate moyety, as
already indicated by our previous work (Rosati and De
Santis, 1980; De Santis et al., 1980).

More than 50 percent of the glycopeptides of the
FG-Bpl fraction are sensitive to alkaline hydrolysis, thus
indicating a high percentage of 0-glycosidic linkages.

2.   The activation of the spermatozoon

Early at the beginning of our work on Ascidian fertilization Rosati and De Santis (1978) discovered that treatment of the eggs with glycerol at a low temperature results
in the shedding of the follicle cells and cytolysis of the
test cells and of the oocyte. On the contrary, the V.C.
not only remains apparently intact, but it retains its
ability to bind spermatozoa species-specifically. These
eggs were called "ghost eggs." An interesting property of
the V.C. of the ghost eggs is that it has lost its ability
to trigger the acrosome reaction of the attached spermatozoa. This situation has thus provided us with a tool

to investigate the events of sperm binding under conditions in which neither an acrosome reaction nor a metabolic reaction of the egg takes place.

Using this system we have been able to show that binding to the V.C. elicits a marked heat production from the spermatozoa not accompanied, however, by oxygen consumption (Elia et al, 1983). In addition, nearly 90 percent of the ATP of the spermatozoa is lost (Rosati and Tosti, unpublished). We suggested that upon binding to the V.C. the spermatozoa undergo a massive breakdown of their ATP content and the energy generated thereby goes into heat rather than into motility (futile heat). This leads to speculate that attachment to the sperm receptors causes a metabolic inactivation of the spermatozoa as a result of the burning of their energy sources (Monroy, 1985).

Once the spermatozoa have overcome the species-specificity barrier of the V.C., fusion with the egg ensues. A prerequisite for fusion to occur is that the spermatozoa must have undergone the acrosome reaction. Fusion is indeed mediated by the acrosome process (or by the exposed inner acrosomal membrane as in the case of mammals which do not form an acrosomal process) and the egg plasma membrane. In the Ascidians and mammals the acrosome reaction is triggered by the interaction of the spermatozoon with the V.C. (or the zona pellucida, respectively). In the starfish it is triggered by a high molecular weight component of the jelly coat that surrounds the egg (Ikedai and Hoshi, 1981). In the sea urchin, although the jelly coat in solution is the most potent trigger of the acrosome reaction, whether this is also the case in vivo, is still an open question. The major difficulty in answering this question, is that in these eggs the V.C. is extremely thin and firmly attached to the egg plasma membrane, which makes essentially impossible to isolate it without cytoplasmic or jelly coat contaminants (reviewed by Monroy and Rosati, 1983).

The acrosome reaction is associated with ionic movements, and in particular with a massive uptake of calcium, increased intracellular pH, depolarization of its membrane, and release of enzymes (Shapiro et al., 1981; Schackmann et al., 1981, 1984; Shapiro et al., 1981; Tilney, 1985). All these events may be relevant to the following step, sperm fusion with the egg.

3.   Fusion of the spermatozoon with the egg

Information about the mechanisms underlying fusion is
scanty. In fact it does not go much beyond the pioneering
electron microscopic studies of the Colwins which illustrated the details of the fusion of the acrosomal process
with the egg plasma membrane (reviewed by Colwin and
Colwin, 1967).

As a first approximation, the problem can be discussed
in the context of fusion of artificial phospholipid membranes and vesicles (Monroy, 1985). The first prerequisite
for fusion of such membranes to occur is that they must
approach one another so as to attain molecular contact.
That means overcoming the electrostatic repulsion and the
much greater resistance offered by the hydrated polar
groups of the phospholipid molecules: this is called the
hydration barrier. In the case of curved surfaces, the
repulsive forces decrease with the decrease of their radius
of curvature and reach a minimum at a radius of a curvature of 0.1 µm or less. This is indeed the radius of curvature at the tip of the acrosomal process in the spermatozoa in which a long and thin filament arises as a result of
the acrosome reaction (such as in the Echinoderms, see
Tilney, 1985). In cases in which the acrosome reaction
leads to the formation of a number of blunt tubules (such
as in Hydroides, Colwin and Colwin, 1961, and in the
Ascidians, Rosati et al., 1985) the published electron
micrographs suggest that their molecular contact with the
egg plasma membrane may be established with mechanisms
analogous to those between flaccid vesicles. In the
extreme case, in which no acrosomal process is formed,
close contact of the exposed inner acrosomal membrane with
the egg plasma membrane may be mediated by bushes of
microvilli arising from the egg surface (Yanagimachi and
Noda, 1970).

An important role in overcoming the electrostatic
repulsion may be played by the surface charges of the
interacting surfaces (Evans and Parsegian, 1983; Gilbert
and Ehrenstein, 1983). Preliminary investigations on the
sea urchin and ascidian spermatozoa carried out by
Dr. L. Koehler in our Laboratory using anionic or cationic
charged microbeads suggest a negative charge of the acrosomal process, while no beads become attached either to the
acrosomal region or to the head of the unreacted

spermatozoa. However, in view of the conditions prevailing in the sea water – in particular the high pH and the high contents of divalent ions – it is difficult to be certain whether the attachment of the beads is due to the electrical charges of the surface of the acrosomal process or to e.g. the "stickness" of the bindin that ensheathes the acrosomal process (Moy and Vacquier, 1979).

Close apposition of phospholipid membranes does not necessarily lead to their fusion. Fusion is greatly enhanced by calcium as a result of the formation of Ca-phospholipid complexes between the adjoining membranes (trans-complex). This results in membrane destabilization due to the crystallization of the acyl chains (phase transition) with release of heat in the region of contact. The heat released, in turn enhances the rate of molecular mixing at the domain boundaries (Papahadiopoulos, 1978; Portis et al., 1979). Furthermore, inclusion of Ca-binding proteins or pore-forming proteins (such as porin, Zimmerberg et al., 1980; Cohen et al., 1982) in the vesicles enhances fusion.

In the case of fertilization, the presence of calcium in the medium, though an absolute requirement for the acrosome reaction to take place (J.C. Dan, 1952) does not seem to be required for sperm-egg fusion (Chambers, 1980; Schmidt et al., 1982) (at least in the sea urchin, while it seems to be required in mammals). However, it is now known that a massive calcium uptake by the spermatozoon accompanies the acrosome reaction (Schackmann and Shapiro, 1981), though it is not known in which sperm compartment it accumulates. At least some of it could be taken up by the acrosomal process and become bound to its surface (Monroy, 1985). This among other things may shield the electrical charges at the surface of the acrosomal process thus helping its approaching the egg plasma membrane.

However, neither the acrosomal process nor the egg plasma membrane are pure phospholipid membranes: indeed, proteins are important components of both. Proteins can participate in sperm-egg fusion in two ways. One is in a fusogenic capacity. This is suggested by the recent observations of Glabe (1985) that bindin promotes fusion of dipalmytol phosphatidylcholine-phosphatidylcholine vesicles. The second concerns the role of the membrane intrinsic proteins in membrane fusion (Satir et al., 1973; Orci et al.,

1977). Clearance and/or translocation of intramembrane proteins-the IMP-at the site of contact between cells or in the process of exocytosis has been claimed to be required for fusion. Such studies are very difficult to carry out in the case of sperm-egg fusion in view of the enormous difference in size of the two gametes and of the extremely small area of the egg surface where fusion occurs. Yet in the spermatozoon of the ascidian, Ciona intestinalis, bound to the V.C. but prior to the onset of the acrosome reaction, the particles of the "inner circlet" become disarranged, though neither their number nor their size change (Rosati et al., 1985). Hence it is possible that translocation of intramembrane proteins, both in the acro-somal process and in the egg plasma membrane, which does not necessarily involve clearance, may be a step toward destabilization of the two adjoining membranes - that of the acrosomal process and the egg plasma membrane - in preparation to their fusion. Translocation may be trigger-ed when the two membranes reach molecular contact. Alternatively, molecular contact may induce a conforma-tional change of some of the intramembrane proteins that is a prerequisite for fusion to occur (Monroy, 1985).

Finally, release of lysophosphatides due to the activa-tion of phospholipases may be an important fusogenic factor. This has indeed been observed to take place both in in vitro systems (Monroy, 1956; Conway and Metz, 1976) in which acrosome reacted spermatozoa were shown to be able to release lysophosphatides from hens egg yolk, and in the course of the acrosome reaction (SeGall and Lennarz, 1981). An attractive aspects of phospholipase activation as the initiator of the reactions leading to sperm-egg fusion is that this is a self-regulating reaction in the sense that the active lyso-products are very rapidly degraded into non-lyso, i.e. non-fusogenic, products.

4. Conclusions

In this presentation we have discussed three problems related to the mechanisms of sperm-egg interaction and fusion. First, we show that in the ascidians the sperm receptors are very high (higher than 1.5×10^6 daltons) MW glycoprotein complexes. They selectively bind to the tip of the unreacted spermatozoa and this results in the loss of the ability of the spermatozoa to bind to the V.C.

From the active complex several glycopeptide fractions have been obtained; one of them was still able to bind to the spermatozoa and to inhibit their attachment to the V.C.

From calorimetric studies of the interaction of the spermatozoa with the V.C. under conditions in which binding is not followed by the acrosome reaction, we suggest that upon binding to the sperm receptors the spermatozoa undergo metabolic inactivation.

Finally, we discuss the mechanisms of fusion of the spermatozoon with the egg. We suggest that this is controlled by processes analogous to those controlling fusion of artificial phospholipid membranes. In particular, the key event for fusion to occur is that the acrosomal process and the egg plasma membrane come into molecular contact. Molecular contact is, however, a necessary but not sufficient requirement for fusion to occur. In the case of artificial phospholipid membranes a most important role is played by calcium as a result of the formation of calcium-phospholipid complexes between the adjoining membranes. Although calcium in the external medium does not seem to be required for sperm-egg fusion, in view of the very large uptake of calcium in conjunction with the acrosome reaction, it is suggested that some calcium may be incorporated into the acrosomal process thus facilitating its fusion with the egg plasma membrane. Furthermore, proteins at the surface of the acrosomal process may be endowed with fusogenic activity: relevant to this is the fusogenic activity of bindin. The organization and the topology of the membrane proteins, in particular in the egg plasma membrane may play a critical role in allowing or preventing the approach of the acrosomal process to the egg plasma membrane at the molecular distance required for fusion. This would confer to the egg plasma membrane selective properties in addition to those of the vitelline coat.

An important fusogenic role may also be played by phospholipases activated in conjunction with the acrosome reaction resulting in the transient formation of lysophosphatides.

The investigations of our group have been supported by Grants from the Consiglio Nazionale delle Ricerche through the "Progetto Finalizzato Biologia della Riproduzione" and "Progetto Finalizzato Chimica Fine e Secondaria" and from the Ministry of Education.

REFERENCES

Boveri Th (1902). Das Problem der Befruchtung. G Fischer Verl, Jena
Chambers EL (1980). Fertilization and cleavage of eggs of Lytechynus variegatus in Ca^{2+} free sea water. Europ J Cell Biol 22:476.
Cohen FS, Akabas MH, Finkelstein A (1982). Osmotic swelling of phospholipid vesicles causes them to fuse with planar phospholipid bilayer membrane. Science 217: 458-460.
Colwin AL, Colwin LH (1961). Changes in the spermatozoon during fertilization in Hydroides hexagonus (Annelida). 2. Incorporation with the egg. J Bioph Bioch Cytol 10:255-274.
Colwin LH, Colwin AL (1967). Membrane fusion in relation to sperm-egg association in "Fertilization" C.B. Metz and A. Monroy, Eds, Ac Press vol 1:295-368.
Conway AF, Metz ChB (1976). Phospholipase activity of sea urchin sperm: its possible involvement in membrane fusion. J Exptl Zool 198:39-48.
Dan JC (1952). Studies on the acrosome. 1. Reaction to egg water and other stimuli. Biol Bull 103:54-66.
De Santis R, Jamunno G, Rosati F (1980). A study of the chorion and of the follicle cells in relation to sperm egg interaction in the Ascidian, Ciona intestinalis. Dev Biol 74:490-499.
De Santis R, Pinto MR, Cotelli F, Rosati F, Monroy A, D'Alessio G (1983). A fucosyl glycoprotein component with sperm-receptor and sperm-activating activities from the vitelline coat of Ciona intestinalis eggs. Exptl Cell Res 148:508-513.
Elia V, Rosati F, Barone G, Monroy A, Liquori AM (1983). A thermodynamic study of sperm-egg interaction. The EMBO J 2:2053-2058.
Evans EA, Parsegian VA (1983). Energetics of membrane deformation and adhesion in cell and vesicle aggregation. Ann NY Acad Sci 416:13-33.
Gilbert DL, Ehrenstein G (1983). Membrane surface charge. Curr Topics in Membr & Transp 22:407-421.
Glabe CG (1985). Interaction of the sperm adhesive protein, bindin, with phospholipid vesicles. 2. Bindin induces the fusion of mixed-phase vesicles that contain phosphatidylcholine and phosphatidylserine in vitro. J Cell

Biol 100:800–806.

Ikedai H, Hoshi M (1981). Biochemical studies on the acrosome reaction of the starfish, Asterias amurensis. 2. Purification and characterization of acrosome reaction-inducing substance. Dev Growth Differ 23:81–88.

Lambert CC, Epel D (1979). Calcium-mediated mitochondrial movement in Ascidian sperm during fertilization. Dev Biol 69:296–604.

Monroy A (1956). Some experiments concerning the chemical mechanisms of the activation of the sea urchin egg. Exp Cell Res 10:320–323.

Monroy A (1985a). Processes controlling sperm-egg fusion. Europ Journ Biochem (in press).

Monroy A (1985b). Sperm-egg interactions preparatory to fertilization in "The Molecular and Cellular Biology of Fertilization". J Hedrick, Ed. (in press).

Monroy A, Rosati F (1983). A comparative analysis of sperm-egg interaction. Gamete Res 7:85–102.

Moy GW, Vacquier VD (1979). Immunoperoxidase localization of bindin during the adhesion of sperm to sea urchin eggs. Curr Topics Dev Biol 13:31–44.

Orci L, Perrelet A, Friend DS (1977). Freeze fracture of membrane fusion during exocytosis in pacreatic B cells. J Cell Biol 75:23–30.

Papahadjopoulos D (1978). Calcium-induced phase changes and fusion in natural and model membranes. in "Membrane Fusion" G. Poste & G.L. Nicolson, Eds. Elsevier/North Holland 765–790.

Pinto MR, De Santis R, D'Alessio G, Rosati F (1981). Studies on fertilization in the Ascidians. Fucosyl sites on the vitelline coat of Ciona intestinalis. Exptl Cell Res 132:289–295.

Portis A, Newton C, Pangborn W, Papahadjopoulos D (1979). Studies on mechanism of membrane fusion: Evidence for an intermembrane Ca^{2+}-phospholipid complex, synergism with Mg^{2+}, and inhibition. Biochemistry 18:780–790.

Rosati F, De Santis R (1978). Studies on fertilization in the Ascidians. 1. Self-sterility and specific recognition between gametes of Ciona intestinalis. Exptl Cell Res 112:111–119.

Rosati F, De Santis R (1980). The role of the surface carbohydrates in sperm-egg interaction in Ciona intestinalis. Nature 283:762–764.

Rosati F, Cotelli F, De Santis R, Monroy A, Pinto MR (1982). Synthesis of fucosyl-containing glycoproteins of the vitelline coat in oocytes of Ciona intestinalis (Ascidia).

Proc Natl Acad Sci USA 79:1908-1911.

Rosati F, Pinto MR, Casazza G (1985). The acrosomal region of the spermatozoon of Ciona intestinalis; its relationship with binding to the vitelline coat of the egg. Gamete Res 11:379-390.

Satir B, Schooley L, Satir P (1973). Membrane fusion in a model system. Mucocyst secretion in Tetrahymena. J Cell Biol 56:153-176.

Schackmann RW, Shapiro BM (1981). A partial sequence of ionic changes associated with the acrosome reaction of Strongylocentrotus purpuratus. Dev Biol 81:145-154.

Schackmann RW, Christen R, Shapiro BM (1981). Membrane potential depolarization and increased intracellular pH accompany the acrosome reaction of sea urchin sperm. Proc Natl Acad Sci USA 78:6066-6070.

Schackmann RW, Christen R, Shapiro BM (1984). Measurement of plasma membrane and mitochondrial potentials in sea urchin sperm. Changes upon activation and induction of acrosome reaction. J Biol Chem 259:13914-13922.

Schmidt T, Patton C, Epel D (1982). Is there a role for the Ca^{2+} influx during fertilization of the sea urchin egg? Dev Biol 90:284-290.

SeGall GK, Lennarz WJ (1981). Jelly coat and induction of the acrosome reaction in Echinoid sperm. Dev Biol 86:87-93.

Shapiro BM, Schackman RW, Gabel CA (1981). Molecular approaches to the study of fertilization. Ann Rev Biochem 50:815-843.

Tilney LG (1985). The acrosomal reaction. in "Biology of Fertilization", Ch.B. Metz & A. Monroy, Eds., Acad Press NY vol.2:157-213.

Yanagimachi R, Noda YD (1970). Physiological changes in the postnuclear cap region of mammalian spermatozoa: a necessary preliminary to the membrane fusion between sperm and egg cell. J Ultrastr Res 31:486-494.

Zimmerberg J, Cohen FS, Finkelstein A (1980). Micromolar Ca^{2+} stimulates fusion of lipid vesicles with planar bilayers containing a calcium-binding protein. Science 210:906-908.

Progress in Developmental Biology, Part B, pages 69–73
© 1986 Alan R. Liss, Inc.

PROTEIN SULFHYDRYL REACTIVITY AND SPERM ACTIVATION

*Akiya Hino, Robert W. Schackmann and
Bennett M. Shapiro

Department of Biochemistry, University
of Washington, Seattle, WA 98195, USA;
*present address, Department of Biology,
Nagoya University, Nagoya, 464 Japan

Intracellular pH (pH_i) has a determinant effect on sperm behavior: sperm are stored in the testes at low pH_i; upon spawning, they undergo an activation of respiration and motility that is dependent upon a 0.5 unit increase in pH_i (Christen et al., 1982). As sperm pass through the egg jelly coat, the acrosome reaction (AR) is triggered, due to elevated pH_i and Ca^{2+} (Christen et al., 1983a,b).

Heavy metals, especially Zn^{2+}, affect sperm motility and the acrosome reaction, perhaps due to a role of Zn^{2+} in pH_i regulation (for recent data and references, see Clapper et al., 1985). A possible target for Zn^{2+} effects is the sulfhydryl group, which may form thiol-metal complexes (Jocelyn, 1972). In order to explore the possibility that sperm protein sulfhydryl groups are involved in pH_i regulation, we have measured the SH group reactivity in quiescent, activated, and acrosome reacted sperm, with special attention to their interrelationships with pH_i.

(I) CHANGES IN THE REACTIVITY OF SULFHYDRYL GROUPS IN QUIESCENT AND ACTIVATED SPERM.

Sperm were incubated with ^{14}C-iodoacetamide (IAA), and the TCA-precipitable radioactivity was measured as an estimate of SH reactivity. Sperm motility and respiration are activated as [Na^+] increases, with half-maximal activation at 5-10 mM Na^+. Fig. 1 shows the change in SH reactivity as a function of [Na^+]. The number of reactive SH groups in quiescent sperm ([Na^+] <5 mM) was about 11 n mole SH/10^{10} sperm and doubled in fully

activated sperm. Sea urchin sperm are quiescent in high
[K^+] seawater, and addition of 10 mM NH_4Cl causes sperm
activation due to increased pH_i (Christen et al., 1982).
As shown on the right side of Fig. 1, upon addition of
10 mM NH_4Cl to sperm in K_{200}, SH reactivity increased.
Moreover, SH reactivity increased along with a gradual
increase in pH_i (Fig. 2), whereas the respiration sharply
increased in the range of 13-15 n mole $SH/10^{10}$ sperm.
Thus, quiescent sperm have relatively lower SH reactivity;
over a small range of pH_i and SH group reactivity there
is a dramatic increase in respiration and motility.

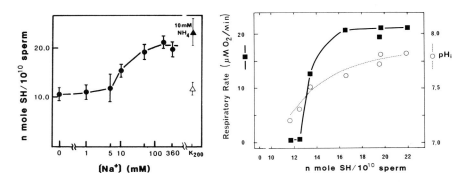

Fig. 1. (left) Changes in the reactivity of SH groups upon
the activation of sperm. Sperm were incubated with ^{14}C-IAA
(0.5 uCi/ml, 25 mCi/mmol; 5 x 10^8 sperm/ml) for 20 min in
several concentrations of Na^+. Quiescent sperm in K_{200}
seawater (200 mM KCl, 160 mM NaCl) were activated by adding
10 mM NH_4Cl. Incubations were stopped with 5% TCA and 1 mM
DTT. The sperm were trapped on GF/C filters and washed
with five volumes of 2% TCA solution.

Fig. 2 (right) The relationship between the number of SH
groups and sperm activation parameters. Sperm were activated by increasing Na^+ of ASW. The respiratory rate of
sperm was measured in an oxygen electrode and pH_i by the
accumulation of ^{14}C-diethylamine (Schackmann et al., 1982).

(II). CHANGES IN SULFHYDRYL GROUPS UPON INDUCTION
      OF THE ACROSOME REACTION.

     Fig. 3 shows the change in the number of SH groups of
sperm after the addition of egg jelly to induce the AR.
Sperm were incubated with tracer quantities of ^{14}C-IAA for

15 min prior to the initiation of the experiment and then egg jelly was added (Fig. 3, open squares). The apparent number of SH groups in sperm decreased just after the addition of egg jelly and recovered to a higher level gradually. Egg jelly can be separated into at least three components. A small molecule, speract, activates sperm respiration and motility at acidic pH (e.g., Suzuki and Garbers, 1984); this had little effect upon the number of reactive SH groups (Fig. 3, open triangles). The high molecular-weight components were separated into a fucose sulfate polysaccharide fraction (F) that induces the AR and a protein fraction (P) that eluted just before V_i by Sepharose CL 4B (SeGall, G. and Lennarz, W., 1979). F caused a transient decrease in reactive SH groups, as did unfractionated egg jelly (Fig. 3). P does not induce the acrosome reaction but causes sperm mitochondrial movement (Hino, unpublished data); it did not affect the SH reactivity (Fig. 3). The initial decrease in SH reactivity after induction of the AR was unexpected; it must be caused by a loss of TCA-precipitable material from the

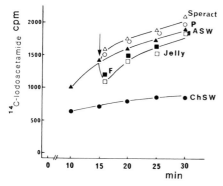

Effects of Iodoacetamide on Sperm Activities

	Motility	pHi	AR	Resp.
None	+++	7.3	94%	100%
0.2 mM	++	7.2	80%	68%
0.5 mM	+	6.9	46%	32%
1.0 mM	-	6.6	7%	0%

5×10^7 sperm /ml   (pHe=8.0)

Fig. 3 (left) Change in SH groups after addition of egg jelly components. Sperm were incubated for 15 min with ^{14}C-IAA, then jelly components were added and SH group reactivity measured as in Fig. 1. See text for jelly fractions used. ChSW is Na$^+$-free, where sperm are immotile and non-respiring.

TABLE I. (right) The effects of IAA on sperm activities. Sperm were incubated (4×10^7/ml) in several concentrations of IAA for 5 min, then washed and the indicated parameters were studied, as previously described (Christen et. al, 1983).

labeled sperm, for the alkylation reaction forms a covalent bond and IAA was present before AR induction.

(III) THE EFFECTS OF SH REAGENTS ON SPERM BEHAVIOR

IAA at higher concentrations caused an inhibition of sperm respiration and motility. For example, after five min incubation with 1 mM IAA, sperm became immotile, respiration decreased, and the AR could not be induced. The pH_i also decreased after addition of iodoacetamide (Table 1). The decreased respiration and inability to induce the AR can be explained by this decrease in pH_i, since neither process can be activated at low pH_i.

At our current state of knowledge it is difficult to arrive at a unitary mechanism to tie these correlations between sperm SH reactivity and sperm behaviors together. Altered SH group reactivity could be due to a change in cysteine thiol pK (reaction with alkylating agents increases along with $[RS^-]$); alternatively, it may reflect a difference in the thiol-disulfide ratio, suggested to play a third messenger role in response to alterations in cAMP in other cell types (Gilbert, H. F., 1982). The simplest and most direct correlation was between increases in pH_i during sperm activation and increased SH reactivity. To link the results of Clapper et al. and previous studies of heavy metal effects with the observations reported here, one can speculate that sperm thiol groups may form complexes with Zn^{2+}, to drive proteins into conformations more compatible with the elevated pH_i state, thereby activating respiration and motility. However, much more information is needed to identify specific molecular targets and mechanisms for these cases.

REFERENCES

Christen R, Schackmann RW, Shapiro BM (1982). Elevation of the intracellular pH activates respiration and motility of sperm of the sea urchin, Strongylocentrotus purpuratus. J Biol Chem 257:14881.
Christen R, Schackmann RW, Shapiro BM (1983a). Metabolism of the sea urchin sperm. J Biol Chem 258:5392.
Christen R, Schackmann RW, Shapiro, BM (1983b). Interaction between sperm and sea urchin egg jelly. Dev Biol 98:1-14.
Clapper DL, Davis JA, Lamothe PJ, Patton C, Epel D (1985).

Involvement of zinc in the regulation of pH_i, motility, and acrosome reactions in sea urchin sperm. J Cell Biol 100:1817-1824.

Gilbert HF (1982). Biological Disulfides: The third messenger. J Biol Chem 57:12086.

Jocelyn PC (1973). Biochemistry of the SH Group. Academic Press, New York.

Lee HC, Johnson C, Epel D (1983). Change in internal pH associated with initiation of motility and acrosome reaction of sea urchin sperm. Devel Biol 95:31.

Schackmann, RW, Christen R, Shapiro BM (1981). Membrane potential depolarization and increased intracellular pH accompany the acrosome reaction of sea urchin sperm. Proc Natl Acad Sci USA 78:6066.

Segall GK, Lennarz WJ (1979). Chemical characterization of the component of the jelly coat from sea urchin eggs responsible for induction of the acrosome reaction. Devel Biol 71:33.

Suzuki N, Garbers DL (1984). Stimulation of sperm respiration rates by speract and resact at alkaline extracellular pH. Biol of Repro 30:1167.

ACKNOWLEDGMENTS

This work was supported by USPHS Grant GM23910. Speract was a gift from Dr. D. Garbers. We are grateful to Mary Patella for careful typing of the manuscript.

Progress in Developmental Biology, Part B, pages 75–78

A CALCIUM-ACTIVATED SODIUM CONDUCTANCE CONTRIBUTES TO THE FERTILIZATION POTENTIAL IN THE EGG OF THE NEMERTEAN WORM, CEREBRATULUS LACTEUS

Douglas Kline, Laurinda A. Jaffe, and Raymond T. Kado

Department of Physiology, University of Connecticut Health Center, Farmington CT 06032 (D.K. and L.A.J.) and Laboratoire de Neurobiologie Cellulaire, C.N.R.S. 91190 Gif-sur-Yvette, France (R.T.K.)

INTRODUCTION

The egg cell membrane of many species contains ion channels that produce the fertilization potential, a prolonged change in membrane potential that accompanies fertilization (reviewed by Jaffe and Gould, 1985). As part of a continuing study of the ionic mechanisms responsible for this conductance change, we have studied the fertilization potential in the egg of the nemertean worm, Cerebratulus lacteus, which has an exceptionally long-lasting fertilization potential (about 80 min in duration, Kline et al., 1985). We tested the hypothesis that a calcium-mediated opening of sodium channels contributes to the long-lasting fertilization potential. The fertilization potential in the egg of Cerebratulus and in the eggs of many other species functions in the prevention of polyspermy (Kline et al., 1985; reviewed by Jaffe and Gould, 1985).

We present here a brief summary of some of our experiments. Obtaining and handling gametes, sea water solutions, and electrophysiological methods are described in the paper by Kline et al. (1985). We lowered calcium and sodium concentrations to determine the ionic requirements of the fertilization potential, and injected the calcium chelator, EGTA, by pressure or iontophoresis, to demonstrate a calcium-dependent sodium conductance.

RESULTS AND DISCUSSION

An example of the fertilization potential in the egg of Cerebratulus is shown in Figure 1A. The peak potential was calcium dependent; it was reduced from an average of +43 mV to +23 mV when the extracellular calcium concentration was reduced by 10 fold. The plateau potential was sodium dependent; its value (averaged over the first 30 min for each egg) was reduced from an average of +22 mV to -27 mV when the extracellular sodium concentration was reduced by 10 fold (choline substitution). An example of the fertilization potential in low sodium sea water is shown in Figure 1B.

Injection of EGTA by pressure or by iontophoresis to a final concentration of 2 to 5 mM had little effect on the initial peak of the fertilization potential; however, the positive plateau phase was dramatically reduced. An example of the fertilization potential after EGTA injection is shown in Figure 2A. Prior to the record shown, 60 pl of 90 mM EGTA and 500 mM MOPS buffer at pH 7.4 was injected by pressure, resulting in a final concentration of 4.5 mM EGTA and 25 mM MOPS in the egg. When sperm were added, the fertilization potential showed an initial peak but never developed a positive plateau phase. In this egg, more sperm were added and another spike was produced, but the plateau remained below 0 mV.

Injections that gave higher EGTA concentrations in the egg were even more effective in lowering the plateau potential. MOPS buffer was included in the injection solution to control for possible intracellular pH changes caused by proton release as EGTA binds calcium in the cell. Eggs injected with buffer alone had normal fertilization potentials. The egg shown in Figure 2B was injected with 56 pl of 600 mM MOPS at pH 7.4 giving a final concentration of about 28 mM MOPS in the egg and the fertilization potential was normal.

These experiments indicate that a calcium-activated sodium conductance contributes to the fertilization potential. Some preliminary experiments suggest that this conductance may depend, at least in part, on the release of calcium from intracellular stores. Addition of 250 μM (8-(N,N-diethylamino)octyl-3,4,5-trimethoxybenzoate HCl) during the plateau phase lowered the average plateau potential by 58 mV. TMB-8 is believed to antagonize the release of calcium in

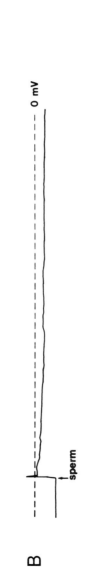

Figure 1. Fertilization potentials in normal sea water (486 mM sodium) (A) and in low sodium sea water (51 mM sodium) (B). (From Kline et al., 1985, with permission of Alan R. Liss, Inc.)

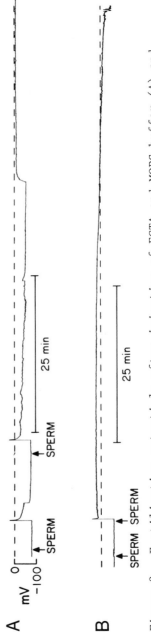

Figure 2. Fertilization potentials after injection of EGTA and MOPS buffer (A) and after injection of MOPS buffer only (B).

skeletal and smooth muscle (Chiou and Malagodi, 1975) and may
have the same effect in the Cerebratulus egg.

The fertilization potential of the Cerebratulus egg
depends on a calcium-activated sodium conductance, since
reduction of external sodium or injection of EGTA reduces
its amplitude. The source of the calcium may be in part
extracellular, since the initial peak of the fertilization
potential depends on extracellular calcium, and in part
intracellular, since TMB-8 reduces the plateau potential.
It has been suggested that calcium-activated conductances are
also responsible for all or part of the fertilization potential
in eggs of other animals, including starfish (Lansman, 1983),
frog (Cross, 1981), and hamster (Miyazaki and Igusa, 1982).
A calcium-activated ion conductance could be a general
feature of the fertilization potential in many eggs, although
the particular ion channel being opened differs (sodium in
the starfish and Cerebratulus, chloride in the frog, and
potassium in the hamster). This hypothesis might be tested
by injection of calcium chelators into eggs of other species.

This work was supported by an NIH training grant
(5-T35-HD07098) awarded to the Embryology Course, Marine
Biological Laboratory, Woods Hole, and NIH grant HD14939
to L.A.J.

REFERENCES

Cross NL (1981). Initiation of the activation potential
  by an increase in intracellular calcium in eggs of the
  frog, Rana pipiens. Dev Biol 85: 380-384.
Chiou CY, Malagodi MJ (1975). Studies on the mechanism
  of action of a new Ca^{2+} antagonist, 8-(N,N-diethylamino)
  octyl-3,4,5-trimethoxybenzoate hydrochloride in smooth
  and skeletal muscle. Br J Pharmacol 53: 279-285.
Jaffe LA, Gould M (1985). Polyspermy-preventing mechanisms.
  In Metz CB, Monroy A (eds): "Biology of Fertilization,
  Vol 3" Orlando: Academic Press, pp 223-250.
Kline D, Jaffe LA, Tucker RP (1985). Fertilization
  potential and polyspermy prevention in the egg of the
  nemertean, Cerebratulus lacteus. J Exp Zool 235: in press
Lansman JB (1983). Voltage-clamp study of the conductance
  activated at fertilization in the starfish egg.
  J Physiol 345: 353-372.
Miyazaki S, Igusa Y (1982). Ca-mediated activation of a K
  current at fertilization of golden hamster eggs.
  Proc Natl Acad Sci USA 79: 931-935.

Progress in Developmental Biology, Part B, pages 79–83
© 1986 Alan R. Liss, Inc.

THE ROLE OF β-N-ACETYLGLUCOSAMINIDASE IN SEA URCHIN SPERM-EGG INTERACTION

Marcello G. Cacace and Alfonso Sada

Institute of Protein Biochemistry and Enzymology
National Council of Research
Via Toiano, 6 80072 Arco Felice, Naples, Italy.

INTRODUCTION

The binding of spermatozoa to the egg is the first event in a series of complex interactions which precede fusion between the two gametes. It seems that terminal oligosaccharide residues of glycoproteins of the cell surface of gametes are involved in sperm-egg interaction in much the same way as they are in the cell-cell adhesion phenomena observed in other systems. These glycoproteins contain a variety of sugars and aminosugars such as mannose, galactose, fucose, N-acetylglucosamine and N-acetylgalactosamine (Lennarz, 1980).

The molecular mechanisms by which these residues are recognized by complementary structures on the cell surface of gametes are at present poorly understood. It has still to be clarified which molecule(s) is (are) responsible for the binding of the sperm to the egg investments, although a number of proteins capable of specifically binding to sugar residues have been described (Vacquier and Moy, 1977; Bleil and Wassarman, 1980; Isaka and Ikemori, 1980; Yamada and Aketa, 1982).

Little attention has been paid to the possibility that the gamete surface may have bound enzymes which could be of importance either as "receptor" proteins, or, via their enzymatic activities, as modifiers of carbohydrate structures (Shur and Hall, 1982). We present evidence for the existence of a loosely bound β-N-acetylglucosaminidase in the sperm of various sea urchin species from different habitats, Anthocidaris crassispina, Strongylocentrotus purpuratus and Paracentrotus lividus. The enzyme activities have been solubilized and characterized.

MATERIALS AND METHODS

p-nitrophenyl-2-acetamido-2-deoxy-β- D-glucopyranoside was from Sigma Chemical Co. DE-52 DEAE cellulose was from Whatman. AcA 34 gel filtration medium was from LKB. All other chemicals were of analytical grade purity. Gametes were obtained by lantern excision and intracoelomic injection of 0.5 M KCl. Sperm were collected as "dry" as possible by aspiration from the gonadophores and used immediately or kept frozen at -70 °C.

β--N-acetylglucosaminidase was assayed using p-nitrophenyl glucoside substrate (Ceccarini et al., 1983). p-nitrophenol released was measured using an extinction coefficient of 14.4 $mM^{-1}cm^{-1}$ at 401 nm. The assay mixture contained in a total volume of 0.2 ml substrate at a concentration of 1 mg/ml and enzyme in 0.15 M McIlvaine buffer at the appropriate pH. The reaction was quenched with 1 ml of 1 M Na_2CO_3. In the case of sperm suspension, color was developed after the sperm were removed by centrifugation at 15,000 rpm for 5 min. Protein concentration was measured by the Bradford method with bovine serum albumin as standard (Bradford, 1976).

RESULTS AND DISCUSSION

Spermatozoa incubated in the presence of McIlvaine buffer, pH 6.0, released β-N-acetylglucosaminidase activity. Various extraction methods were tested, and freezing and thawing proved to be the most satisfactory. However, the enzyme could also be extracted by Triton X-100 treatment. One cycle was sufficient to liberate up to 30% of the activity present in the sperm. The solubilized enzyme was partially purified by ammonium sulfate fractionation, gel filtration and ion exchange chromatography. Enzyme activities are relatively stable and can be purified by conventional purification steps with a relatively low yield.

The apparent molecular weight of the β-N-acetyl-glucosaminidase as determined by gel filtration on AcA 34 matrix was 210,000 daltons for the A. crassispina enzyme and 160,000 daltons for the P. lividus enzyme. The enzymes were optimally active in the acidic range (pH 3.5-4.5).Enzyme activity for all species was remarkably stable against thermal denaturation and exhibited optimal activity in the range 40-50 °C. Figure 1 shows the temperature dependence of the activity of P. lividus β-N-acetylglucosaminidase.

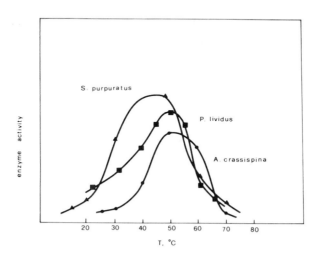

Figure 1. Effect of temperature on β-N-acetylglucosaminidase activity. The enzyme was incubated at various temperatures for 30 min at pH 4.5 in the presence of the p-nitrophenyl-glucoside substrate.

The β-N-acetylglucosaminidase activity is released from Paracentrotus lividus sperm by mild detergent treatment. This treatment is known not to damage gametes, although it causes the acrosome reaction to occur and it probably induces other cell surface alterations. Enzyme activity is not present in the seminal plasma and it is not released by gentle washing of the spermatozoa with sea water. Egg jelly had a marked effect on the release of enzyme activity from spermatozoa. In fact, soluble β-N-acetylglucosaminidase level increased when spermatozoa were treated with solubilized jelly coat. This effect was more pronounced when a fraction purified by ethanol precipitation (mainly composed of a highly sulfated polysaccharide (SeGall and Lennarz, 1979)) was used (Fig. 2).

One intriguing property is the fact that optimal activity is observed at a pH value too low to be of physiological significance and a question open to further investigation is that relative to the nature of the substrate(s) of this β-N-acetylglucosaminidase.

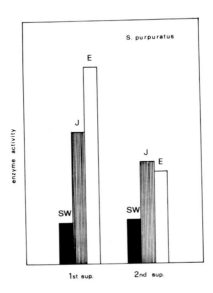

Figure 2. Effect of jelly coat on the release of β-N-acetylglucosaminidase from S. purpuratus spermatozoa. Activity in the supernatant after two subsequent washes with sea water (SW), total jelly coat extract (J) and ethanol-purified fraction (E). The two (E) supernatants contained 80% of total sperm activity.

The β-N-acetylglucosaminidase activities described in the present work have some distinctive properties which, together with their apparent surface localization suggest that this protein may be involved in functions other than simple glycoside hydrolysis. A number of sugar derivates are involved in sperm-egg recognition in the sea urchin (Glabe et al., 1982) and ascidians (Pinto et al., 1981) or as marker groups present in mammalian egg investments (Huang et al., 1982). Our findings suggest that a similar role could be ascribed to β-N-acetylglucosamine residues and to β-N-acetylglucosaminidase present in sea urchin gametes.

REFERENCES

Bleil JO, Wassarman PM (1980). Mammalian sperm-egg interaction : identification of a glycoprotein in mouse egg zonae pellucidae possessing receptor activity for sperm. Cell 20:873-882.

Bradford MM (1976). A rapid and sensitive method for the quantitation of microgram quantities of protein utilizing the principle of protein-dye binding. Anal Biochem 72:248-254.

Ceccarini C, D'Aniello A, Cacace MG, Atkinson PH (1983). Purification and characterization of a β-N-acetylglucosaminidase from Octopus vulgaris. Eur J Biochem 132:469-476.

Glabe CG, Grabel LB, Vacquier VD, Rosen SD (1982). Carbohydrate specificity of sea urchin sperm bindin: a cell surface lectin mediating sperm-egg adhesion. J Cell Biol 94:123-128.

Huang TTF Jr, Ohzu E, Yanagimachi R (1982). Evidence suggesting that L-fucose is part of a recognition signal for sperm-zona pellucida attachment in mammals. Gamete Res 5:355-361.

Isaka S, Ikemori M (1980). Glycoside hydrolases of sea urchin spermatozoa and their possible involvement in sperm isoagglutination by egg water. Devel Growth Diff 22:475-481.

Lennarz WJ, ed, (1980). The Biochemistry of Glycoproteins and Proteoglycans, Plenum Press, New York.

Pinto MR, De Santis R, D'Alessio G, Rosati F (1981). Studies on fertilization in the ascidians. Fucosyl sites on vitelline coat of Ciona intestinalis. Exp Cell Res 132:289-295.

SeGall GK and Lennarz WJ (1979). Chemical characterization of the component of the jelly coat from sea urchin eggs responsible for induction of the acrosome reaction. Dev Biol 71:33-48.

Shur BD and Hall NG (1982). A role for mouse sperm surface galactosyltransferase in sperm binding to the egg zona pellucida. J Cell Biol 95:574-579.

Vacquier VD, Moy GW (1977). Isolation of bindin: The protein responsible for adhesion of sperm to sea urchin eggs. Proc Natl Acad Sci USA 74:2456-2460.

Yamada Y, Aketa K (1982). Purification and partial characterization of hemagglutinins in seminal plasma of the sea urchin, Hemicentrotus pulcherrimus. Biochem Biophys Acta 709:220-226.

Progress in Developmental Biology, Part B, pages 85–89
© 1986 Alan R. Liss, Inc.

ULTRASTRUCTURAL AND EXPERIMENTAL INVESTIGATIONS OF SPERM-
EGG INTERACTIONS IN THE ASCIDIAN, PHALLUSIA MAMILLATA

Thomas G. Honegger

Zoological Institute, University of Zürich,
Winterthurerstrasse 190, CH-8057 Zürich,
Switzerland

INTRODUCTION

It is well established that in a great number of species the extracellular egg coat plays a key role in sperm-
egg interaction (Monroy and Rosati, 1983; Lopo, 1983). In
ascidians the egg is surrounded by a glycoprotein envelope,
the chorion or vitelline coat (VC). In several ascidian
species the VC represents the site for species-specific
recognition (Minganti, 1959) and in the self sterile species Ciona intestinalis (Morgan, 1939; Rosati and DeSantis,
1978) and Halocynthia roretzi (Fuke, 1983) the VC acts as
a barrier preventing self fertilization. Evidence has been
presented that binding of sperm to the VC is a prerequisite
for the induction of the sperm reaction (Lambert and Epel,
1979) and for sperm activation (DeSantis et al., 1983).
However, detailed studies on sperm-viteline coat interaction have been performed only on a small number of ascidian
species and there is almost no information on sperm-egg
membrane fusion.

The present paper summarizes ultrastructural and experimental investigations on sperm-vitelline coat and sperm-
egg interactions in the self fertile ascidian Phallusia
mamillata in order to contribute to a better understanding
of the basic mechanismus of sperm-egg interactions in ascidians.

RESULTS

The Ph. mamillata egg (140-145μm diameter) is enclosed
in a rigid acellular VC. Spherical highly vacuolated follicle cells are attached to the outer surface of the VC
(Fig.1). In the perivitelline space between the VC and the
egg plasma membrane test cells are found, single or in
groups (Fig.1). The VC itself consists of three distinct
layers, a fibrous surface, a homogenous electron dense central layer and a thick innermost layer with thin fibers and
globular elements (Fig.2).

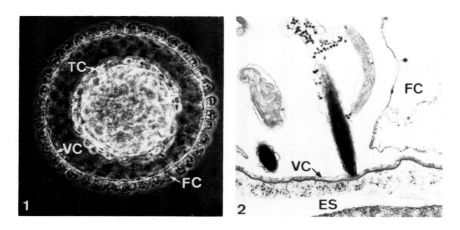

Figure 1. Egg of Ph. mamillata showing follicle cells (FC),
vitelline coat (VC) and test cells (TC) X 200.
Figure 2. Sperm attaching to the VC. Note the three layers
of the VC. FC, follicle cells. ES, egg surface. X 22'500.

The sperm of Ph. mamillata exhibits the typical ascidian structure. The elongated head (5,5μm) contains the nucleus alongside which the single mitochondrium is located
(Fig.2). Freeze-fracture studies reveal a cap-like structure
at the sperm apex (Fig.3) which encloses a number of vesicles of 50-60nm in diameter (Fig.4). Whether the lysins to
dissolve the VC are located in these vesicles or not is
still a point of issue (Fukumoto, 1984a,b; Rosati et al.,
1985).

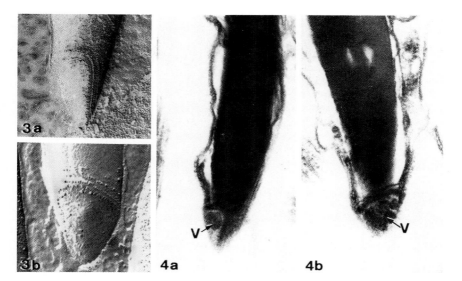

Figure 3a,b. Freeze-fracture replicas of sperm apex. Note the three rows of particles bordering the cap-like structure. X 65'000.
Figure 4a,b. Vesicles (V) in the same structure of quick frozen and freeze-substituted sperm. X 65'000.

An acrosomal process containing F-actin, as found in many marine invertebrates, is not present in any ascidian sperm investigated so far. Firm sperm binding is established between the tip of the sperm and the fibrous outer layer of the VC at sites which are not covered by follicle cells. In Ph. mamillata wheat germ agglutinin which binds to N-acetyl-glucosamine- and N-acetylneuraminic-like receptors of the VC (Fig.5), inhibits sperm binding and consequently fertilization (Honegger, 1983; Honegger, in prep.). The inhibitory effect of WGA is concentration dependent and can be completely abolished by low concentrations of competing sugars such as N,N,N, Triacetylchitotriose (1mM). On the other hand, WGA is not bound to and has no effect on the fertilization capacity of sperm. Studies aiming at a characterization of the interacting surface molecules of the VC and sperm are now in progress.

On contact with the VC, the sperm reaction (Lambert and Epel, 1979), i.e. shifting of the swollen mitochondrium along

the tail, is initiated in a number of sperm. However, only
a few of these sperm are observed to penetrate the VC
(Fig.6). From ultrastructural analysis the following conclusions can be drawn: 1. No physical contact between the sperm
apex and the central layer of the VC must be established to
dissolve the latter. 2. The VC lysins are most probably released by exocytosis of sperm bound vesicles and may act
over a certain distance (Fig.6). 3. Sperm having penetrated
the VC still exhibit the cap like apical structure.

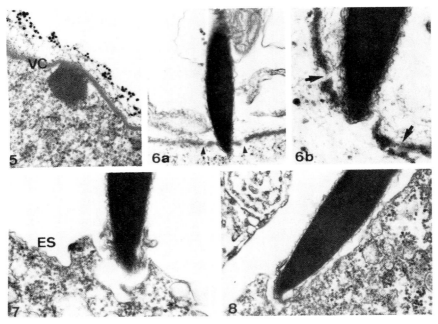

Figure 5. Gold granules labelled with WGA bound to the outer
VC layer. X 37'500.
Figure 6a,b. Sperm penetrating the VC. Note the dissolution
of the VC (arrows). X 15'000
Figure 7. Sperm establishing contact with egg. X 45'000.
Figure 8. Sperm partially engulfed by the egg. X 38'000.

        Sperm-egg fusion is initiated by contact between the
membranes of the sperm apex and microvilli-like protrusions
of the egg surface (Fig.7). Then the sperm head contacts the
egg membrane sideways and becomes engulfed by the egg (Fig.8)

Membrane fusion seems to occur in the postacrosomal region of the head, a feature common with mammalian fertilization.

REFERENCES

DeSantis R, Pinto MR, Cotelli F, Rosati F, Monroy A, D'Alessio G (1983). A fucosyl glycoprotein component with sperm receptor and sperm-activating activities from the vitelline coat of Ciona intestinalis eggs. Exp Cell Res 148: 508-513.

Fuke TM (1983). Self and non-self recognition between gametes of the ascidian, Halocynthia roretzi. Roux s Arch Dev Biol 192: 347-352.

Fukumoto M (1984a). The apical structure in Perophora annectens (Tunicate) spermatozoa: Fine structure, differentiation and possible role in fertilization. J Cell Sci 66: 175-187.

Fukumoto M (1984b). Fertilization in Ascidians: Acrosome fragmentation in Ciona intestinalis spermatozoa. J Ultrastruct Res 87: 252-262.

Honegger TG (1982). Effect on fertilization and localized binding of lectins in the ascidian Phallusia mamillata. Exp Cell Res 138: 446-451.

Lambert C, Epel D (1979). Calcium mediated mitochondrial movement in ascidian sperm during fertilization. Dev Biol 69: 296-304.

Lopo AC (1983). Sperm-egg interactions in invertebrates. In Hartmann JF: "Mechanism and Control of Animal Fertilization", New York: Academic Press p. 269-324.

Minganti A (1959). Lo sviluppo embrionale e il comportamento dei cromosomi in ibridi tra 5 specie di Ascidie. Acta Embryol Morphol Exptl 2: 269-301.

Monroy A, Rosati F (1983). Review article: A comparative analysis of sperm-egg interaction. Gamete Res 7: 85-102.

Morgan TH (1939). The genetic and physiological problems of self-sterility in Ciona. J Exptl Zool 80: 19-55.

Rosati F, DeSantis R (1978). Studies on fertilization in the ascidians. I. Self-sterility and specific recognition between gametes of Ciona intestinalis. Exp Cell Res 112: 111-119.

Rosati F, Pinto MR, Casazza G (1985). The acrosomal region of the spermatozoon of Ciona intestinalis: Its relationship with the binding to the vitelline coat of the egg. Gamete Res 11:379-389.

Progress in Developmental Biology, Part B, pages 91–94

CENTROSOMES AND MICROTUBULE ORGANIZATION DURING MOUSE AND SEA URCHIN FERTILIZATION

Heide Schatten and Gerald Schatten

Department of Biological Science
Florida State University
Tallahassee, FL 32306-3050

INTRODUCTION

Cytoskeletal activity is essential for the motions culminating in the union of the sperm and egg nuclei during fertilization and investigations on the egg cytoskeleton may prove crucial for generating a full understanding of the biology of the cytoskeleton. In keeping with the themes of this monograph this report will summarize several new technologies for investigating cell structure which are leading towards new discoveries in developmental biology. The advent of routine methods for mammalian fertilization in vitro is now being coupled with the powerful method of immunocytochemistry, especially in conjuction with well characterized antibodies against only poorly understood cellular structures from human autoimmune patients.

Centrosomes, the pericentriolar material [PCM] typically found surrounding centrioles which serve as microtubule organizing centers [MTOCs], are localized in sea urchin eggs and mouse oocytes during fertilization and cell division along with the corresponding patterns of microtubules and nuclei or chromosomes. The centrosomes are precise and reliable predictors of the sites of microtubule assembly, and they mirror the activity of chromatin during the cell cycle: they duplicate during interphase when they are dispersed and at mitosis they condense and separate. As predicted by Boveri [reviewed in Wilson, 1928 and Mazia, 1984], the sea urchin centrosome is contributed by the sperm along with the sperm centriole. Astongishingly, the mouse egg violates this rule and centrosomes in this mammal are maternally inherited.

CENTROSOMES AND MICROTUBULE ORGANIZATION IN SEA URCHINS

Centrosomes are introduced to the unfertilized sea urchin egg by the sperm. During the pronuclear migrations, this paternal centrosome widens and nucleates the sperm aster [Balczon and Schatten, 1983]. At syngamy it is split and two discrete poles are detected at the streak stage. At prophase and metaphase, the centrosomes remain as a pair of tight aggregates surrounding the centrioles. However at anaphase, as the microtubules within the mitotic poles begin to disassemble, these centrosomes flatten and broaden with axes perpendicular to the mitotic axis. In figure 1 centrosomes, microtubules and chromosomes are depicted at telophase. They have enlarged into hemispheres as the astral microtubules have disassembled at their interiors and continued to assemble at their peripheries; the chromosomes have both moved from the metaphase plate to the mitotic poles but their arrangement has also widened as the centrosomes spread.

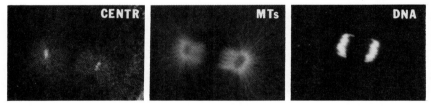

Figure 1. Centrosomes (left: CENTR), Microtubules (Middle: MTs) and Chromosomes (Right: DNA) during First Mitosis in a Triple Labeled Sea Urchin Egg. Centrosomes are of paternal origin and after duplication during first interphase nucleate the two mitotic poles. At prophase and metaphase, the centrosomes are tight spherical aggregates and they enlarge into ellipses by telophase, as shown here.

CENTROSOMES AND MICROTUBULES ORGANIZATION IN MICE

Mouse sperm do not bind centrosomal antibodies, and remarkably unfertilized mouse eggs display sixteen cytoplasmic centrosomal particles (figure 2) in addition to the broad bands at the meiotic poles recently described by Calarco-Gillam et al. (1983). The unfertilized mouse oocyte does not have any centrioles (Szollosi et al., 1972). Each centrosomal particle nucleates an aster of microtubules (figure 2) and larger particles nucleate larger asters. During the initial phase of sperm incorporation, centrosomes are not found in association with the sperm. As the pronuclei develop centrosomes and their attached microtubules associate with each pronuclear surface. This pattern of microtubules during mouse fertilization has recently been described (Schatten et al., 1985a) and centrosome localization has been reported by Schatten et al. (1986).

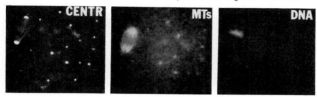

Figure 2. Centrosomes are Found in Unfertilized Mouse Oocytes. Centrosomes (left: CENTR), Microtubules (middle: MTs) and the Maternal Meiotic Chromosomes (right: DNA) are detected in this triple labeled oocyte. Unexpectedly, the mouse oocyte retains centrosomes during oogenesis which nucleate asters in unfertilized eggs.

During the first cell cycle, the centrosomal particles duplicate from around sixteen to perhaps fifty and the first mitotic spindle is organized independent of the introduced sperm centriole. Towards the completion of first interphase, all the centrosomal particles move to the pronuclear surface nucleating a circumnuclear microtubule sheath. As the nuclear envelopes dissolve at prophase the nuclear lamins disperse throughout the cytoplasm (Schatten et al., 1985b). In figure 3 at first metaphase in the mouse zygote, the numerous centrosomal particles have clustered into irregular mitotic poles. These centrosomes organize barrel-shaped anastral mitotic spindles during the first few mitoses. Between the third (Schatten et al., 1985a) and fifth (Calarco-Gillam et al., 1983) divisions, centrioles may develop and they are expected to be of maternal origin.

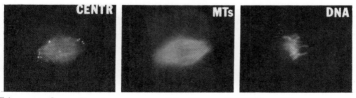

Figure 3. Centrosomes (left: CENTR), Microtubules (middle: MTs) and the Mitotic Chromosomes (right: DNA) during First Division in a Triple Labeled Mouse Zygote. The centrosomal particles aggregated into irregular mitotic poles and organize an anastral spindle with broad mitotic poles.

THE MOUSE CENTROSOME IS MATERNALLY INHERITED

This investigation demonstrates a surprising observation: the mouse centrosome is maternally inherited unlike that in sea urchins which is of paternal origin. Paternal centrosomes are expected to be found in most animals since in most systems the sperm nucleates a sperm aster adjacent to the male pronucleus. Teleologically, the paternal centrosome ensures biparental inheritance and requires extranuclear contributions by each parent. It is not clear why this mammal, and perhaps other mammals, have deviated from this pattern.

REFERENCES

Balczon, R, Schatten, G (1983). Microtubule-containing detergent-extracted cytoskeletons in sea urchin eggs from fertilization through cell division. Cell Motil 3:213-226.

Calarco-Gillam, PD, Siebert, MC, Hubble, R, Mitchison, T, Kirschner, M (1983). Centrosome development in early mouse embryos as defined by an autoantibody against pericentriolar material. Cell 35:621-629.

Mazia, D (1984). Centrosomes and mitotic poles. Exp Cell Res 153:1-15.

Schatten, G, Simerly, C, Schatten, H (1985a). Microtubule configurations during fertilization, mitosis and early development in the mouse and the requirement for egg microtuble-mediated motility during mammalian fertilization. Proc Natl Acad Sci USA 82:4152-4156.

Schatten, G, Maul, G, Schatten, H, Chaly, N, Simerly, C, Balczon, R, Brown DL (1985b). Nuclear lamins and peripheral nuclear antigens during fertilization and embryogenesis in mice and sea urchins. Proc Natl Acad Sci USA 82: in press.

Schatten, H, Schatten, G, Mazia, D, Balczon, R, Simerly, C (1986). Centrosomes during mouse and sea urchin fertilization and cell division. Under review.

Szollosi, D, Calarco, P, Donahue, RP (1972). Absence of centrioles in the first and second meiotic spindles of mouse oocytes. J Cell Sci 11:521-541.

Wilson, EB (1928). "The Cell in Development and Heredity." New York: Macmillan and Company, p. 440.

Progress in Developmental Biology, Part B, pages 95–98
© 1986 Alan R. Liss, Inc.

PARTIAL CHARACTERIZATION OF A PROTEIN KINASE ACTIVITY THAT
INCREASES AT GERMINAL VESICLE BREAKDOWN OF STARFISH AND
SURF CLAM OOCYTES

Kiyoshi Sano, Haruo Kanatani[+] and Samuel S. Koide

Kitasato University School of Medicine, Sagamihara 228, Japan (K.S.), National Institute for
Basic Biology, Okazaki 444, Japan (H.K.), Population Council, New York 10021 (S.S.K.) and Marine
Biological Laboratory, Woods Hole, MA 02543

INTRODUCTION

Resumption of meiotic maturation of prophase-arrested
starfish oocytes is induced by 1-methyladenine (1-MeAde).
1-MeAde acts on the surface membrane of the oocytes, producing maturation-promoting factor (MPF) in the cytoplasm.
MPF is a cytoplasmic factor which triggers germinal vesicle
breakdown (GVBD) and subsequent processes of meiotic maturation. In addition, MPF is supposed to be a general inducer of nuclear envelope breakdown and certain processes
of cell division both in meiosis of oocytes and in mitosis
of somatic cells.

In the maturing oocytes, a burst of protein phosphorylation occurs shortly before GVBD. The phosphorylation
burst has been shown to be closely involved with both the
appearance of MPF and the induction of GVBD. Therefore, a
certain protein kinase, activated shortly before GVBD, is
suggested to participate in the phosphorylation burst and
to be involved with the induction of GVBD.

We have successfully extracted a protein kinase which
is highly activated in starfish (Sano, 1985) and surf clam
oocytes undergoing GVBD.

RESULTS AND DISCUSSION

To obtain supernatants of oocytes, immature oocytes
and maturing oocytes, which were undergoing GVBD, were
homogenized in the buffer modified from the extraction

buffer for amphibian MPF (Wu and Gerhart, 1980). After
centrifuging the homogenates at 160,000 x g for 1 hr at
2°C, the translucent layer was collected and used as
"oocyte supernatant".

In the starfish Asterina pectinifera, when the
supernatant protein of immature oocytes was used as an
endogenous substrate and self-phosphorylation by the
substrate was subtracted, the protein kinase activity in
the supernatant of maturing oocytes was approximately
7-fold higher than that of immature oocytes (Sano, 1985).

The substrate specificity of the protein kinases in
the supernatants of both immature and maturing oocytes was
examined using various exogenous substrates, including
histone subfractions, protamine, phosvitin, and casein.
A distinctive feature of the protein kinase detected in the
supernatant of maturing starfish oocytes was its high
phosphorylating activity for histone H1 as an exogenous
substrate (Sano, 1985). As shown in Figure 1, since the
protein kinase activity observed in maturing oocytes was
found to be very labile, the kinase activity was assayed
immediately after thawing the freeze-stocked enzyme preparation. The immediate assay has revealed that the protein
kinase activity of maturing oocytes for histone H1 was 6-
to 7-fold higher than that of immature oocytes. This
difference in the kinase activities coincides well with
that obtained when the supernatant protein of immature
oocytes was used as a substrate.

In the surf clam Spisula solidissima, a high phosphorylating activity for histone H1 was also observed in the
supernatant of maturing oocytes. The kinase activity of
maturing oocytes was 3-fold higher than that of immature
oocytes.

The stability of the protein kinases in the supernatant of immature and maturing starfish oocytes was
further examined. The protein kinase in maturing oocytes
responsible for high phosphorylating activity was very
labile and lost its activity much more easily than that of
immature oocytes (Fig. 1). This labile protein kinase
specifically observed in the maturing oocytes is referred
to as "maturation-specific protein kinase". The unstable
nature of this kinase seems to be a requisite feature for a
protein kinase, the activity of which must be promptly

Figure 1. Stability of the protein kinases in the supernatants of immature and maturing starfish oocytes. The

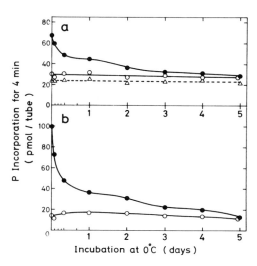

supernatant was diluted
10-fold with distilled
water and incubated at
0°C. At various times,
protein kinase activity
was assayed. The
substrates used are
(a) supernatant protein
of immature oocytes and
(b) calf thymus histone
H1. (O) immature
oocytes, (●) ma-
turing oocytes, (▲)
the phosphorylating
activity of the super-
natant protein of
immature oocytes used
as a substrate. (Sano,
1985, with permission)

controlled concomitantly with the proceeding of the cell
cycle. The observed rapid inactivation of the maturation-
specific protein kinase in vitro may correspond to the
inactivation of this kinase in vivo.

The maturation-specific protein kinase was inhibited
neither by adding 2 mM ethylene glycol bis(β-aminoethyl
ether)N,N,N',N'-tetraacetic acid (EGTA), nor by adding the
heat-stable inhibitor protein of cyclic AMP-dependent
protein kinase. When a heat-stable inhibitor protein from
bovine heart, obtained from Sigma (type II, partially
purified), was added, the activity of the maturation-specific protein kinase increased by 70% above the basal activity
(Sano, 1985). However, when we used the inhibitor protein
purified more than 50-fold (a generous gift from Dr.
Hiroshi Murofushi, University of Tokyo) over that of the
Sigma inhibitor, activation due to the inhibitor preparation disappeared. Therefore, the activation observed with
the inhibitor protein of Sigma seems to be due to contaminating proteins within the preparation. These results have
shown that the maturation-specific protein kinase is Ca-
and cAMP-independent.

A possible candidate for the initial activator of the latent maturation-specific protein kinase in vivo may be an endogenous protease in the oocytes, because a protease inhibitor, chymostatin, inhibits starfish oocyte maturation most strongly in the latter half of the hormone-dependent period (Sano and Kanatani, 1983), corresponding to the time when the burst of protein phosphorylation begins in the maturing oocytes.

One of the possible target proteins within the oocytes for the maturation-specific protein kinase may be histone H1, since the kinase has a high substrate specificity for histone H1 as an exogenous substrate, and since phosphoryl-ation of histone H1 has been shown to be involved in the initiation of chromosome condensation in culture cells.

Recently, Miake-Lye and Kirschner (1985) have shown that MPF, partially purified from amphibian eggs, induces phosphorylation of lamins A and C of CHO nuclei as well as the resulting depolymerization of the nuclear lamina, fol-lowed by nuclear envelope breakdown in vitro. The present maturation-specific protein kinase has been extracted from maturing oocytes undergoing GVBD, in which MPF activity has nearly reached a maximum, and the burst of protein phospho-rylation is occurring within the oocytes. Therefore, an-other possible target protein of the maturation-specific protein kinase may be the nuclear lamins or other proteins that are involved with GVBD. Supported by grants from Ministry of Educa. Sci. & Cult. of Japan, U.S.-Japan Coope-rative Sci. Program, and Rockfeller Found. grant GA PS8418.

REFERENCES

Miake-Lye R, Kirschner MW (1985). Induction of early mitotic events in a cell-free system. Cell 41: 165-175.
Sano K, Kanatani H (1983). Effects of various protease inhibitors on starfish oocyte maturation. Biomed Res 4: 139-146.
Sano K (1985). Calcium- and cyclic AMP-independent, labile protein kinase appearing during starfish oocyte maturation: its extraction and partial characterization. Develop Growth Differ 27: 263-275.
Wu M, Gerhart JC (1980). Partial purification and characterization of the maturation-promoting factor from eggs of Xenopus laevis. Devel Biol 79:465-477.

Progress in Developmental Biology, Part B, pages 99–101
© 1986 Alan R. Liss, Inc.

ACTIN – LIKE PROTEIN ASSOCIATED WITH CORTICAL CYTOSKELETON
OF MOTH OOCYTES (HYLAPHORA CECROPIA, MANDUCA SEXTA)

Bruce M. Jarnot and Spencer J. Berry

Department of Biology, Wesleyan University,
Middletown, CT 06457.

INTRODUCTION

Eggs of giant moths (H. cecropia, M. sexta) display a
pattern of molecular events during early embryogenesis which
is similar to that described for sea urchins. During
oogenesis, messenger RNA and other components of the trans-
lational machinery accumulate, but protein synthesis in the
oocyte is suppressed until after fertilization. Early post-
fertilization translation occurs in the absence of transcription, which is initiated during blastoderm stages. Moon
et al (1983) have demonstrated a cortical cytoskeleton in
sea urchin embryos. Maternal mRNA and polysomes are associated with this structure. Since the first cells that form
in the insect egg subdivide the cortex during syncytial
blastoderm formation, immobilization of specific maternal
mRNAs by the cortical cytoskeleton could represent a mechanism for spatial determination. We have observed localization of poly A(+) RNA in the cortex of oocytes of M.
sexta (Jarnot and Berry, 1985). In this paper, we describe
an actin-rich cortical cytoskeleton and propose the fatbody
as the site of actin synthesis.

RESULTS AND DISCUSSION

Extraction of fragments of chorionated eggs with 1.0%
Triton X-100 and subsequent fixation in glutaraldehyde
reveals a filamentous cortical cytoskeleton (Fig.1a). The
actin basis for the cytoskeletal structure is demonstrated
by Fig. 1b in which similar preparations were treated with
rhodamine-conjugated phalloidin. When intact, unextracted

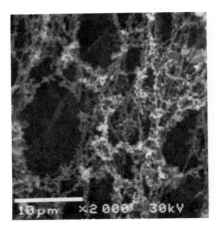
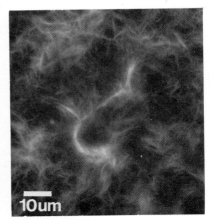

Figure 1 (a) - Scanning electron micrograph of the cortical cytoarchitecture of M. sexta oocyte following extraction with 1% Triton X-100. (b) - Fluorescent photomicrograph of a similar cortical fragment labelled with rhodamine conjugated phalloidin.

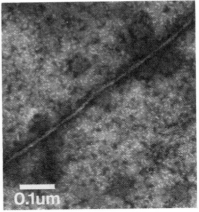

Figure 2 - Fluorescent photmicrograph of female M. sexta fatbody labelled with rhodamine conjugated phalloidin. Fluorescence appears localized to vitellogenic secretory vesicles.

Figure 3 - Transmission electron micrograph of polymerized actin fiber associated with two distinct globular protein species. Proteins isolated by DNAse I affinity chromatography from female H. cecropia hemolymph.

follicles were treated with rhodamine-phalloidin, fluorescence was heaviest in the region of the developing cortex.

When electropherograms of ooplasm are inspected, a prominent band is observed at 43 kD which co-migrates with vertebrate actin. Cell-free translation assays of early embryo cytoplasm show incorporation of ^{3}H leucine in many bands, but radioactivity is excluded from the vitellin and putative actin bands. A band at 43 kD is found in the blood of vitellogenic females in high concentration. This protein is not found in the blood of males or pre-vitellogenic females. Blood and oocyte "actin" yield identical peptide fragments when subjected to partial proteolysis with Staphylococcus aureus V8 protease. The preceeding results suggest that, like vitellogenins, actin may be synthesized in the fatbody, transported to the ovary by the hemolymph, and taken up into the oocytes by endocytosis. Further support for this mechanism is derived from phalloidin staining of fatbody where heavy fluorescence is detected in the secretory vesicles (Fig. 2).

When blood proteins and oocyte homogenates are passed over a Sephadex G-200 column, actin is detected in a very large aggregate which resists dissociation in high salt (0.6 M), but is resolved into "actin" and two larger globular proteins by SDS. This complex also binds to a Sepharose 4B-DNAse I affinity column. If the complex is released from DNAse I, and the salt concentration adjusted to promote polymerization of f-actin, negative-stained EM preparations show fibers composed of two helical chains, and two large globular proteins (Fig. 3).

We are now examining the possibility that the formation of actin-vitellogenin complexes is required for yolk uptake and processing in the oocytes.

REFERENCES

Jarnot B, Berry S J (1985) Regulation of translation during oogenesis and embryogenesis in the tobacco hornworm Manduca sexta. Intl J. Invert Rep and Dev In press.
Moon Randall T, Nicosia Roberto F, Olsen Cherie, Hille Merrill B, Jeffery William R. (1983) The cytoskeletal framework of sea urchin eggs and embryos:Developemntal changes in the association of messenger RNA. Dev Biol 95:447-458.

Progress in Developmental Biology, Part B, pages 103–106
© 1986 Alan R. Liss, Inc.

PROTEIN METABOLISM IN PREIMPLANTATION MOUSE EMBRYOS

Peter L. Kaye, Lucia B. Pemble and Jill G. Hobbs

Department of Physiology and Pharmacology, University of Queensland, Brisbane, Australia 4067

INTRODUCTION

The mouse egg is fertilized and develops to a blastocyst in the oviduct/uterus with access to the complex nutrient environment of the luminal fluids. Information for the mouse is limited, but the more easily studied rabbit luminal fluid, contains high protein levels (Shapiro *et al.*, 1971) and most amino acids (Miller, 1984). The importance of this material to the embryo is largely unknown. Development of 2-cell mouse embryos to blastocysts can occur in media lacking protein and amino acid. But absence of free amino acids from the medium reduces the total amino acid pool of the embryos, whilst protein levels remain unchanged in protein-containing medium (Sellens *et al.*, 1981). We investigated the capacity of embryos to take up these amino nutrients *in vitro*. BSA labelled with ^{125}I (Greenwood *et al.*, 1963) and ^{3}H-glycine were used to measure protein and glycine uptake from media by standard techniques (Hobbs and Kaye, 1985).

RESULTS

Protein Uptake

At 37°C, 2-cell embryos, morulae and blastocysts all took up protein from the medium but blastocysts were much more active (Fig. 1A). In blastocysts, uptake was temperature dependent and the kinetics, measured over

30 min indicated at least two components; one saturable at low protein levels and one unsaturable (Fig. 1B). The likely uptake mechanism in blastocysts is by endocytosis of ^{125}I-BSA bound to the membrane (saturable) and soluble (unsaturable) in the pinocytosed fluid medium.

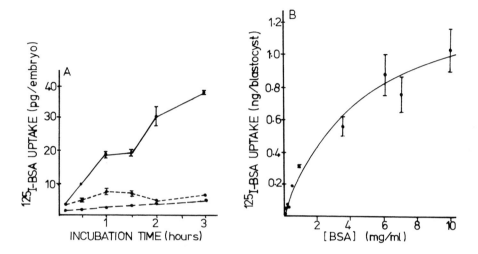

Fig. 1A. ^{125}I-BSA uptake (18 g/ml, 13 mCi/mg) by 2-cell embryos (•–•), morulae (•---•) and blastocysts (•—•) at 37°C. **B.** Dependence of ^{125}I-BSA uptake (30 min) by blastocysts on ^{125}I-BSA concentration at 37°C. (Means ± sem).

Once associated with the embryos, ^{125}I-BSA rapidly dissappeared, suggesting rapid catabolism of endocytosed material. At the protein levels in uterine fluids endocytosis would represent a significant source of amino acids to the embryo which has previously remained unassessed. Uptake of BSA by mouse embryos *in vivo* has been observed but not quantified by immunochemical procedures (Glass, 1963), indicating that this process probably occurs normally *in vivo*.

Glycine Uptake

Glycine is a major component of the embryonic free

amino acid pool and its level decreases significantly during development (Shultz *et al.*, 1981).

Both 2-cell embryos and blastocysts concentrated glycine from the medium by temperature dependent, Na^+ requiring systems. In 2-cell embryos only sarcosine competed for glycine uptake; however in blastocysts, methionine, alanine and leucine but not sarcosine competed. Kinetic analysis revealed uptake to be by a combination of a saturable, high activity Na^+-dependent system and a non-saturable, low activity Na^+-independent route.

We conclude that 2-cell embryos possess a specific saturable glycine transport system. During development either *in vivo* or *in vitro* this system is modified or replaced by a similarly active but less specific system which was stimulated by insulin (1.7 nM, 90 min preincubation) and by the complete absence of an amino-source during 72 h culture (Table 1). These effects are characteristic of "A-like" systems which have previously been proposed to transport methionine in blastocysts (Kaye *et al.*, 1982).

Table 1. Regulation of blastocyst glycine uptake by exogenous insulin and amino source (pmol/blastocyst/ 10 min, mean ± sem (n)).

	Freshly collected (96 h post hCG)	Cultured 24 h from morulae
Control	0.30 ± 0.03 (9)	0.40 ± 0.03 (6)
Insulin	0.43 ± 0.05 (8)*	0.66 ± 0.03 (7)***

Cultured from 2-cell embryos (120 h post hCG)

No protein, no glycine	1.14 ± 0.13 (14)
+ BSA	0.89 ± 0.14 (16)
+ BSA, + glycine	0.59 ± 0.05 (16)***

(* P < 0.05, *** P < 0.001)

So during development mouse embryos acquire a glycine uptake system which may be regulated by the levels of Na^+, amino source or insulin in the tract fluid.

Particularly interesting is the apparent interaction between the supply of amino acids whether from amino acid or protein in the medium and the activity of the glycine transport system. This suggests that the embryo does utilize exogenous protein for amino acid pool regulation.

The non-saturable Na^+-independent component of blastocyst glycine uptake has approximately the same diffusion constant as the non-saturable component of ^{125}I-BSA uptake (i.e. ~ 4 pl/min/embryo) compared with an embryonic volume of about 200 pl. This represents a high rate of fluid transport by blastocysts.

REFERENCES

Glass LE (1963). Transfer of native and foreign serum antigens to oviducal mouse eggs. Amer Zool 3: 135-156.

Greenwood F, Hunter W, Glover J (1963). The preparation of ^{131}I-labelled human growth hormone of high specific activity. Biochem J 89: 114-123.

Hobbs JG, Kaye PL (1985). Glycine transport in mouse eggs and pre-implantation embryos. J Reprod Fert 74: 77-84.

Kaye PL, Schultz GA, Johnson MH, Pratt HPM, Church RB (1982). Amino acid transport and exchange in preimplantation mouse embryos. J Reprod Fert 65: 367-380.

Miller JGO (1984). Amino acid transport in preimplantation mammalian embryos. PhD Thesis, University of Calgary, Canada.

Schultz G, Kaye P, McKay D, Johnson M (1981). Endogenous amino acid pool sizes in mouse eggs and preimplantation embryos. J Reprod Fert 61: 387-393.

Sellens MH, Steins S, Sherman MI (1981). Protein and free amino acid content in preimplantation mouse embryos and in blastocysts under various culture conditions. J Reprod Fert 61: 307-315.

Shapiro S, Jentsch J, Yard A (1971). Protein composition of rabbit oviducal fluid. J Reprod Fert 24: 403-408.

Supported by grants to PLK from the NHMRC and University of Queensland Special Projects.

Pattern Formation in Nervous System

Progress in Developmental Biology, Part B, pages 109–112
© 1986 Alan R. Liss, Inc.

DEVELOPMENT OF RETINAL CENTRAL PROJECTION IN <u>XENOPUS</u> TADPOLES

Hajime Fujisawa and Shin Takagi

Department of Anatomy, Kyoto Prefectural University of Medicine, Kamikyo-ku, Kyoto 602, Japan

INTRODUCTION

The establishment of specific neuronal connection between the retina and the tectum in amphibians is well studied, and several developmental mechanisms responsible for the ordered retinotectal connection have been proposed.

In regeneration of the retinotectal projection in amphibians, several regenerating retinal axons arrived at their correct sites of innervation within the tectum, after passing through anomalous routes (Udin, 1978; Fujisawa, 1981 a, b; Fujisawa et al., 1982). In normally developing <u>Xenopus</u> tadpoles, the pathway of retinal axons is not so clearly seggregated, and also, the developing retinal axons arrived at their sites of normal innervation within the tectum, after passing through ectopic termination sites for those axons (Fujisawa, 1984). These findings indicate that some kinds of direct interaction between retinal axons and tectal cells are primarily important to establish the orderly map of the retinotectal projection.

One of the practical approaches to elucidate the interaction between retinal axons and tectal cells is an anatomical mapping of ingrowing retinal axons. As shown in previous studies (Fujisawa et al., 1981a, b), a direct detection of the trajectories and patterns of branching of individual regenerating retinal axons after filling with anterograde neuronal tracer horseradish peroxidase (HRP) enable us to clarify the mode of axonal growth toward targets, and to predict an involvement of active interaction between

retinal axons and tectal cells during the reestablishment
of the retinotectal connection, in the adult newts.

In this study, we performed an anatomical detection of
the trajectories and patterns of branching of developing
retinal axons in Xenopus tadpoles, and posturated developmental mechanisms for the orderly map formation between the
retina and the tectum. Moreover, to clarify the molecular
background of the specific neuronal connection between the
retina and the tectum, we tried to screen target specific
cell surface molecules by the monoclonal antibody technique.

RESULTS

Mode of Growth of Retinal Axons Toward Tectum

To clarify the spatial and temporal mode of growth of
retinal axons toward the tectum, a restricted regional population of retinal axons of Xenopus tadpoles at different
stages of development were filled with HRP. And, the trajectories and patterns of branching of the HRP-filled retinal axons were mapped in whole-mounted brains. Through
this analysis, two different steps of axonal growth which
may account for the establishment of the orderly map of the
retinotectal projection.

The first step was a global retinotopical alignment of
terminals of newly added retinal axons within the tectum.
Newly added retinal axons which had derived from the periphery of the retina invaded the tectum, and arrived approximately at their sites of normal innervation; the nasal, temporal, ventral and dorsal retinal axons arrived at the caudal, rostral, dorsal and ventral parts of the tectum, respectively. The most important finding was that those newly added retinal axons started sprouting at first when they
had arrived at their sites of normal innervation within the
tectum. The global alignment of newly added retinal axons
within the tectum may be accomplished by a direct interaction between growth cones of ingrowing retinal axons and
tectal cells.

The second step of axonal growth was a sequential bifur-
cation of those globaly aligned retinal axons and a following preferential selection of appropriate branches. Axonal

sprouting and selection of branches continued throughout larval life, untill the growth of the retina and the tectum completely stopped. As the result, the retinotectal projection became more accurate, and the terminal sites of individual retinal axons were shifted to produce a final retinotectal projection map.

Growth of Retinal Axons Toward Minor Visual Centers

The present HRP-filling of retinal axons was also feasible to detect the mode of growth of retinal axons toward such minor visual centers in the diencephalon and the midbrain as the nucleus of Belonci, the corpus geniculatum thalamicus, the pretectal area and the basal optic nucleus. Similar to the retinal axons toward the tectum, retinal axons projected to those minor visual centers started sprouting at first when they had arrived at their targets.

Monoclonal Antibodies That Recognize Tectal Cell Surface Molecules

To obtain monoclonal antibodies that specifically recognize cell surface molecules of the visual centers, mechanically dissociated tectal cells of Xenopus tadpoles at stage 50 to 52 were injected into BALB/c mice, and immune spleen cells were fused with myeloma cells (P3X63Ag8U1). Screening of hybridoma cells were performed by immunofluorescence staining of frozen section of Xenopus tadpole brains. From more than two thousands hybridoma cells, two monoclonal antibodies which recognized different tectal laminas were screened.

Monoclonal antibody A5 (Mab-A5) bound to the laminas 8 and 9 of the tadpole and frog tecta, and monoclonal antibody B2 (Mab-B2) bound to all plexiform layers of the tectum except laminas 8 and 9. Mab-A5 bound to the laminas 8 and 9 of the tectum of eye-enucleated tadpoles, but not to the optic nerve. A5 antigen was a cell surface molecule, because the pattern of immunohistochemical staining of Mab-A5 in intact brains was exactly same to the one in the paraformaldehyde-fixed brains. A5 antigen was detectable also in the minor visual centers in the diencephalon and the midbrain. A5 antigen appeared in the tectum at first at stage 39 when the tectal invasion of retinal axons initiated. These immunohistochemical features suggest that the A5 antigen may act as a marker molecule of optic nerve targets.

REFERENCES

Fujisawa H (1981a). Retinotopic analysis of fiber pathways in the regenerating retinotectal system of the adult newt Cynops pyrrhogaster. Brain Res 206: 27-37.

Fujisawa H (1981b). Persistence of disorganized pathways and tortuous trajectories of regenerating retinal fibers in the adult newt Cynops pyrrhogaster. Dev Growth and Differ 23: 215-219.

Fujisawa H (1984). Pathways of retinotectal projection in developing Xenopus tadpoles revealed by selectively labeling of retinal axons with horseradish peroxidase (HRP). Dev Growth and Differ 26: 545-553.

Fujisawa H, Watanabe K, Tani N, Ibata Y (1981a). Retinotopic analysis of fiber pathways in amphibians. I. The adult newt Cynops pyrrhogaster. Brain Res 206: 9-20.

Fujisawa H, Watanabe K, Tani N, Ibata Y (1981b). Retinotopic analysis of fiber pathways in amphibians. II. The frog Rana nigromaculata. Brain Res 206: 21-26.

Fujisawa H, Tani N, Watanabe K, Ibata Y (1982). Branching of regenerating retinal axons and preferential selection of appropriate branches for specific neuronal connection in the newt. Dev Biol 90: 43-57.

Udin SB (1978). Permanent disorganization of the regenerating optic tract in the frog. Exp Neurol 58: 455-470.

Progress in Developmental Biology, Part B, pages 113–127

A VITAL-DYE FIBER-TRACING TECHNIQUE TO EXAMINE NEURONAL PATTERNING AND PATTERN REGULATION IN THE *XENOPUS* EYEBUD

Nancy A. O'Rourke and Scott E. Fraser

Developmental Biology Center and
Department of Physiology and Biophysics,
University of California,
Irvine, California 92717

INTRODUCTION

During development, groups of neurons send out axons to form precise connections with their targets in neighboring regions of the embryo. Thus, pattern formation in the nervous system becomes a complex issue involving both the spatial order within groups of neurons and the order found within their projections. A striking feature of the patterning of these projections is the apparent specificity of axonal connections. Evidence in a number of systems strongly suggests that neurons are equipped with positional information which allows them to innervate their correct targets.

One important system for studying the patterning of neural connections has been the retinotectal projection in which the retinal ganglion cells of the eye send a topographically ordered projection into the tectum of the midbrain via the optic nerve. The projection pattern is highly regular, demonstrating a reliable order both during development and after regeneration. Axons from the dorsal part of the eye project to the lateral tectum, from the ventral eye to medial tectum, from the nasal eye to caudal tectum, and from the temporal eye to rostral tectum. In addition, the projection displays a smooth internal order; that is, neighboring cells in the eye project to neighboring locations in the tectum. This paper will review some of the data on the patterning of the retinotectal projection and the nature of the positional information that brings order to the system, and then present our studies which focus on determining mechanisms by which positional information is provided to the cells of the developing eyebud.

Patterning of the Retinotectal System

Evidence for positional information in the retinotectal system has been found both during development and regeneration of the projection. Developing optic nerve fibers in *Xenopus laevis* grow to their correct dorsoventral position in the tectum, even in the absence of nerve activity or normal timing of ingrowth (Holt & Harris, 1983; Harris, 1984; Holt, 1984). Furthermore, when small wedges of eyebud tissue are grafted to ectopic sites in the eyebud, the descendants of the grafted tissue in the adult eye are often observed to project to the tectum in a manner appropriate for their position of origin (c.f. Conway. et al, 1980; Cook & Gaze, 1983). During regeneration, misrouted optic nerve fibers have been shown to travel through unfamiliar regions of the tectum to relocate their correct termination sites (c.f. Meyer, 1984; Fujisawa, et al, 1981, 1982). When small pieces of the tectum are surgically excised and then reimplanted in a different position or orientation, regenerating optic nerve fibers are able to locate and terminate on the proper, though malpositioned, piece of tectum (c.f. Yoon, 1975; see review, Fraser and Hunt, 1980). These results are all consistent with the interpretation that each optic nerve fiber has an inherent "knowledge" of its position in the eye and uses this "knowledge" to navigate over positional markers in the tectum.

Additional experiments highlight another very important characteristic of the patterning in the projection. The neurons display plasticity, changing their projection pattern in response to changes in their environment. For example, if one half of the tectum is removed, the optic nerve fibers from the entire eye will innervate the remaining half tectum in a compressed, but ordered, projection. Conversely, if half the retina is removed, the remaining half set of optic fibers will expand to innervate the entire tectum, again in an ordered fashion. This plasticity will take place even in cases where controls show there is no regeneration of the deleted tissues (see reviews: Meyer, 1982, Fraser & Hunt, 1980).

The neurons in the retinotectal system show a well-documented ability to find their correct target sites. The specificity displayed by the neurons in the retinotectal system has led to the proposal of such models as the chemoaffinity model (Sperry, 1963) in which a precise one-to-one system of positional cues is set up in the retina and the tectum. The model requires some modification, however, since the plasticity in the system indicates that the cues are not exact, but relative. The optic nerve fibers maintain order in their projection while responding to changes in the tectal environment. Thus, the ordered projection between the eye and the brain appears to be the product of a dynamic process in which the retinal ganglion cells extend and retract neurites, responding to the positional cues and

competitive influences in the tectum, in a search for their
termination site.

Regulation in the Retinotectal System

The presence of positional information has been implicated in
the patterning of many embryonic tissues. Unfortunately, very little
is known about how this information is assigned to the cells during
development. One powerful approach to this problem has been the
study of regulatory interactions which reveal changes in the
positional information of developing tissues following the
rearrangement or removal of part of the tissue. In many embryos,
the tissue will respond to this perturbation by replacing the missing
parts of the tissue or by forming anomolous spatial patterns.
Examination of these changes has provided clues to the mechanisms
by which positional information might be originally assigned to the
cells in the embryo.

The reliable order of the amphibian retinotectal projection and
the accessibility of the embryonic eyebud to surgical manipulation
has made it a popular system for studies of regulation. In the
eyebud of *Xenopus laevis*, studies have focused on regulation in
eyebud fragments, on interactions between eyebud fragments and on
interactions between the whole eyebud and its surrounding tissue.
The basic paradigm of these studies is to remove or rearrange part or
all of the embryonic eye rudiment, raise the animal to
metamorphosis, and then assay the projection pattern. Although some
controversy exists as to whether regulation occurs after certain
manipulations (c.f. Conway et al, 1980, Cooke & Gaze, 1984), many
operations lead to dramatic and reproducible changes in the adult
pattern. Efforts are now focusing on how these changes come about.

Two major questions being considered are when and in what
cells the changes in positional information occur. The eye of lower
vertebrates undergoes dramatic growth during post-embryonic
development, increasing its size as much as a thousand fold (c.f.
Fernald, 1984). Cells are added to the margin of the eye such that
the descendants of a given cell form a radial wedge in the adult eye.
The relative position of grafted tissue is thought to be maintained
but the vast majority of the retina is added long after the grafting
operation. Thus, when the final pattern is assayed in the adult eye,
this growth limits the information that experiments can yield about
the timing of interactions that bring about pattern regulation. In
addition, the few cell markers for the neural retina previously
available made the actual positions of the descendants of the grafted
cells uncertain. New approaches to this problem must include ways

of identifying cells and assaying their behavior throughout development.

CELL LABELING TECHNIQUE

In our study we have developed a cell marking technique which allows us to 1) mark the cells of the neural retina and 2) assay the topography of the retinotectal projection during early stages of development. We utilized the fluorescent vital dye lysinated fluorescein dextran (LFD) (Gimlich & Braun, 1985). The dye consists of a 10,000 MW dextran molecule with fluorescein and lysine residues added along its length, creating a stable dye which can be fixed in the tissue using aldehyde fixatives. The large molecular weight of the dye and its hydrophilic nature prevent it from leaking out of the cells or passing between cells through gap junctions. In our experiments we pressure injected the dye into fertilized *Xenopus* eggs, yielding embryos in which all the cells were brightly labeled (O'Rourke & Fraser, 1985). The injected animals developed normally and had the same survival rates as uninjected siblings. The development of labeled cells could then be followed by grafting them into unlabeled host animals.

Application of the technique to the retinotectal system first required characterization of the behavior of the dye in eyebud tissue. Labeled whole eyebuds or half-eyebud fragments were exchanged with the equivalent tissues in unlabeled hosts at st 32. The dye remained visible in the grafted cells for a period of weeks. Initially, the dye could be visualized in the grafted eyebud *in vivo*. With further development, the outer pigmented epithelium covered the inner neural retina and the label was hidden from view. At this point, histological sections were necessary to visualize the label in the cells. Figure 1 shows a frozen section through an eye with a labeled dorsal half at st 47 (four days after surgery). The label is clearly visible in all layers of the grafted neural retina and a sharp graft-host boundary is observed. In the center of the eye, where there is little or no cell division, the dye remains bright. Around the ciliary margin at the edge of the eye, cell division occurs throughout development and the dye has been diluted. This shows both that the dye provides a long term marker for grafted cells in the neural retina and that these cells remain healthy and divide normally.

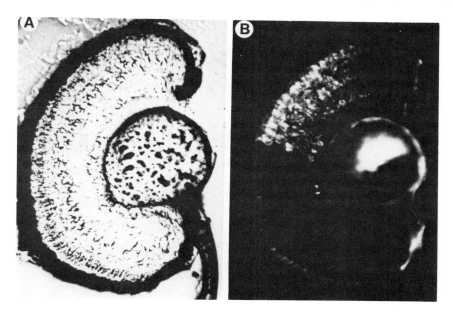

Figure 1. Transverse frozen section through a stage 47 eyebud which has its dorsal half labeled with fluorescein dextran. (A) Bright field illumination. (B) Epifluorescent illumination. Scale bar=50 microns.

DEVELOPMENT OF TOPOGRAPHY IN THE PROJECTION

As development proceeds the head of the tadpole becomes transparent and the growing axons of the labeled retinal ganglion cells can be visualized in the live animal. Half eye grafts were performed in order to determine if the topography of the retinotectal projection could be assayed during early larval development. The projection pattern from the labeled half eyes was followed in individual animals over a period of days, allowing a dynamic view of the appearance of topography in the projection.

The dorsoventral order of the projection was assayed by comparing the projection patterns from dorsal and ventral half eye grafts. The topography was apparent from early stages but was most easily visualized in live animals from stage 47 onward because the shape of the animal allowed it to be reliably aligned on the microscope stage and the shape of the tectum permitted an unhindered (though foreshortened) view of the mediolateral

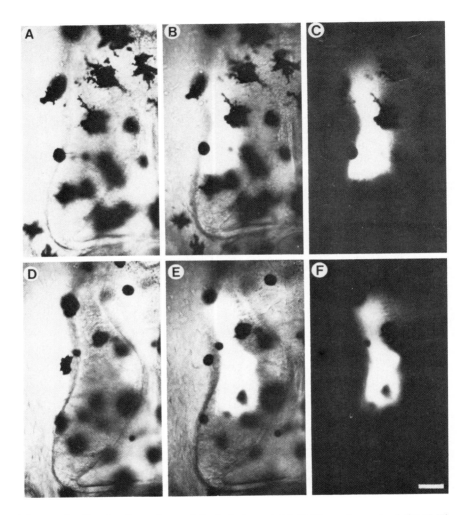

Figure 2. Projections from labeled dorsal (A,B,C) and ventral (D,E,F) half eyebuds at stage 47. (A,D) Bright field, (C,F) Fluorescence, (B,E) Combination bright field and fluorescence. The tecta are oriented with anterior at the top; posterior at the bottom; lateral edges at the left; and medial edges at the right. Scale bar=50 microns.

dimension of the tectal neuropil. At stage 47, labeled dorsal fibers could be seen innervating the lateral portion of the tectum, while ventral fibers projected more medially, leaving a gap of 10-40 microns between the lateral edge of the tectum and the edge of the projection (Fig. 2).

The development of nasotemporal order was explored using a similar approach. At stage 47 when a clear dorsoventral order was already evident, no consistent nasotemporal difference was observed. The fibers from the nasal half and the temporal half of the eye overlapped, covering the same area of the tectal surface. When the same animals were assayed three to five days later at stage 49, however, a clear difference was apparent. The projection from the nasal half eyebud consistently projected more caudally on the tectum than the projection from the temporal half eyebud. The results are summarized diagramatically in Figure 3.

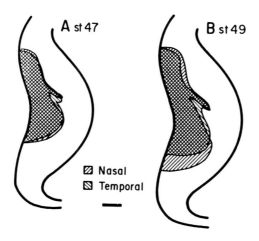

Figure 3. Projections from nasal and temporal half eyes. (A) Tracings of the projections from labeled nasal and temporal half eyebuds at stage 47, and (B) from the same animals four days later at stage 49. The tecta are oriented with anterior to the top; posterior to the bottom; lateral edge to the left; and medial edge to the right. The cross-hatched areas represent the projections of the LFD labeled optic nerve fibers, traced from a video monitor connected to an image intensifying camera. Scale bar=50 microns.

REGULATION IN COMPOUND EYES

We have examined pattern regulation in interactions between eyebud fragments, many of which produce reproducible and dramatic alterations of the adult retinotectal projection pattern. The interaction we have studied is a recombinant or compound eye made up of the nasal half of a right eyebud (N_r) and the temporal half of a left eyebud (T_l) (Hunt & Jacobson, 1973a, Ide et al, 1979, O'Rourke & Fraser, 1985b). These compound "Nasal right-Temporal left" (N_rT_l) eyes are composed of a nasal half with normal dorsoventral orientation and a temporal half with reversed dorsoventral orientation (Fig. 4A). The surgery is performed at embryonic stage 32 when the cells of the eyebud have been shown to have positional information (Hunt & Jacobson 1973b, Gaze et al, 1979). If the eye developed its projection to the tectum in accord with the positional information within the eyebud fragments, the nasal half of the visuotectal projection pattern (corresponding to the T_l fragment) would be expected to have inverted dorsoventral polarity (Fig 4C). Due to inversion of the image by the lens, the nasal visual field is seen by the temporal retina, therefore the dorsoventral polarity of the temporal half of the eye is reflected in the nasal visual field. Instead, when assayed with electrophysiological techniques in a newly metamorphosed frog, the projection formed is always either normal or mirror image duplicated (Fig. 4D,E). Since both of these projection patterns show normal, rather than an inverted, dorsoventral polarity, these results have been taken as evidence that the positional information in the T_l half of the N_rT_l eye has been respecified.

Three mechanisms for patterning in the eyebud have been proposed based on the results of regulation studies:

1. Diffusible signals. Diffusible signals could pass from one part of the eyebud to another and respecify the positional information in the eyebud cells. The results of the N_rT_l eye experiment could be explained by a signal passing from the nasal half of the eye to the grafted temporal half and repolarizing the dorsoventral (and in some cases the nasotemporal) axis of the eyebud fragment.

2. Intercalary growth. In this case, the positional information in the cells would be stable and cell division would be required for regulation to occur. Intercalary growth would give rise to new cells with new positional values. In the N_rT_l eye, the original cells in the grafted temporal left half would maintain their inverted dorsoventral polarity. The normal dorsoventral polarity would arise from the intercalary growth at the graft/host border.

3. Cell movement-cell sorting. In the third mechanism recently proposed by Ide et al (1984) cells would not change their positional

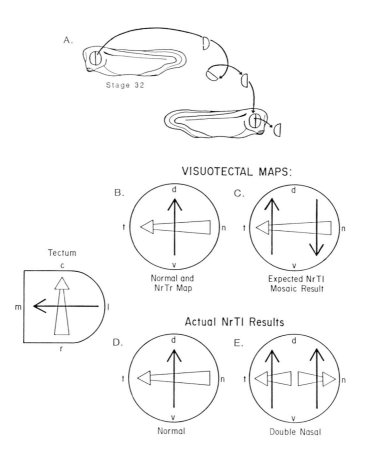

Figure 4. (A) N_rT_1 grafting operation. The temporal half of the right eyebud of a stage 32 host is removed and replaced with the temporal half of a left eyebud. (B) Normal visuotectal projection pattern. (C) Expected pattern from an N_rT_1 eye if the neurons projected according to their original positions in the eyebud. (D,E) Actual maps obtained from N_rT_1 compound eyes. The arrows represent the polarity of the projection pattern. Note that the nasal half of the projection (temporal retina) has normal dorsoventral polarity instead of the expected upside-down polarity. Tectum: c,caudal; r,rostral; m,medial; l,lateral. The circles (B-E) represent the visual fields of the eyes: d,dorsal; v,ventral; n,nasal; t,temporal.

values; instead, they would change their positions within the eyebud, and then sort out into new patterns of positional values. Thus, cells in the temporal half of the N_rT_l eye would have to exchange their dorsoventral positions in order to set up a new polarity in the eye.

The limitations imposed by the techniques used in previous investigations have made it difficult to rule out any of these proposed mechanisms for pattern regulation in the eyebud. Further insight into this problem must rely on a greater knowledge of the events which occur during these interactions. We have therefore used our labeling technique to examine early stages of regulation in the compound N_rT_l eye.

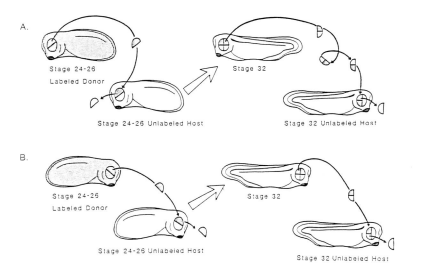

Figure 5. Diagram illustrating grafting operations. (A)To produce a N_rT_l eye with a labeled temporoventral quadrant: The "dorsal" half of the left eyebud of a stage 24-26 unlabeled animal is removed and replaced with the "dorsal" half of a labeled donor of the same stage. At stage 32, the temporal half of this half-labeled left eyebud is used to create an N_rT_l eye. (B)To produce a control N_rT_r eye with a labeled temporodorsal quadrant: A similar "dorsal" half replacement graft is performed, but on the right eyebud. The temporal half of this half-labeled right eyebud is then used to replace the temporal half of the right eyebud of an unlabeled host at stage 32. A similar series of operations were performed to create eyes with label in the ventral half of the eye (st 24-26) which could then be used to create N_rT_l and N_rT_r eyes (st 32).

In a series of two grafting operations (Fig. 5), N_rT_l eyes were created with either the dorsal or ventral portion of the grafted temporal left half labeled. Labeled cells which were initially in the dorsal half of the donor eye ended up in the ventral portion of the grafted temporal half of the final N_rT_l eye. Ventral cells ended up in a dorsal position. A series of control N_rT_r eyes were also constructed in which a simple right temporal half eye replacement was performed. In this case, the labeled cells from the donor eye end up in the same dorsoventral position in the grafted temporal right half fragment.

This experimental paradigm can be used to test two of the proposed mechanisms for regulation in the eyebud. The position of the labeled cells in the eyebud were followed to determine if the grafted cells in an N_rT_l eye remained in the positions in which they were grafted, thereby testing for cell movement. In addition, the retinotectal projection patterns of the labeled cells were assayed to ascertain whether the cells projected according to their original positions in the eyebud or whether they projected as predicted by the regulated pattern seen in the adult map. If the early cells projected in a regulated pattern, this would be strong evidence for respecification in the eyebud cells and against intercalation.

Cell Movement in Compound Eyes

Frozen sections through the temporal half of an N_rT_l eye at st 47 reveal that labeled cells remained in the positions in which they were grafted. There was a sharp graft-host boundary indicating that very little mixing of the cells occurred. In addition, dilution of the dye at the ciliary margin confirmed that the graft cells were healthy and dividing. Thus, there was no cell movement among the original grafted cells during the first few weeks after the surgery.

To test whether cell movement was occurring around the ciliary margin where the dye became diluted, we repeated the same experimental paradigm using the interspecific borealis-laevis nuclear marker. Quinacrine dye stains borealis nuclei in a freckled pattern and laevis nuclei diffusely (Thiebaud, 1983). This permits the graft cells and their progeny to be identified throughout the life of the animal. Preliminary results indicate that the cells remain in the positions in which they were grafted even up to adult stages.

Larval Projection Patterns from Compound Eyes

The labeling technique permits us to perform an *in vivo* assay of dorsoventral topography of the projection formed by the N_rT_l eyes.

The distinct projection patterns formed by dorsal and ventral half-eyes are shown in Figure 6A,B. In the first series of experiments, labeled dorsal cells were grafted to ventral positions in the final N_rT_1 eye (Fig. 6C). The results show that the labeled cells projected along the lateral edge of the tectum, as though they were still in a dorsal position. In the second series of experiments, the ventral half of the donor eyebud was labeled. The cells in the N_rT_1 eyes, which had been grafted from a ventral position into a final dorsal position, projected medially in the tectum as if they were still in a ventral position (Fig. 6D). In control N_rT_r eyes, labeled dorsal or ventral eyebud cells projected indistinguishably from normal eyes. Thus, in all cases the labeled cells projected according to their original positions in the eyebud and not according to either their grafted positions or the regulated pattern seen in the adult map.

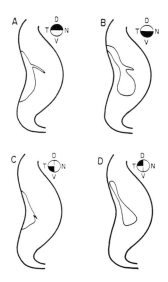

Figure 6. (A,B) Projections from normal dorsal (A) and ventral (B) half-eyes. (C) Projection from an N_rT_1 eye in which labeled dorsal cells have been grafted to a ventral position. (D) Projection from an N_rT_1 eye in which labeled ventral cells have been grafted to a dorsal position. Each of the outlines are tracings of the tectum of stage 47 *Xenopus* larvae. The thinner lines are the outlines of the recorded fluorescent signal from the projections of the labeled fibers from the contralateral eye. The small circles represent the eyebuds; the shaded regions show the position of the labeled cells in the eyebud. Scale bar=50 microns.

SUMMARY

    The projection patterns of the nervous system display an inherent specificity, apparently based on sets of positional cues present in both the neurons and their target cells. Although a wealth of evidence in many different systems supports the existence of these cues, very little is known about how they may be laid down in the embryo. One way of approaching this question has been to study the regulatory interactions which perturb patterning in the embryo.

    We have developed a new cell labeling technique for the study of regulatory interactions in the developing eyebud. The fluorescent vital dye, lysinated fluorescein dextran, was injected into fertilized *Xenopus* eggs, producing embryos in which all the cells were labeled. When labeled eyebud cells were grafted into unlabeled hosts, their development could be followed. The dye persisted in the eyebud cells for a period of weeks and thus provided a useful long-term cell marker. In addition to marking the cell, the dye also filled the growing axons of the retinal ganglion cells. Because the head of the young *Xenopus* tadpole is transparent, the pathway of the labeled fibers could be visualized in a live animal. Video imaging techniques have allowed us to follow development of the projection in individual animals for a period of several days.

    Using the cell marking technique we have been able to document the emergence of topography in the retinotectal projection. We have confirmed that dorsoventral topography is apparent early in development (Holt and Harris, 1983). In contrast, we have found that nasal and temporal fibers overlap early in development and then sort out into their normal topography over a period of days. This demonstrates the dynamic behavior of optic nerve fibers during the formation of the developing retinotectal projection.

    We have applied this fiber-tracing technique to studies of regulation in the developing eyebud. Since the technique permits both the position of grafted cells in the neural retina and their early projection pattern in the tectum to be assayed, it provided a convenient way to explore pattern regulation problems. In the compound N_rT_l eye, cell movement, intercalation, or respecification could be responsible for regulation. We have shown that cells in the grafted temporal half of N_rT_l eyes remained in the positions in which they were grafted, ruling out cell movement as a mechanism for this particular regulatory interaction. The cells remained healthy and continued to divide and contribute to the eye throughout development. In addition, these grafted cells project according to their original positions in the embryo. That is, they do not show the regulated projection pattern seen in the adult eye. Thus, we have not seen any evidence for regulation in the original grafted cells during early larval development.

These studies introduce a new approach for the study of regulation in the developing nervous system. Through the direct observation of the labeled cells, this approach may yield a better understanding of the cellular and molecular basis of regulation. For example, knowledge of the timing of regulation will permit future studies to be concentrated on critical time periods in the interaction. The application of this and other new techniques to the study of regulation should allow insight into the mechanisms responsible for patterning of the nervous system.

REFERENCES

Cooke J, Gaze RM (1983). The positional coding system in the early eye rudiment of *Xenopus laevis*, and its modification after grafting operations. J Embryol exp Morph 77:53-71.

Conway K, Feiock K, Hunt RK (1980). Polyclones and patterns in developing *Xenopus* larvae. Curr Topics Dev Bio 15:216-317.

Fernald RD (1984). Vision and Behavior in an African Cichlid fish. Amer Scientist 72:58-65.

Fraser SE, Hunt RK (1980). Retinotectal specificity: Models and experiments in search of a mapping function. Ann Rev Neurosci 3:319-352.

Fujisawa H, Tani N, Watanabe K, Ibata Y (1982). Branching of regenerating retinal axons and preferential selection of appropriate branches for specific neuronal connections in the newt. Dev Bio 90:43-57.

Fujisawa H, Watanabe K, Tani N, Ibata Y (1981). Retinotopic analysis of fiber pathways in the regenerating retinotectal system of the adult newt *Cynops pyrrhogaster*. Brain Res 206:27-37.

Gaze RM, Feldman JD, Cooke J, Chung S-H (1979) The orientation of the visuotectal map in *Xenopus*: Developmental aspects. JEEM 53:39-66.

Gimlich RL, Braun J (1985). Improved fluorescent compounds for tracing cell lineage. Dev Bio 109:509-514.

Harris WA (1984). Axonal pathfinding in the absence of normal pathways and impulse activity. J Neurosci 4:1153-1162.

Holt CE (1984). Does timing of axonal outgrowth influence initial retinotectal topography in *Xenopus*? J Neurosci 4:1130-1152.

Holt CE, Harris WA (1983). Order in the initial retinotectal map in *Xenopus*: A new technique for labeling growing nerve fibres. Nature 301:150-152

Hunt RK, Jacobson M (1973a). Neuronal locus specificity: Altered pattern of spatial deployment in fused fragments of embryonic *Xenopus* eyes. Science 180:509-511.

Hunt RK, Jacobson M (1973b). Specification of positional information in retinal ganglion cells of *Xenopus laevis*: Assays for analysis of the unspecified state. PNAS USA 70:507-511.

Ide, CF, Kosofsky B, Hunt RK (1979) Control of pattern duplication in the retinotectal system of *Xenopus*: Suppression of duplication by eye-fragment interactions. Dev Bio 69:337-360.

Ide CF, Reynolds P, Tompkins R (1984). Two healing patterns correlate with different neural connectivity patterns in regenerating embryonic *Xenopus* retina. J Exp Zool 230:71-80.

Meyer RL (1982). Ordering of retinotectal connections: A multivariate analysis. Curr Topics Dev Bio 17:101-145.

Meyer RL (1984). Target selection by surgically misdirected optic fibers in the tectum of goldfish. J Neurosci 4:234-250.

O'Rourke NA, Fraser SE (1985). Dynamic aspects of retinotectal map formation as revealed by a vital-dye fiber-tracing technique. Dev Bio (submitted).

O'Rourke NA, Fraser SE (1985). Pattern regulation in the eyebud of *Xenopus* studied with a vital-dye fiber-tracing technique. Dev Bio (submitted).

Sperry, RW (1963). Chemoaffinity in the orderly growth of nerve fiber patterns and connections. PNAS USA 50:703-711.

Thiebaud, CH (1983). A reliable new cell marker in *Xenopus*. Dev Bio 98:245-249.

Yoon MG (1975). Topographic polarity of the optic tectum studied by re-implantation of the tectal tissue in adult goldfish. Cold Spring Harbor Symp Quant Bio 40:503-519.

Progress in Developmental Biology, Part B, pages 129–132
© 1986 Alan R. Liss, Inc.

INVESTIGATING POSSIBLE MECHANISMS OF SPECIFIC NERVE
REGENERATION IN THE AXOLOTL

Nigel Stephens

Anatomy Department Kings College, Strand,
London WC2, England

INTRODUCTION

One of the most striking and complex examples of pattern formation in embryonic development is the assembly of
the nervous system. Central to this process is the formation
of orderly and stereotyped axonal projections between sets
of presynaptic and postsynaptic cells. The most widely –
accepted explanation of this process is the theory of neuronal specificity, which is due to R.W. Sperry (1963). He
envisaged that cells within each pre- and postsynaptic set
have a distinct identity, and may recognise oneanother and
form or avoid forming connections on the basis of this
identity. Many different experiments have demonstrated that
neurones must possess some identification that allows them
to be distinguished from oneanother during neurogenesis.
Nevertheless, within this constraint, many mechanisms may be
proposed a priori to account for the formation of patterns
of connections. Three classes of mechanism may be distinguished:

"Diffusion". Here, each postsynaptic element, when it
is not innervated, secretes an unique diffusible factor.
Axons matched to this element may detect this and respond to
it by growing up a concentration gradient of the factor to
terminate on their target.

"Competition". In this mechanism axonal growth may be
random. When a growth cone by chance encounters a postsynaptic site it makes contact with it. If another growth cone
also contacts the same site, then the two compete, with the

best - matched terminal remaining and the other retracting.
This process is reiterated until a correct pattern of connections is established.

"Labelled Pathways". Here, the substratum with which
the growth cones are in contact has biochemical labels that
they may recognise. These labels are arranged such that
they constitute pathways leading axons to their correct targets.

In order to distinguish between these hypotheses, we
are studying the mechanism of regeneration of a correct patt-
of neuromuscular connections in the axolotl. It has been
known for some time that if axolotl peripheral nerves are
cut or deviated, motor axons within these nerves may somehow
navigate back to their correct muscles and hence restore
coordinated movements (e.g. Holder et al, 1984). A regenerating system has a number of advantages over developing
systems for this type of study. One is that it is larger,
and hence more accessible to surgical manipulations; another
is that an explanation of how specfic reinnervation of muscle
may occur in one species (the axolotl) may have a more direct
bearing on how it fails in another (man).

RESULTS

The first stage of this investigation has been the
development of an assay of the accuracy of the projection
of the spinal cord motorneurones to the limb muscles. We
have found, using the horseradish peroxidase tracing technique, that each muscle studied in the limb is innervated by
a characteristic group of motorneurones in a distinct position
in the spinal cord - the muscle's motorneurone pool.
(Stephens and Holder, 1985).

This technique will demonstrate whether a muscle becomes
innervated by appropriate or foreign neurones after experimental manipulation. One such result is shown in figure 1.
If a forelimb is amputated and allowed to regenerate, the
majority of motorneurones innervating the biceps muscle in
the regenerated limb are in the same position as those innervating the normal biceps. This is evidence for specific
regrowth of a majority of motor axons in the regenerated limb.

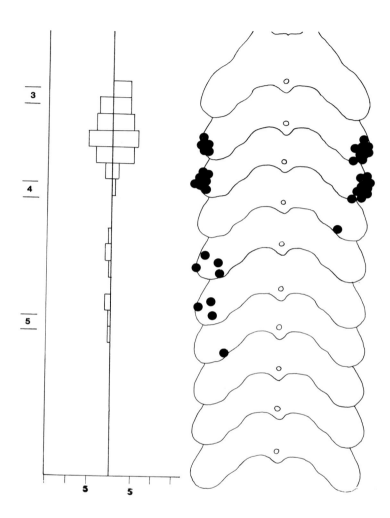

Figure 1. Motorneurone pools innervating a control biceps (right) and a biceps formed in a regenerate limb 108 days after amputation (left). The histogram on the left gives numbers of motorneurones in 500 μm bins in relation to spinal nerve roots in the rostrocaudal axis. Outline drawings of the grey matter on the right plot the position of labelled motorneurones in the transverse plane.

One strategy for testing the hypotheses of specific nerve regeneration outlined above is to alter the normal spatial relationship between axons and their targets. We have investigated the innervation of muscles in one such situation, that of serially duplicated limbs. These monster limbs may be created by amputation through the wrist and vitamin A treatment. We have found that duplicate copies of proximal muscles, such as biceps, in these limbs are innervated by inappropriate, distal limb muscle, motorneurones (Stephens et al, 1985). As has been outlined already, both after nerve damage and during limb regeneration, axolotl motor axons have a remarkable capacity for relocating their target. Why did they not in this case? One explanation is that the axons are guided by pathway cues to their correct muscle. In this experimental situation, axons terminating on the first biceps would have to grow through unfamiliar, distal limb tissues in order to reach their second target, the second biceps.

This experiment therefore provides evidence against diffusion - directed axon growth and is compatible with a pathway guidance hypothesis of specific nerve regeneration.

REFERENCES

Holder N, Tonge DA and Jesani, P (1984) Directed regrowth of axons from a misrouted nerve to their correct muscles in the limb of the adult newt. Proc R Soc Lond B 222:477-489.

Sperry RW (1963) Chemoaffinity in the orderly growth of nerve fibre patterns and connections. Proc Natl Acad Sci USA 55:703-710.

Stephens N and Holder N (1985) A horseradish peroxidase study of the motorneurone pools of the forelimb and hindlimb musculature of the axolotl. Proc R Soc Lond B 224:325-339.

Stephens N, Holder N and Maden, M (1985) Motorneurone pools innervating muscles in vitamin A - induced proximal - distal duplicate limbs in the axolotl. Proc R Soc Lond B 224: 341-354.

Progress in Developmental Biology, Part B, pages 133–136
© 1986 Alan R. Liss, Inc.

CELL MOVEMENTS AND NOVEL GROWTH PATTERNS DURING EARLY HEAL-
ING IN REGENERATING EMBRYONIC <u>XENOPUS</u> RETINA

C. F. Ide, A. Blankenau, J. Morrow and R.
Tompkins

Department of Biology, Tulane University, New
Orleans, Louisiana 70118

Pattern duplication of the visuotectal projection in
embryonic <u>Xenopus</u> eye fragments correlates with cell migration (Ide, et al., 1984), which in turn, leads to unusual
juxtapositioning of retinal cells. Here we report that
surgical removal of migratory cells can suppress pattern
duplication and that migratory cells interact with their
new neighbors to produce unusual growth patterns.

In the embryonic retina, responses to removal of 2/3
of the eye primordium at stage 32 (Nieuwkoop and Faber, 1967)
include an initial "pinching" of the pigmented retinal epithelium to close the wound, followed by movement of some
cells from the interior of the remaining fragment to the
wound edges (Ide, et al., 1984). In some cases, where
wound closure is not complete, moving cells spill into the
region of the ablation and coalesce there to form a secondary
retina (called "tongues" in our previous report due to the
way they protrude from the original fragments). Secondary
retinas, which form within the first 24–48 hours of healing,
range in size from structures as large as the remaining
retinal fragment to very small groups of cells.

Secondary retina formation correlates with pattern duplication of the visuotectal projection (Ide, et al., 1984).
Thus, the normal projection from the eye to the midbrain
optic tectum (assayed after metamorphosis using electro-
physiologic techniques) is a continuous representation of
the visual field across the tectum (Fig. 1a). In pattern
duplicated projections, two different retinal regions project
to the same tectal area (Fig. 1b). However, the size of the

secondary retina viewed at 48 hours post-surgery does not
necessarily predict the size of the pattern duplication which
ultimately forms. Small secondary retinas sometimes correlate
with full mirror-symmetric duplicated projections and large
secondary retinas sometimes correlate with small duplications.

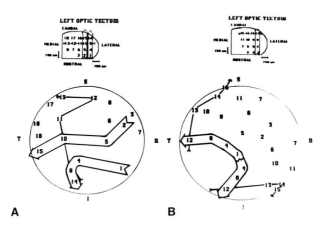

Figure 1. (a) A normal projection. (b) A duplicated projection.

To assess the importance of secondary retinas, we prepared 210 nasal 1/3 fragments at stage 32. Eighteen formed
secondary retinas (Fig 2a) of which 13 were ablated (Fig. 2b).
Only three reformed secondary retinas, and these developed
duplicated projections. Six of the remaining 10 formed normal
projections and four had some duplicated points. Four of five
unablated fragments formed duplicated projections. Thus, a
reduction in the rate of duplication (from 80% to 40%) was
obtained by removal of the secondary retina. However, the
correlation between secondary retina formation and pattern
duplication observed both in this study and in Ide et al.
(1984) was not 100%. This argues that additional processes
may underlie the pattern duplication process.

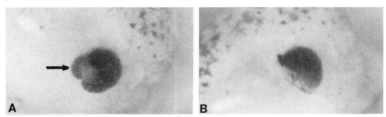

Figure 2. (a) A secondary retina (arrow). (b) After ablation.

To determine if local cell division might also be involved in pattern duplication, we injected embryos with
tritiated thymidine 36 hours after creating the nasal 1/3
fragments at stage 32. After a further 24 hours the animals
were fixed, sectioned and autoradiographs prepared. Internal-
ly, 18/19 eyes showed histological evidence of cell migration
and a single, heavily labelled ciliary margin in the front
of the eyes. However, in the rear (proximal) half of the eyes
secondary retina cells still lying in the region of the ablation between the cut edges of the fragment were heavily
labelled. In addition, heavy local label also appeared in
the ventral portion of the retina abutting the labelled cells
in the region of the ablation (Fig. 3a). In contrast, 4/4
eyes which showed no evidence of cell movements showed no
cell labelling in the region of the ablation, nor any assymetric labelling of cells in the proximo-ventral region of the
eyes. Virtually no label was found in the corresponding
proximal regions of unoperated contralateral eyes (Fig. 3b).

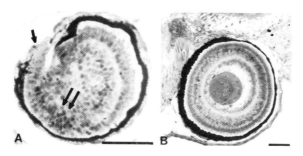

Figure 3. (a) Fragment with label in the secondary retina
(arrow) and in adjoining ventral retina (double arrows).
(b) Contralateral control eye with no localized label. Bar
equals 50 microns.

These data are consistent with the idea that, during
healing, cells which are normally never neighbors become
apposed to one another due to cell movements. Since these
cells are apparently derived from a variety of former positions, they may divide to reconcile their positional differences as proposed by the polar coordinate model (Bryant et
al., 1981). In addition, ventral cells in the original fragment which adjoin the remaining secondary retinal cell mass
also show heavy labelling. This may also be due to mismatch
between these cells and the secondary retina cell mass. The
apparent lack of heavy labelling at the dorsal cut edge may

indicate that dorsal retinal cells have different capacities for cell division compared to ventral cells. Similar assymetric growth has been described during pattern duplication in amphibian limbs (Muneoka and Bryant, 1984).

Thus, pattern duplication in the regenerating embryonic retina appears to consist of at least two phases; first, cell movements which may create positional mismatch, and second, a local cell division which may create new cells of intermediate positional values.

Supported by NSF grants PCM-8316142 and PCM 8209293.

REFERENCES

Bryant SV, French V, Bryant PJ (1981) Distal regeneration and symmetry. Science 212:993-1002.

Ide CF, Reynolds P, Tompkins R (1984) Two healing patterns correlate with different adult neural connectivity patterns in regenerating embryonic Xenopus retina. J. Exp. Zool. 230:71-80.

Muneoka K, Bryant SV (1984) Cellular contribution to supernumerary limbs in the axolotl, Ambystoma mexicanum. Develop. Biol. 105:166-178.

Nieuwkoop PD, Faber J (1967)"Normal Table of Xenopus laevis (Daudin)" Amsterdam: North Holland.

Progress in Developmental Biology, Part B, pages 137–140
© 1986 Alan R. Liss, Inc.

STUDIES ON THE DEVELOPMENT AND GROWTH OF THE MAMMALIAN
NERVOUS SYSTEM BY AGGREGATION CHIMERAS: ANALYSIS OF
CORTICOHISTOGENESIS IN THE CEREBRUM BY REELER MUTANT MICE.

K.Mikoshiba, M.Yokoyama, H.Terashima, Y.Nishimura, Y.
Inoue, H.Okano, K.Takamatsu, T.Nomura and Y.Tsukada
Division of Regulation of Macromolecular Function,
Institute for Protein Research, Osaka University,
Yamadaoka, Suita, Osaka, (K.M.,H.O.), Department of
Physiology (K.T.,Y.T.), and Anatomy (Y.N.) School of
Medicine, Keio University, Shinano-machi, Shinjuku-ku,
Tokyo 160, Central Institute for Experimental Animals,
Nogawa, Kawasaki, Kanagawa, (M.Y.,T.N), Department of
Anatomy, Hokkaido University, Kita-ku, Sapporo, (H.T.,
Y.I.), Japan

INTRODUCTION

Brain cortical structure such as cerebral cortex is
composed of laminated layers of neurons. Each layer is
composed of neurons of similar character in morphology and
function. The cortical architecture is composed of numerous
cells migrating from the proliferation site, the matrix cell
layer, according to an exact time schedule.

The cerebral cortex is composed of six distinct layers.
Formation of the cortical structure would be very important
for increasing the efficiency of the neural network. It
has been already shown by autoradiographic studies after
injection of ^{3}H-thymidine in utero that the cerebral cortex
is formed in a reverse manner. Namely, the early-formed
cells stay at the deeper part of the cerebral cortex and
the late-formed cells stay at the superficial part of the
cortex.

Among the various kinds of mutant animals, the reeler
mutant is characterized by cytoarchitectonic abnormality of
the cerebral cortex, namely, the position of the neurons is
relatively inverted in the cerebral cortex compared to that
of the control (Caviness 1976, Mikoshiba et. al. 1980, 1982,
Terashima et. al. 1983).   Analysis of the reeler
mutant would give us clues to understanding the mechanism
of corticohistogenesis of the cerebral cortex.

In addition to the abnormal positioning of neurons, the

reeler mutant cerebrum is characterized by 1) disordered dendritic processes of neurons in the cortex, 2) absence of plexiform layer, and 3) the fact that the thalamo-cortical myelinated fibers are grouped in bundles and follow a sigmoidal trajectory across the cortical plate while in the normal animal thalamo-cortical fiber originates from the central white matter and climbs up perpendicularly as separate diffuse fibers (Mikoshiba et. al. 1982, 1985, Terashima et. al. 1983).

What is the cause for the abnormality in the reeler mutant? Are there abnormalities in the neurons themselves? Is the guide mechanism abnormal? Is some migration factor abnormal, if such factors exist? In order to answer these questions, we analysed the chimera brain produced from reeler and wild type control mice.

RESULTS

When we first analysed the chimera composed of half-reeler and half-normal animals judged from the coat color and the strain specific GPI isozyme pattern, we found that the cerebral architecture, shape of the neuron, and trajec-tory of the thalamo-cortical projection are all normalized (Mikoshiba et. al. 1985). This suggests that reeler mutation does not directly affect the neurons and that the abnormalities in dendrite formation of neurons and fiber trajectory are consequential upon malposition of the cells.

When we examined the cerebral cortex of the adult chimera in which the reeler contribution was about 95% of the total brain, there were patches of normal and reeler phenotypes judged from the presence of plexiform layer. It is therefore probable that circulating humoral factor does not act to control the cell migration.

We analysed by scanning electron microscopy and found that migrating neuroblasts were attached to bundles of matrix cell processes at 17th embryonic day in the control, while no bundle formation was observed in the reeler (Mikoshiba et. al. 1983). Instead, a very fine meshwork of fibers was observed.

From fractographic analysis of the cerebral cortex of chimera embryos, we could observe heterogeneous figures such as reeler phenotype, wild type phenotype, and inter-mediate phenotype between reeler and wild type control. In the intermediate type, the number of processes that form the bundle was decreased but a column-like architecture was still observed.

Fig. 1. The formation of laminated pattern in the cerebral cortex and abnormal pattern in the <u>reeler</u> mutant mouse.

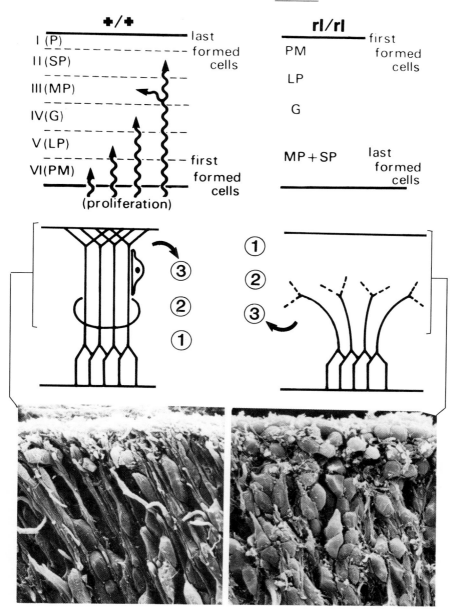

Since the bundles of matrix cell processes are considered to play an important role for creating guide-ropes to the migrating neuroblasts, the absence of the radial bundle structure would be the cause of the incapability of the neuroblasts to move up through the cortical plate.

Reeler mutation would be supposed to be directly related to the absence of a specific molecule that is responsible for the adhesion of the matrix cell processes to form bundle structure.

REFERENCES

Caviness V S Jr (1976). Patterns of cell and fiber distribution in the neocortex of the reeler mutant mouse. J Comp Neurol 170:435-488.

Caviness V S Jr (1982). Neocortical histogenesis in normal and reeler mice: A developmental study based upon (3H) thymidine autoradiography. Develop Brain Res 4: 293-302.

Mikoshiba K, Kohsaka S, Takamatsu K, Aoki E, and Tsukada Y (1980). Morphological and biochemical studies on the cerebral cortex from reeler mutant mice: Development of cortical layers and metabolic mapping by the deoxy-glucose method. J Neurochem 34:53-80.

Mikoshiba K, Takamatsu K, Kohsaka S, Tsukada Y, and Inoue Y (1982). Immunohistochemical and biochemical analyses of development of nervous system of mutant mice (reeler and shiverer). in "Genetic Approaches to Developmental Neurobiology" (ed. Y. Tsukada) Univ Tokyo Press pp. 195-221.

Mikoshiba K, Nishimura Y, Tsukada Y (1983/84). Absence of bundle structure in the neocortex of the reeler mouse at the embryonic stage, Studies by scanning electron microscopic fractography. Dev Neurosci 6:18-25.

Mikoshiba K, Yokoyama M, Terashima T, Sekiguchi M, Inoue Y, Takamatsu K, Nomura T, Shimai K and Tsukada Y (1985). Analysis of abnormality of corticohistogenesis in the reeler mutant mice by producing chimera mice: absence of abnormality in neurons in the reeler. Acta Histochem Cytochem 18:113-124

Terashima T, Inoue K, Inoue Y, Mikoshiba K, and Tsukada Y (1983). Distribution and morphology of corticospinal tract neurons in reeler mouse cortex by the retrograde HRP method. J Comp Neurol 218:314-326.

Progress in Developmental Biology, Part B, pages 141–144
© 1986 Alan R. Liss, Inc.

EARLY PRENATAL APPEARANCE OF SUBSTANCE P IN THE HUMAN
VISUAL CORTEX

Raj D. Mehra, M.K. Bhondeley and V.Bijlani

Neuroanatomy Laboratory, Department of Anatomy,
All India Institute of Medical Sciences,
New Delhi-110 029, INDIA.

INTRODUCTION

Following our studies on the ontogeny of substance P
containing neuronal systems in the developing human spinal
cord where it was shown to be present in the very early
stages of intrauterine life (8 weeks), the neuropeptide was
further localized in the occipital cortex. In the human
brain, existence of substance P has been shown in several
areas both pre- as well as postnatally (Pickel et al.,1980;
Cooper et al., 1981). Substance P immunoreactive projections have also been observed in the frontal and temporal
cortices (Hokfelt et al., 1976). Keeping this in view, the
present studies were planned on the developing human calcarine cortex.

Fetuses 13,15 and 18 weeks gestational age groups were
available at hysterotomy from the legalized abortions at
the hospital of the All-India Institute of Medical Sciences.
The cranial cavity was cut open and the calcarine cortex
dissected out quickly and immersed in fixative (Somoygi and
Takagi, 1982). It was then processed for immunohistochemical localization of substance P according to the Avidin-
Biotin-Horseradish Peroxidase (ABC) staining technique of
Hsu et al., 1981. The antibody (Ab 56) used was of rabbit
origin and was provided by kind courtesy of Drs.D.M.White
and R.D.Helme, Monash University, Australia. The control
sections were either incubated with the antiserum preabsor-
bed with antigen or incubation with the primary antibody
was omitted.

RESULTS AND DISCUSSION

The visual cortex was seen to be comprised of clearly identifiable five zones at all the three fetal stages studied. The five zones from within outwards were the ventricular zone, subventricular zone, intermediate zone, cortical plate and the marginal zone (Fig. I). Likewise, the substance P like immunoreactivity (SPLI) was seen to be present at all the three fetal stages. The SPLI was observed in the nerve fibres and terminals and revealed a characteristic pattern. The positive fibres and terminals were located in the marginal zone (Fig. IIA) and deep to the cortical plate in the intermediate zone (Fig.IIB). The cortical plate which separates these two zones remained relatively free of immunoreactivity. In the intermediate zone, the immunoreactive fibre bundles were separated by non-immunoreactive regions whereas in the marginal zone, the positive fibres were more widely spread.

Radioimmunoassay analysis has revealed presence of small quantities of substance P in the adult rat visual cortex (Kanazawa and Jessel, 1975). However, the distribution pattern of immunoreactivity seen in the current investigations could have an important bearing on the cortical development. The recent view that the cortex has a dual origin (Marin-Padilla, 1978) may further be analysed in light of the present findings wherein it could be presumed that substance P containing corticopetal fibres are the early fibres to arrive and induce the process of maturation in the deeper region (layer VII) and in the layer I (marginal zone) since these are the two regions where the immunoreactivity is observed at these early fetal stages. The cortical plate which forms layers II to VI has neglegible SPLI. The formation of cortical plate is a later step in the cortical development and it is known to be slow in the process of maturation as indicated by synapse formation etc. (Molliver et al., 1973). However, whether the same fibres spread out to the region of cortical plate to induce further maturation is yet to be seen. Another possibility to be explored is whether these PLI fibres formed a continuous network in early embryonic stages and were divided into two distant zones only on arrival of the cortical plate. This could be the reason why we see two more mature zones viz., layer VII and layer I separated by a relatively immature zone (cortical plate) in sections of the fetal cortex. A somewhat similar type of distribution pattern of catecholamine containg nerve fibres has been observed earlier in the rat cerebral cortex (Schleumpe et al., 1980). According to these authors, the catecholamine containing fibres formed a continuous network before the arrival of cortical plate. Later, this plate divides the fibre network into a

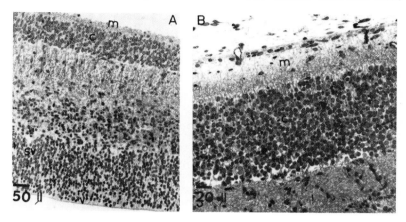

Fig. I. Coronal section of fetal visual cortex. A) shows five zones at 10 wks of gestation; ventricular (v), sub-ventricular (sv), intermediate (i), cortical plate (c) and marginal (m). B) marginal zone, cortical plate and part of intermediate zone at 15 wks.

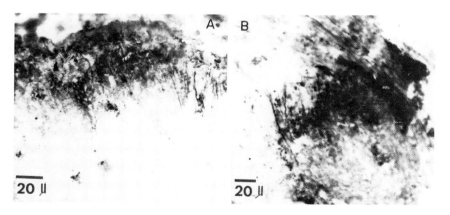

Fig.II. SPLI in the (A) marginal zone and (B) intermediate zone (deep to cortical plate) at 15 wks gestation.

superficial (under the pia within the marginal zone) and a deeper band (situated in the deeper neocortical zones) which helps in early induction and differentiation in these cortical layers. 13 weeks is a very early stage in human cortical development and presence of substance P at such an early stage would possibly be inducing a trophic influence.

REFERENCES

Cooper PE, Fenestrom MH, Rorstad OP, Leeman SE, Martin JB (1981). The regional distribution of somatostain, substance P and neurotensin in human brain. Brain Res 218: 219-232.

Hokfelt T, Meyerson B, Nilsson G, Pernow B, Sachs C (1976). Immunohistochemical evidence for substance P containing nerve endings in the human cortex. Brain Res 104: 181-186.

Hsu SM, Raine L, Franger H (1981). A comparative study of the peroxidase-antiperoxidase method and an Avidin-Biotin complex method of studying polypeptide hormones with radioimmunoassay antibodies. Am J Clin Pathol 75: 734-38.

Kanazawa I, Jessel T (1976). Post mortem changes and regional distribution of substance P in the rat and mouse nervous system. Brain Res 117: 362-367.

Marin-Padilla M (1978). Dual origin of mammalian neocortex and evolution of cortical plate. Anat Embryol 152:109-26.

Molliver ME, Kostovic I, Vander Loos H (1973). The development of synapses in cerebral cortex of human fetus. Brain Res 50: 403-407.

Pickel VB, Sumal KK, Reis DJ, Miller RJ and Hervonen A(1980). Immunocytochemical localization of enkephalin and substance P in the dorsal tegmental nuclei in human fetal brain. J Comp Neurol 193: 805-814.

Schlumpe M, Shoemaker WJ, Floyd E (1980). Innervation of embryonic rat cerebral cortex by catecholamine-containing fibres. J Comp Neurol 192: 361-376.

Somoygi P, Takagi H (1982). A note on the use of picric acid-paraformaldehyde-glutaral-dehyde fixative for correlated light and electronmicroscopic immunocytochemistry. Neuroscience 7: 1779-1783.

Progress in Developmental Biology, Part B, pages 145–148
© 1986 Alan R. Liss, Inc.

ALKALINE PHOSPHATASE ACTIVITY IN THE NEURAL TUBE OF THE MOUSE EMBRYO

Kohji A. Matsui, Harukazu Nakamura, and Mineo Yasuda
Department of Anatomy, Hiroshima University School of Medicine, Kasumi 1-2-3, Minami-ku, Hiroshima 734, Japan

INTRODUCTION

Transient activities of alkaline phosphatase (ALP) in the developing central nervous system have been reported in chick (Moog, 1943), mouse (Chiquoine, 1954; Kwong and Tam, 1984), rat (McAlpine, 1959) and human (Mori, 1965) embryos. Nevertheless the functional significance of ALP activity in the course of the CNS histogenesis has not yet been clarified. The present study aims to investigate the precise distribution and the time course of ALP activity. The pattern of ALP activity is interpreted in relation to the neuronal differentiation and to the formation of the interneuronal connections.

MATERIALS AND METHODS

Colony bred Jcl:ICR mice were used. Embryos at days 9.0-17.5 (VP=day 0) were fixed for 1 hour at 4°C in a mixture of 1% glutaraldehyde and 2% formaldehyde in 0.1 M cacodylate buffer (pH 7.2-7.4) containing 8% sucrose. Sections cut at 20 μm with a cryostat for light microscopy, or cut at 50 μm with a Microslicer for electron microscopy, were processed with the lead citrate method (Mayahara et al., 1967) for 30 minutes at 37°C. For the control, 3 mM levamisole was added to the incubation medium, resulting in complete disappearance of reaction products. For electron microscopy, the sections were postfixed in 1% OsO_4 , dehydrated and embedded in epoxy resin.

RESULTS

Typically ALP activity is restricted in part of the basal plate and marked in the matrix layer.

Sequential changes in ALP activity in the spinal cord at the level of the forelimb bud are as follows. Activity first appears at day 10.0, as a crossband in the middle of the basal plate. At day 11.5, activity attains its peak. Activity is observable in the matrix layer and also noted on fine processes radiating from the matrix layer into the mantle layer. Ventrolateral marginal layer is also ALP positive. By day 12.5, the mantle layer of the basal plate has well developed, however, the motor column and the ventral root are free of ALP staining. With further development, activity gradually weakens and the stained area in the matrix layer becomes narrower as the matrix layer becomes thinner, but remains evident in the ventral and intermediate gray matter, and the adjacent marginal layer.

ALP activity is detected along the entire length of the spinal cord, and ALP positive structures form a continuous column through the brain stem up to the level of the rhombencephalic isthmus, where the ALP positive column is suddenly interrupted. But there remains the ALP positive marginal layer extending further cephalad. More cephalically, part of the floor of the diencephalon has ALP activity.

Electron microscopically, ALP activity is localized on the lateral membranes of the matrix cells, but not on the luminal membranes facing to the central canal. ALP positive mitotic cells are also present. Some of the neurons in the mantle layer near to the matrix layer have activity. In the marginal layer, ALP activity is localized on the cranio-caudally oriented axons, and on the endfeet consisting of the lateral processes of the matrix cells.

DISCUSSION

Our major findings are as follows (Fig. 1). (1) In the matrix layer, there is an absolute spatial and temporal restriction of ALP positive matrix cells. (2) The ALP positive structures make a continuous column throughout the spinal cord up to the rhombencephalic isthmus, in which

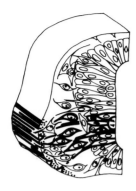

Figure 1. A schematic summary of our major findings. Thick lines indicate ALP positive structures. ALP positive structures, especially endfeet and cranio-caudally oriented axons in the marginal layer, seem to contact closely with each other.

each ALP positive structure (matrix cells and their radiating lateral processes, some of the neurons, and the cranio-caudally oriented axons) seems to make a close contact.

It is generally believed that the matrix layer has a mosaic organization specified to produce different subpopulations of neurons in a sequential order, but there has been little morphological evidence which proves this principle. Our first finding might make some contribution to this principle. Although McAlpine (1959) noted that ALP activity might be associated with the somatic motor neurogenesis, we could not find ALP activity on the motor neurons nor ventral roots. Moreover, the time course of ALP activity did not correspond to that of the somatic motor neurogenesis (McConnell, 1981; Wentworth, 1984). We speculate that ALP positive matrix cells might be precursors of a kind of interneurons in the ventral and intermediate gray matter probably belonging to the reticular formation.

As for the second finding, we interpret that ALP activity might play an important role in "contact guidance", namely it might relate to the formation of some neuronal pathways and the interneuronal connections. It is suggested that neuroepithelial endfeet provide adhesive pathways for the axonal elongation (Silver and Rutishauser, 1984). In this sense the existence of ALP activity on the matrix cells is quite reasonable. Other evidences suggest that among the first to develop in the marginal layer may be reticulospinal pathways (Das and Hine, 1972; Kevetter and Lasek, 1982). Judging from their position, we are tempted to think that ALP positive cranio-caudal axons correspond to these pathways.

REFERENCES

Chiquoine AD (1954). Distribution of alkaline phosphomono-esterase in the central nervous system of the mouse embryo. J Comp Neurol 100:415-439.
Das GD, Hine RJ (1972). Nature and significance of sponta-neous degeneration of axons in the pyramidal tract. Z Anat Entwickl-Gesch 136:98-114.
Kevetter GA, Lasek RJ (1982). Development of the marginal zone in the rhombenecephalon of Xenopus laevis. Develop Brain Res 4:195-208.
Kwong WH, Tam PP (1984). The pattern of alkaline phospha-tase activity in the developing mouse spinal cord. J Embryol Exp Morph 82:241-251.
Mayahara H, Hirano H, Saito T, Ogawa K (1967). The new lead citrate method for the ultracytochemical demonstra-tion of activity of non-specific alkaline phosphatase (orthophosphoric monoester phosphohydrolase). Histo-chemie 11:88-96.
McAlpine RJ (1959). Selected observations on the early development of the motor neurons in the brain stem and spinal cord of the white rat as revealed by the alkaline phosphatase technique. J Comp Neurol 113:211-243.
McConnell JA (1981). Identification of early neurons in the brainstem and spinal cord. II. An autoradiographic study in the mouse. J Comp Neurol 200:273-288.
Moog F (1943). The distribution of phosphatase in the spinal cord of chick embryos of one to eight days' incu-bation. Proc Natl Acad Sci USA 29:176-183.
Mori T (1965). Histochemical studies on the distribution of alkaline phosphatase in early human embryos. III. Embryos in Streeter's Horizon XII. Okajimas Fol Anat Jpn 40:765-793.
Silver J, Rutishauser U (1984). Guidance of optic axons in vivo by a preformed adhesive pathway on neuroepithelial endfeet. Develop Biol 106:485-499.
Wentworth LE (1984). The development of the cervical spi-nal cord of the mouse embryo. I. A Golgi analysis of ventral root neuron differentiation. J Comp Neurol 222:81-95.

Progress in Developmental Biology, Part B, pages 149–151
© 1986 Alan R. Liss, Inc.

SUBSTANCE P LIKE IMMUNOREACTIVITY ALONG THE LATERAL SIDE OF
THE DORSAL HORN OF HUMAN SPINAL CORD

Raj D.Mehra and Veena Bijlani
Department of Anatomy
All India Institute of Medical Sciences
New Delhi-110 029, INDIA

INTRODUCTION

Substance P is considered to be a putative neurotransmitter of primary afferent fibres transmitting the sensat-
ion of pain (Nicoll et al., 1980; Pearson et al., 1982).
Though numerous investigators have studied the distribution
pattern of substance P like immunoreactivity (SPLI) in the
spinal cord of experimental animals (Takahashi and Otsuka,
1975; Barber et al., 1979) and man (Pearson et al., 1982)
employing radioimmunoassay and immunohistochemical techniques, only one report is available on the localization of
this neuropeptide in the developing human spinal cord
(Charnay et al., 1983). The latter authors used immunofluorescence technique and studied fetuses from 12 weeks
gestational age onwards. We have been conducting a sequential study on the localization of the neuropeptide in fetuses of various age groups (beginning 8 weeks) employing the
more sensitive peroxidase-anti-peroxidase (PAP) technique.
However, only a part of the results are reported here.

The substance P like immunoreactivity was localized in
the human fetal cords of 8,10,12,15,18,20 and 22 weeks gestational age, obtained by hysterotomy from legalized abortions. The lower thoracic and lumbar region was studied.
The anti-substance P was provided by the kind courtesy of
Drs. D.M.White & R.D.Helme, Prince Henry's Hospital, Monash
University, Melbourne, Australia and had been raised in
rabbit. The antibody had been duly tested against cross
reactivity and found to be reacting only with the specific
antigen (substance P). The immunohistochemical technique

as adapted by Somogyi and Takagi (1982) was followed. The
specificity of immunoreaction was checked by incubating
tissue sections with antiserum absorbed with synthetic substance P. In the second type of control sections, incubation with primary antiserum was omitted.

RESULTS AND DISCUSSION

    SPLI was clearly visible in the dorsal horn even at 8
weeks of gestation. Most dense immunoreactivity was obtained in the superficial portion of the dorsal horn. A somewhat similar distribution pattern has recently been reported
by Charnay and coworkers (1983). However, we observed an
additional, rather consistent and conspicuous band of radially running immunoreactive fibers bordering the lateral side
of dorsal horn in fetal cords of 15 weeks gestational age
and onwards (Fig.I). Such a bundle of fibres has not been
described in any of the earlier publications though one could draw a parallel to it in the description of Hunt and coworkers (1982). These investigators studied two autopsy
specimens of deafferented L3-S2 segments of spinal cord(the
patients had undergone above knee amputation on one side for
over a month in one case and over two years in the other)and
observed a marked loss of substance P like immunoreactivity

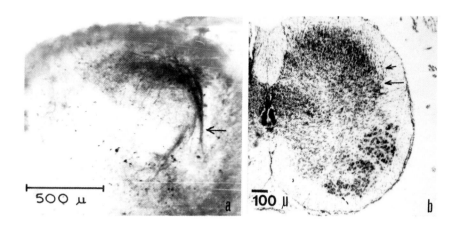

Fig. I : Crossection of 15 wks fetal spinal cord.(a) shows
substance P like immunoreactivity. Note a band of immunoreactive fibres (arrow) bordering the lateral side of the
dorsal horn. (b) A corresponding Nissl stained section.
Arrow indicates the position of the lateral band.

in the dorsal horn. Interestingly, these investigators did not observe any such decrease of immunoreactivity along the lateral most edge of the dorsal horn. Though the authors did not attach much significance to it in their description, it is reasonable to presume that a band of immunoreactive fibres on the lateral side of the dorsal horn remains unaffected at least in its substance P content on deafferentiation of the particular segments of the spinal cord. The origin and termination of this hitherto unfocussed SPLI containing fibre bundle needs to be further investigated.

REFERENCES

Barber RP, Vaughn JE, Slemmon JR, Salvaterra PM, Roberts E, Leeman SE (1979). The origin, distribution and synaptic relationships of substance P axons in rat spinal cord. J Comp Neurol 184: 331–352.

Charnay Y, Paulin C, Chayvialle JA, Dubois PM (1983). Distribution of substance P like immunoreactivity in the spinal cord and dorsal root ganglion of the human foetus and infant. Neuroscience 10: 41–55.

Hunt SP, Rossor MN, Emson PC, Clement Jones V (1982). Substance P and enkephalins in spinal cord after limb amputation. Lancet i: 1023.

Nicoll RA, Schenker C, Leeman SE (1980). Substance P as a transmitter candidate. Annual Rev Neurosci 3: 227–268.

Pearson J, Brainders I, Cuello AC (1982). Depletion of substance P containing axons in substantia gelatinosa of patients with diminished pain sensitivity. Nature 295: 61–63.

Somogyi P and Takagi H (1982). A note on the use of picric acid-paraformaldehyde-glutter-aldehyde fixative for correlated light and electron microscopic immunocytochemistry. Neuroscience 7: 1779–1783.

Takahashi T, Otsuka M (1975). Regional distribution of substance P in the spinal cord and nerve roots of the cat and the effect of dorsal root section. Brain Res 87: 1–11.

Extracellular Matrix in Development

Progress in Developmental Biology, Part B, pages 155-168
© 1986 Alan R. Liss, Inc.

ADHESION AND MIGRATION OF AVIAN NEURAL CREST CELLS: AN
EVALUATION OF THE ROLE OF SEVERAL EXTRACELLULAR MATRIX
COMPONENTS.

Jean Paul Thiery*, Jean-Loup Duband*, Sylvie
Rocher* and Kenneth M. Yamada+.
*Institut d'Embryologie du CNRS et du Collège de
France, 49 bis avenue de la Belle Gabrielle,
94130 Nogent-sur-Marne, FRANCE, and +Laboratory
of Molecular Biology, National Cancer Institute,
Bethesda, Maryland 20205, USA.

The neural crest represents a remarkable model system
to study mechanisms operating during epithelium-mesenchyme
interconversion and individual cell migration. In this
brief review, we analyze the possible roles played during
these events by some of the extracellular matrix components
known to be adhesive molecules.

CELL TO SUBSTRATE ADHESION MOLECULES

The extracellular matrices (ECM) produced by
mesenchymal cells and by epithelial tissues contain several
adhesive glycoproteins, including collagens, laminin, and
fibronectin (Hay, 1981). Collagens form a large family of
proteins represented by at least 9 distinct types. They are
large (300kd MW) and highly conserved molecules composed of
three chains (alpha units) linked by hydrogen bonds. Each
chain comprises an helical peptide that contains a repeating
triplet motif, Gly-X-Y, and two non-helical peptides termed
telopeptides and located at both ends of the chain. The
various collagen chains are coded by a minimum of 17 genes
that contain as many as 50 short exons. The exons are all
multiples of the 9 bp that codes for the sequence Gly-X-Y.
Interestingly, such a family of genes is widely dispersed on
chromosomes (Emanuel et al., 1985; Soloman et al., 1985).
In humans, type I collagen is encoded by the $\alpha_1(I)$ gene on
chromosome 17, and the $\alpha_2(I)$ on chromosome 7. The $\alpha_1(II)$
and $\alpha_1(III)$ genes are located respectively on chromosome 12
and 2. One of type IV collagen chains is on chromosome 13,
and the $\alpha_2(V)$ gene is on chromosome 2.

Collagens type I, III, and V are often expressed in the same cells. They form highly ordered fibers associated into a complex meshwork. They are also present in the basement membranes lining epithelia. Collagen type IV cannot form fibrils and is located exclusively in basement membranes. Finally, collagen type II is only found in cartilage. During embryogenesis, collagens type I and III have been detected as early as during gastrulation in the ECM among mesenchymes and in basal laminae of epithelia (Hay, 1973; Duband et al., in preparation). Collagen type IV appears early concommitant with the epithelial structure (Duband et al., in preparation), whereas collagen type II appears later with the differentiation of cartilages (von der Mark et al., 1976). The roles of collagens during embryogenesis are various, but they might not interfere with the early morphogenetic events, since mice carrying deficiencies in type I collagen gene can reach day 12 of incubation (Löhler et al., 1984).

Laminin (LN) is a large glycoprotein (900kd MW) specific for epithelia. It contains several distinct binding domains for attachment and spreading of cells, and for binding to other basal lamina components including type IV collagen (Timpl et al., 1983). LN is composed of 4 different chains forming a cross. A high-affinity receptor for LN has been isolated and characterized (Liotta et al., 1985). LN appears very early during development; in the mouse embryo, one chain is synthesized during oogenesis, while two and ultimately all four polypeptides appear in the cytoplasm of the 2 to 8 cell-stage embryo. LN is finally expressed on the surface of blastomeres at the 16 cell-stage (Leivo et al., 1980; Cooper and McQueen, 1983). In the chick embryo, LN appears under the epiblast just prior to gastrulation; later in development, most epithelia, whether transient or permanent, express LN (Duband et al., 1985).

Fibronectins (FNs) compose another family of large adhesive glycoproteins (220kd MW) found in most ECM and in the blood (for reviews, see Yamada, 1983; Furcht, 1983). FN is composed of two similar but not identical polypeptides, each containing approximately 2350 amino acids. FN is encoded by a single gene (Kornblihtt et al., 1983; Tamkun et al., 1984) containing 48 exons in the chick (Hirano et al., 1983). In humans, the FN gene is located on chromosome 2 (Kornblihtt, personal communication). Alternative splicing has been described during the processing of the primary transcript of this gene. One class of mRNA completely lacks sequences corresponding to the so-called extra-domain (Kornblihtt et al., 1984; Vibe-Pedersen et al., 1984). Interestingly, this splicing occurs only in the liver where plasma FN is synthesized (Kornblihtt et al., 1983, 1984). Incomplete or complete splicings also occur for another exon termed IIICS (Tamkun et al., 1984). It results that as many as ten distinct mRNA molecules can be produced from the FN gene (Kornblihtt et al., 1985).

FN molecules are multifunctional proteins, all with similar binding domains along their polypeptide chains (Hynes and Yamada, 1982). Plasma FN is soluble, in contrast to cellular FN which readily assembles into fibrils. However, so far, the sequences responsible for fibrillogenesis have not been identified. Recently, the region of FN involved in interactions with the cell membrane was shown to contain a unique peptide sequence Arg-Gly-Asp-Ser (RGDS) that is required for the attachment of cells to intact FN or FN fragments (Pierschbacher and Ruoslahti, 1984a,b; Yamada and Kennedy, 1984, 1985; Akiyama and Yamada, 1985b). Variants of this sequence have been tested for their ability to inhibit binding of cells to FN or of the FN cell-binding region to the cell surface. Most substitutions except at the carboxy terminus inactivate the peptide (Pierschbacher and Ruoslahti, 1984b). Interestingly, specific spacing between two charged amino acids (R and D) is required. In addition, adjacent sequences can also modify the binding capacity of the RGDS peptide (Yamada and Kennedy, 1985).

Studies on the binding of FN to cell surfaces have revealed membrane receptors with a fairly low affinity constant (Akiyama and Yamada, 1985a). A leading candidate for the FN receptor is a complex of three glycoproteins of 120, 140, and 160kd that can be isolated by monoclonal antibodies (Greve and Gottlieb, 1982; Chen et al., 1985a; Knudsen et al., 1985) and affinity chromatography (Pytela et al., 1985). In the chick embryo, this complex is widely distributed in almost all epithelial and mesenchymal tissues and is enriched at sites close to concentrations of FN (Duband et al., submitted). On cultured cells, the complex colocalizes with actin microfilaments and FN fibrils and is enriched in close contacts (Chen et al., 1985a,b; Damsky et al., 1985; Duband et al., submitted). Interestingly, this complex has been recently shown to be also a receptor for LN

(Horwitz et al., submitted).

THE NEURAL CREST

The neural crest (NC) is a transient embryonic structure occupying the dorsal border of the entire neural axis. After their detachment from the neural tube, NC migrate to various sites where they undergo differentiation. NC cells give rise to a large number of cell types as diverse as pigment cells, most types of peripheral neurons and glia, myoblasts, chondrocytes, and connective tissues in the head (for a review, see Le Douarin, 1982). A variety of experiments (Weston, 1963; Le Douarin and Teillet, 1974) have suggested that the morphology of the embryo plays a major role in the pattern of migration and ultimate fate of NC cells. In addition, the behavior of NC cells appears to depend on the control of adhesion between themselves and to the ECM.

Separation from the Neural Tube (Fig. 1)

The release of the NC cells from the neuroectodermal epithelium involves the disappearance of intercellular junctions. Gap and tight junctions are lost among the premigratory NC cells (Revel and Brown, 1975; Tosney, 1978, 1982; Newgreen and Gibbins, 1982). However, the most striking event during the emigration of NC cells is the change in the interaction of the cells with the ECM; NC cells lose their adhesion to LN and acquire a strong adhesion to FN (Duband and Thiery, 1982; Thiery et al., 1982; Duband et al., submitted). Such a change might result from either mechanical forces created by the various tissue reorganizations (Karfunkel, 1974; Jacobson, 1985) or proteases and collagenases released by crest cells (Valinsky and Reich, 1981; Liotta et al., 1982).

Patterns of Migration

The numerous studies on crest migratory pathways have shown that morphogenesis of tissues neighboring NC cells is a major element controlling the pattern of NC cell migration. Structures adjacent to the neural tube are metamerized; the somitomeres in the head (Anderson and Meier, 1981) and the somites in the trunk (Thiery et al., 1982) thereby provide several distinct pathways. For

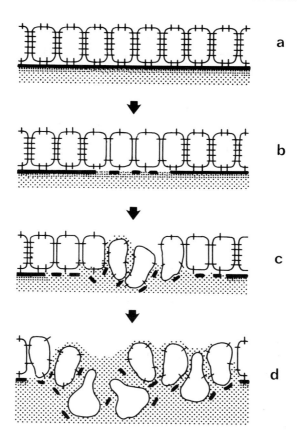

Figure 1: Schematic representation of the mechanism of dissociation of the neural epithelium during the release of NC cells. a) Prior to its dissociation, the neural epithelium is limited by a basal lamina that contains LN and FN. b) Concommitant with a decrease of cell-cell binding, the basal lamina is disrupted locally. c) NC cells facing the disrupted basal lamina dissociate from the epithelium; they become surrounded by FN; the disruption of the basal lamina expends to the neighboring cells. d) NC cells express motile properties and leave the neural epithelium.
━ LN;   🦞FN in basal lamina;   ∴∵∴ FN in ECM;
— cell-cell binding

example, in the trunk, one can identify one pathway between
two consecutive somites, and a second one between the somite
and the neural tube. The first pathway leads NC cells to
the aortic and mesonephric area, where autonomic
differentiation occurs. Cells within the other pathway give
rise to the dorsal root ganglia and to the Schwann cells
lining motor and sensory nerves. Subsequently, the
metameric pattern in the trunk is rapidly modified, as two
adjacent half-somites fuse to form a vertebra. This
extensive reorganization of the mesoderm surrounding the
neural tube contributes to the formation of new pathways,
but primarily creates physical barriers achieving a complete
separation of different NC cell populations.

Substrate of migration

The NC cell migratory pathways contain an ECM limited
by one or two LN-rich basal laminae, which provide defined
channels. FN, vitronectin, type I and III collagens,
hyaluronate and small amounts of chondroitin sulfate are the
major constituents of the matrix (Derby, 1978; Pratt et al.,
1975; Duband and Thiery, 1982; Thiery et al., 1982; Brauer
et al., 1985; Duband et al., in preparation; Newgreen,
personal communication). The matrix is deposited prior to
NC migration. However, so far, there is no direct evidence
for its role in triggering NC emigration from the neural
tube. Furthermore, potential pathways are not always used
by NC cells. For example, the presence of high levels of
chondroitin sulfate around the notochord (Derby, 1978) and
of a non-defined factor in the skin of the white axolotl
(Spieth and Keller, 1984) seem to prevent NC cell migration.
Therefore, in addition to defined pathways, NC cell
migration may be further restricted according to the
chemical composition of the matrix.

FN alone or associated with other matrix components
greatly promotes the attachment, spreading and motility of
crest cells. In contrast, serum proteins, collagens,
hyaluronate, chondroitin sulfate and LN are very poor
substrates for crest cell attachment and movement and
frequently induce their aggregation (Newgreen et al., 1982;
Rovasio et al., 1983). While collagens may provide a
scaffold for the organization of the ECM, hyaluronate is
thought to expand the space and indirectly enhances the
speed of locomotion (Tucker and Erickson, 1984).

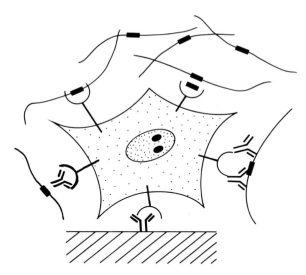

Figure 2: Cell attachment and migration can be altered by several different procedures. Antibodies to the cell binding sequence of FN, peptides containing such a sequence, and antibodies to the FN-receptor on cell membrane prevent the interaction of the cell to FN and inhibit the migration. In contrast, antibodies to FN-receptor can mediate attachment of cells, but do not support as much cell migration.

The essential role of FN in NC cell migration has been confirmed by in vivo and in vitro perturbation experiments (Figs. 2, 3). Monovalent antibodies to the cell-binding sequence of FN or a decapeptide which competes for the cell binding sequence of FN reversibly block the migration of NC cells (Rovasio et al., 1983; Boucaut et al., 1984; Thiery, 1985). In addition, antibodies to the 140kd FN-receptor complex inhibit both the adhesion and migration of motile NC cells in vitro. In contrast, these same antibodies adsorbed to substrata readily mediated adhesion and spreading of NC cells, but were much less effective for cell migration (Duband et al., submitted).

Behavior of crest cells

The dispersal of NC cells is also the result of their specific motile behavior, which differs strikingly from that

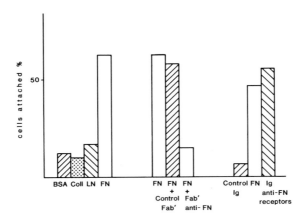

Figure 3: Diagram showing the role of FN on NC cell attachment. FN can mediate the attachment of NC cells onto the substratum in contrast to bovine serum albumin (BSA), type I collagen (coll), and LN. Antibodies to the cell-binding sequence of FN prevent the attachment of NC cells. Finally, antibodies to the FN-receptor on NC cells can mimick the effect of FN itself.

of other embryonic cells (Erickson et al., 1980; Newgreen et al., 1979; Newgreen and Thiery, 1980; Tucker et al., 1985; Duband et al., submitted). In contrast to somitic and notochordal fibroblasts which are polarized, NC cells on a two dimensional substrate are stellate with numerous filopodia.

NC cells display very little organized cytoskeleton, very few focal contact sites, and exert a weak tractional force on their substratum (Tucker et al., 1985; Duband et al., submitted). Moreover, the FN-receptor complex has a uniform distribution on NC cell surface, in contrast to other mesenchymal cells, where it is concentrated in the cell-to-substratum contact sites (Duband et al., submitted). In addition, most crest cells lack the ability to synthesize and deposit FN as a matrix in their immediate environment (Newgreen and Thiery, 1980; Sieber-Blum et al., 1981). In contrast, they synthesize large amounts of hyaluronate (Greenberg and Pratt, 1977), a property that may favor their displacement (Tucker and Erickson, 1984). A similar

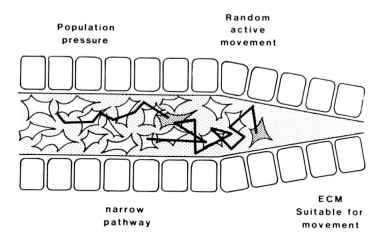

Figure 4 : Model of migration of neural crest cells. This
diagram represents the various parameters that have been
found to govern crest cell migration and ensure a proper
directionality ot the different target sites. They concern
either crest cells themselves (active cell migration,
population pressure and expansion of space by hyaluronate,
H.A.) or their immediate environment (narrow pathways, ECM
suitable for migration).

situation was observed for mesenchymal cells emigrating from
embryonic heart explants on exogenous FN (Couchman et al.,
1982); these cells become stationary when they begin
secreting and assembling FN fibrils at their surface. These
observations prompt the hypothesis that the ability to
migrate is directly linked to a particular distribution of
FN receptors and the inability to synthesize and organize FN
fibrils at the cell surface. The influence of the various
extrinsic and intrinsic factors on NC cell migration is
summarized in Figure 4.

ACKNOWLEDGMENTS

Research by the authors is supported by grants from INSERM (CRL 824018), CNRS (ATP 3701), MRT (84C1312), the Ligue Nationale Française contre le Cancer, the Fondation pour la Recherche Médicale, and the National Cancer Institute. Excellent technical assistance was provided by Monique Denoyelle and Dorothy Kennedy. The authors thank Lydie Obert for typing, Sophie Tissot and Stephane Ozounoff for illustrations. We are particularly grateful to our colleagues involved in the original work we describe.

REFERENCES

Akiyama SK, Yamada KM (1985a). The interaction of plasma fibronectin with fibroblastic cells in suspension. J Biol Chem 260: 4492-4500.

Akiyama SK, Yamada KM (1985b). Synthetic peptides competitively inhibit both direct binding to fibroblasts and functional biological assays for the purified cell binding domain of fibronectin. J Biol Chem in press.

Anderson CB, Meier S (1981). The influence of the metameric pattern in the mesoderm on migration of cranial neural crest cells in the chick embryo. Dev Biol 85: 385-402.

Boucaut JC, Darribère T, Poole TJ, Aoyama H, Yamada KM, Thiery, JP (1984). Biological active synthetic peptides as probes of embryonic development: A competitive peptide inhibitor of fibronectin function inhibits gastrulation in amphibian embryos and neural crest cell migration in avian embryo. J Cell Biol 99: 1822-1830.

Chen W-T, Hasegawa E, Hasegawa T, Weinstock C, Yamada KM (1985a). Development of cell surface linkage complexes in cultured fibroblasts. J Cell Biol 100: 1103-1114.

Chen W-T, Greve JM, Gottlieb DI, Singer SJ (1985b). Immunocytological localization of 140 kd cell adhesion molecules in cultured chicken fibroblasts, and in chicken smooth muscle and intestinal epithelial tissues. J Histochem Cytochem 33: 576-586.

Cooper AR, McQueen H (1983). Subunits of laminin are differentially synthesized in mouse eggs and early embryos. Dev Biol 96: 467-471.

Couchman JR, Rees DA, Green MR, Smith CG (1982). Fibronectin has a dual role in locomotion and anchorage of primary chick fibroblasts and can promote entry into the division cycle. J Cell Biol 93: 402-410.

Damsky CH, Knudsen KA, Bradley D, Buck CA, Horwitz AF (1985). Distribution of the cell substratum attachment (CSAT) antigen on myogenic and fibroblastic cells in culture. J Cell Biol 100: 1528-1539.

Derby MA (1978). Analysis of glycosaminoglycans within the extracellular environments encountered by migrating neural crest cells. Dev Biol 66: 321-336.

Duband J-L, Thiery JP (1982). Distribution of fibronectin in the early phase of avian cephalic neural crest cell migration. Dev Biol 93: 308-323.

Emanuel BS, Cannizzaro LA, Seyer JM, Myers JC (1985). Human α_1 (III) and α_2 (V) procollagen genes are located on the long arm of chromosome 2. Proc natl Acad Sci USA 82: 3385-3389.

Erickson CA, Tosney KW, Weston JA (1980). Analysis of migratory behavior of neural crest and fibroblastic cells in embryonic tissues. Dev Biol 77: 142.

Furcht LT (1983). Structure and function of the adhesive glycoprotein fibronectin. Modern Cell Biology 1: 53-117.

Greenberg JH, Pratt, RM (1977). Glycosaminoglycan and glycoprotein synthesis by cranial neural crest cells in vitro. Cell Diff 6: 119-132.

Greve JM, Gottlieb DI (1982). Monoclonal antibodies which alter the morphology of cultured chick myogenic cells. J Cell Biochem 18: 221-229.

Hay ED (1973). Origin and role of collagen in the embryo. Amer Zool 13: 1087-1107.

Hay ED (1981). Cell biology of extracellular matrix. New York: Plenum Press.

Hirano H., Yamada Y, Sullivan M, De Crombrugghe B, Pastan I, Yamada KM (1983). Isolation of genomic DNA clones spanning the entire fibronectin gene. Proc natl Acad Sci USA 80: 46-50.

Hynes RO, Yamada KM (1982). Fibronectins: multifunctional modular glycoproteins. J Cell Biol 95: 369-377.

Jacobson AG (1985). Adhesion and movements of cells may be coupled to produce neurulation. In Edelman GM, Thiery JP (eds) "The cell in contact: Adhesions and junctions as morphogenetic determinants". New York: John Wiley and Sons in press.

Karfunkel P (1974). The mechanism of neural tube formation. Intern Rev Cytol 38: 245-271.

Knudsen KA, Horwitz AF, Buck CA (1985). A monoclonal antibody identifies a glycoprotein complex involved in cell substratum adhesion. Exp Cell Res 157: 218-226.

Kornblihtt AR, Vibe-Pedersen K, Baralle FE (1983). Isolation and characterization of cDNA clones for human and bovine fibronectins. Proc natl Acad Sci USA. 80: 3218-3223.
Kornblihtt AR, Vibe-Pedersen K, Baralle FE (1984). Human fibronectin: molecular cloning evidence for two mRNA species differing by an internal segment coding for a structural domain. EMBO J 3: 221-226.
Kornblihtt AR, Umezawa K, Vibe-Pedersen K, Baralle FE (1985). Primary structure of human fibronectin: Differential splicing may generate at least 10 polypeptides from a single gene. EMBO J 4: 1755-1759.
Le Douarin NM, (1982). The Neural Crest. Cambridge: Cambridge University Press
Le Douarin NM, Teillet M-A (1974). Experimental analysis of the migration and differentiation of neuroblasts of the autonomic nervous system and of neuroectodermal mesenchymal derivatives, using a biological cell marking technique. Dev Biol 41: 162-184.
Leivo I, Vaheri A, Timpl R, Wartiovaara J (1980). Appearance and distribution of collagens and laminin in the early mouse embryo. Dev Biol 76: 100-114.
Liotta LA, Thorgeirsson UP, Garbisa S (1982). Role of collagenases in tumor cell invasion. Cancer Metastasis Rev 1: 277-288.
Liotta LA, Horan-Hand P, Rao CN, Bryant G, Barsky SH, Schlom J (1985). Monoclonal antibodies to the human laminin receptor recognize structually distinct sites. Exp Cell Res 156: 117-126.
Löhler J, Timpl R, Jaenish R (1984). Lethal mutation of mouse collagen I gene causes rupture of blood vessels and is associated with erythropoietic and mesenchymal cell death at day 12 of gestation. Cell 38: 597-607.
Newgreen DF, Ritterman M, Peters EA (1979). Morphology and behaviour of neural crest cells of chick embryo in vitro. Cell Tiss Res 203: 115-140.
Newgreen D, Thiery JP (1980). Fibronectin in early avian embryos: Synthesis and distribution along the migration pathways of neural crest cells. Cell Tiss Res 211: 269-291.
Newgreen DF, Gibbins IL, Sauter J, Wallenfels B, Wütz R (1982). Ultrastructural and tissue-culture studies on the role of fibronectin, collagen and glycosaminoglycans in the migration of neural crest cells in the fowl embryo. Cell Tiss Res 221: 521-549.
Newgreen DF, Gibbins IL (1982). Factors controlling the time of onset of the migration of neural crest cells in the

fowl embryo. Cell Tiss Res 224: 145-160.

Pierschbacher MD, Ruoslahti E (1984a). Cell attachment activity of fibronectin can be duplicated by small synthetic fragments of the molecule. Nature 309: 30-33.

Pierschbacher MD, Ruoslahti E (1984b). Variants of the cell recognition site of fibronectin that retain attachment-promoting activity. Proc natl Acad Sci USA 81: 5985-5988.

Pratt RM, Larsen MA, Johnston MC (1975). Migration of cranial neural crest cells in a cell-free hyaluronate-rich matrix. Dev Biol 44: 298-305.

Pytela R, Pierschbacher MD, Ruoslahti E (1985). Identification and isolation of a 140 kd cell surface glycoprotein with properties expected of a fibronectin receptor. Cell 40: 191-198.

Revel JP, Brown SS (1975). Cell junctions in development with particular reference to the neural tube. Cold Spring Harbor Symp Quant Biol 40: 433-455.

Rovasio RA, Delouvée A, Yamada KM, Timpl R, Thiery JP (1983). Neural crest cell migration: Requirement for exogenous fibronectin and high cell density. J Cell Biol 96: 462-473.

Sieber-Blum M, Sieber F, Yamada KM (1981). Cellular fibronectin promotes adrenergic differentiation of quail neural crest cells in vitro. Exp Cell Res 133: 285-295.

Solomon E, Hiorns LR, Spurr N, Kurkinen M, Barlow D, Hogan B.L.M, Dalgleish R (1985). Chromosomal assignments of the genes coding for human types II, III, and IV collagen: A dispersed family. Proc natl Acad Sci USA 82: 3330-3334.

Spieth J, Keller RE (1984). Neural crest cell behavior in white and dark larvae of Ambystoma mexicanum: Differences in cell morphology, arrangement and extracellular matrix as related to migration. J exp Zool 229: 91-107.

Tamkun JW, Schwarzbauer JE, Hynes RO (1984). A single rat fibronectin gene generates three different mRNAs by alternative splicing of complex exon. Proc natl Acad Sci USA 81: 5140-5144.

Thiery JP (1985). Roles of fibronectin in embryogenesis. In Mosher DF (ed) "Fibronectin" New York: Academic Press in press.

Thiery JP, Duband J-L, Delouvée A (1982). Pathways and mechanism of avian trunk neural crest cell migration and localization. Dev Biol 93: 324-343.

Timpl R, Johansson S, Van Delden V, Oberbaümer I, Höök M (1983). Characterization of protease-resistant fragment of laminin mediating attachment and spreading of rat

hepatocytes. J Biol Chem 158: 8922-8927.
Tosney KW (1978). The early migration of neural crest cells
   in the trunk region of the avian embryo. An electron
   microscopic study. Dev Biol 62: 317-333.
Tosney KW (1982). The segregation and early migration of
   cranial neural crest cells in the avian embryo. Dev Biol
   89: 13-24.
Tucker RP, Erickson CA (1984). Morphology and behavior of
   quail neural crest cells in artificial three dimensional
   extracellular matrices. Dev Biol 104: 390-405.
Tucker RP, Edwards BF, Erickson CA (1985). Tension in the
   culture dish: Microfilament organization and migratory
   behavior of quail neural crest cells. Cell Motility 5:
   225-237.
Valinsky JE, Reich E (1981). Plasminogen in the chick
   embryo. Transport and biosynthesis. J Biol Chem 256:
   12470-12475.
Vibe-Pedersen K, Kornblihtt AR, Baralle FE (1984).
   Expression of a human α globin/fibronectin gene hybrid
   generates two mRNAs by alternative splicing. EMBO J 3:
   2511-2516.
Vincent M, Thiery JP (1984). A cell surface marker for
   neural crest and placodal cells: Further evolution in
   peripheral and central nervous system. Dev Biol 103:
   468-481.
Von der Mark K, Von der Mark S, Gay S (1976). Study of
   differential collagen synthesis during development of the
   chick embryo by immunofluorescence. I. Preparation of
   collagen type I and type II specific antibodies and their
   application to early stages of the chick embryo. Dev Biol
   48: 237-249.
Weston JA (1963). A radioautographic analysis of the
   migration and localization of trunk crest cells in the
   chick. Dev Biol 6: 279-310.
Yamada KM (1983). "Cell Interactions and Development:
   Molecular Mechanisms". New York: John Wiley and Sons.
Yamada KM, Kennedy DW (1984). Dualistic nature of adhesive
   protein function: Fibronectin and its biologically active
   peptide fragments can auto inhibit fibronectin function. J
   Cell Biol 99: 29-36.
Yamada KM, Kennedy DW (1985). Aminoacid sequence
   specificities of an adhesive recognition signal. J Cell
   Biochem 28: 99-104.

Progress in Developmental Biology, Part B, pages 169–172
© 1986 Alan R. Liss, Inc.

TISSUE–SPECIFIC EXPRESSION OF SHORT–CHAIN COLLAGENS

Hiroshi Konomi, Yoshifumi Ninomiya and Bjorn
R. Olsen
Department of Biochemistry, UMDNJ–Rutgers
Medical School, Piscataway, New Jersey 08854

INTRODUCTION

The collagen gene family comprises a large number of
genes that are differentially expressed by different cell
types. Although the protein products of all collagen
genes contain triple–helical, or collagenous, amino acid
sequences, it is now clear that there are several classes
of collagens, each containing proteins with distinct structural and functional properties. Many defined collagen
types, such as type I through V, contain molecules with
relatively large triple–helical domains. In contrast, the
newly discovered collagens types IX and X contain short
triple–helical domains and relatively large non–collagenous
sequences. We define type IX and X collagens as short–chain
collagens because the polypeptides of these collagens in
their unprocessed, biosynthetic form are shorter than those
of fibrillar collagens (Olsen et al., 1985).

We have studied the structure of type IX polypeptides by
isolating and characterizing cDNAs specific for this collagen (Ninomiya and Olsen, 1984; Ninomiya et al., 1985). We
have used the DNA probes and specific antibodies to study
the tissue–specific expression of the corresponding genes.

MATERIALS AND METHODS

cDNA cloning

The isolation of mRNA from 17–day–old chick embryo
sternal cartilage and synthesis of cDNA has been described

(Ninomiya et al., 1984). The screening of recombinant clones and the characterization of the cDNA clones pYN1738 and
pYN1731 has been reported (Ninomiya and Olsen, 1984;
Ninomiya et al., 1985).

Synthesis of oligopeptides and generation of anti-peptide antibodies

In collaboration with Drs. M. van der Rest (Montreal)
and J. Seyer (Memphis) we have developed polyclonal antibodies against peptides synthesized on the basis of
nucleotide-derived sequences from the α 1(IX) and α 2(IX)
chains and amino acid sequences of the α 3(IX) chain. The
synthetic peptides were coupled to keyhole limpet hemo-
cyanin, and the hapten-carrier complexes were injected into
rabbits. The antisera were assayed as described (Olsen et
al., 1985).

Transfer-blot analyses and immunohistochemistry

Chondrocytes obtained from 17-day-old chick embryo
sternal cartilage were incubated in suspension culture.
Type IX collagen was precipitated from culture media with
30% ammonium sulfate. After reduction with dithiothreitol
in 6 M urea, and alkylation with iodoacetate, polypeptides
in the precipitate were separated by SDS-polyacrylamide gel
electrophoresis. After blotting the SDS-polyacrylamide gel
onto nitrocellulose, the blot was reacted with anti-α1(IX),
anti-α2(IX), or anti-α3(IX) chain specific antibodies.
For immunohistochemistry, frozen sections of 17-day-old
chick embryo sterna were fixed with 4% paraformaldehyde and
treated with 0.2% testicular hyaluronidase before antibody
staining. The anti-α3(IX) chain antibody, a monoclonal
antibody against type II collagen (provided by Dr. T.
Linsenmayer), and pre-immune serum were used for staining.

RESULTS AND DISCUSSION

Two cDNAs, pYN1738 and pYN1731, hybridize to embryonic
sternal cartilage mRNA of lower molecular weight than mRNA
specific for type II collagen, the major collagen in cartilage.

By comparing the amino acid sequences derived from the
nucleotide sequences of pYN1738 and pYN1731, with those
obtained by direct amino acid sequencing of collagenous

fragments (HMW, LMW) isolated by Dr. R. Mayne (Birmingham) from chicken sternal cartilage by pepsin extraction, the two cDNAs have been shown to encode two of the three genetically distinct polypeptide chains of a collagen molecule that we have designated type IX collagen (van der Rest et al., 1985; Ninomiya et al., 1985). We have named the polypeptide chain encoded by pYN1738, the α1 chain and the polypeptide chain encoded by pYN1731, the α2 chain. Based on the complete nucleotide sequence of pYN1738 we have concluded that type IX collagen contains three triple-helical domains (COL 1, COL 2, COL 3) interspersed with non-collagenous domains (NC1, NC2, NC3, NC4).

SDS-polyacrylamide gel analysis of chondrocyte culture medium polypeptides, followed by blotting of the gels onto nitrocellulose, and reaction of the blots with anti-α1(IX), α2(IX), and α3(IX) chain antibodies, has allowed us to identify a relatively sharp 110 Kd band as the α1(IX) chain and a diffuse band at 90 Kd as the α3(IX) chain. Molecular weight estimates are based on globular molecular weight standards.

No reaction with α2(IX) chain specific antibodies was observed on the nitrocellulose blots unless the chondrocyte culture medium polypeptides were treated with chondroitinase ABC prior to electrophoresis. After treatment, the antibody clearly recognized a 90 Kd band. These results are in agreement with a recent report from Dr. P. Bruckner's laboratory, that type IX collagen contains covalently bound glycosaminoglycans (Vaughan et al., 1985). We interpret our data to indicate that the glycosaminoglycan component is attached to the α2 chain of the molecule.

In immunofluorescent staining of frozen sections of 17-day-old chick embryo sterna, the anti-type IX collagen antibody shows reaction with the extracellular matrix of cartilage.

REFERENCES

Ninomiya Y, Olsen BR (1984). Synthesis and characterization of cDNA encoding a cartilage-specific short collagen. Proc Natl Acad Sci USA 81: 3014-3018.

Ninomiya Y, Showalter AM, van der Rest M, Seidah NG, Chretien M, Olsen BR (1984). Structure of the carboxyl propeptide of chicken type II procollagen determined by DNA and protein sequence analysis. Biochemistry 23: 617-624.

Ninomiya Y, van der Rest M, Mayne R, Lozano G, Olsen BR (1985). Construction and characterization of cDNA encoding the the α2 chain of chicken type IX collagen. Biochemistry 24: 4223-4229.

Olsen BR, Ninomiya, Lozano G, Konomi H, Gordon M, Green G, Parsons J, Seyer J, Thompson H, Vasios G (1985). Short-chain collagen genes and their expression in cartilage. Annals of the NY Acad of Sci (in press).

van der Rest M, Mayne R, Ninomiya Y, Seidah NG, Chretien M, Olsen BR (1985). The structure of type IX collagen. J Biol Chem 206: 220-225.

Vaughan L, Winterhalter KH, Bruckner P (1985). Proteoglycan Lt from chicken embryo sternum identified as type IX collagen. J Biol Chem 260: 4758-4763.

Progress in Developmental Biology, Part B, pages 173–176

COLLAGEN BINDING PROTEINS ASSOCIATED WITH THE CHICKEN
EMBRYONIC CELL SURFACE

Roy C. Ogle, Dominique M. Piguet and
Charles D. Little

Cell and Molecular Biology Program and Department
of Anatomy, University of Virginia,
Charlottesville, Virginia 22908

INTRODUCTION

The cells of vertebrate embryos synthesize an abundant
extracellular matrix (ECM) that includes collagens, fibronectin and proteoglycans. Cellular morphology, proliferation, migration and differentiation are influenced by adhesive interaction with the ECM (Hay, 1984). Matrix "receptors" are membrane-associated glycoproteins involved in
the process of cellular adhesion, perhaps interacting with
the actin-based cortical cytoskeleton. Candidates for matrix
receptors include substrate adhesion molecules identified by
antibodies that round and detach cultured cells (Greve and
Gotlieb, 1979, Wylie et al, 1979) as well as glycoproteins
isolated by affinity chromatography (Mollenhauer and von
der Mark, 1983, Pytela et al, 1985).

We have identified and isolated polypeptides from
plasma membranes of chicken embryonic fibroblasts that bind
specifically to native type I collagen in vitro (Ogle and
Little, 1984). These collagen binding proteins (CBP) share
similarities in electrophoretic mobility with other described matrix receptors (Yamada et al, 1985). Preliminary
studies suggest that CBP may alter the native conformation
of the collagen molecule by binding to regions of the polypeptide involved in fibril formation.

CBP purified by two rounds of affinity chromatography
on immobilized collagen type I were used to raise polyclonal
antibodies in rabbits that recognize each of the polypeptides. Affinity purified antibodies to CBP were employed

along with antibodies to type I collagen and fibronectin
(raised in heterologous species) to study the distribution
of these antigens in chicken embryos (Stage 13, Hamburger
and Hamilton, 1951) by double indirect immunofluorescence
microscopy.

RESULTS

Specificity of Antibodies

CBP isolated by affinity chromatography were further
purified by detergent removal and resolubilization of precipitated protein (Fig. 1, lane c). Cell surface polypeptides recognized by antibodies to CBP (Fig. 1, lane a)
shifted upward in electrophoretic mobility (upon reduction),
a characteristic of protein with a high degree of intra-
chain disulfide bonding. Antibodies to collagen and fibronectin were prepared as described (Little and Chen, 1982).

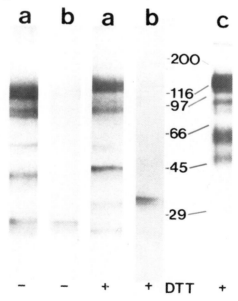

Figure 1. Autoradiogram of lactoperoxidase iodinated polypeptides resolved by electrophoresis following immune precipitation with antibodies to CBP (a) or pre-immune antiserum
(b). CBP purified by collagen affinity chromatography (c).

Immunofluorescence Microscopy

Frozen frontal sections (8μm) passing through somites and neural tube were prepared from stage 13 embryos. Sections were double-stained with antibodies to CBP, type I collagen and fibronectin in a pair-wise fashion. Second antibody conjugates, controls, microscopy and photography were conducted as described (Little and Chen, 1982).

ECM recognized by antibodies to both fibronectin (Fig. 2, d) and collagen (Fig. 2, b) surrounded the somites and neural tube. More matrix staining was associated with somites than with neural tube. CBP staining (Fig. 2, a and c) was restricted to cell surface, most pronounced at basal surfaces that contact the ECM (arrowhead).

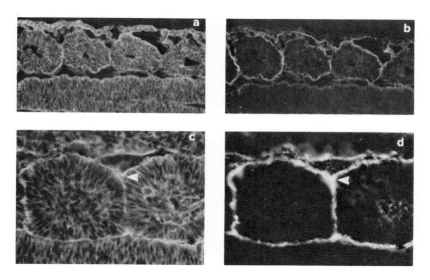

Figure 2. Visualization of CBP (a,c), collagen (b) and fibronectin (d) by double indirect immunofluorescence microscopy.

CONCLUSIONS

Type I collagen is a constituent of the embryonic ECM detectable by immuno-reagents even though mRNA levels are low as measured by cDNA probes (Merlino et al, 1983). CBP are associated with the embryonic cell surface, concentrated at substrate adhesion sites. The temporal and spatial expression of ECM components and their receptors appear to be a significant morphogenetic mechanism as their location in the embryo define the form of somites and neural tube.

REFERENCES

Greve JM, Gotlieb DI (1979). Morphological changes in developing muscle cultures induced by monoclonal antibodies. J Cell Biol 83:51a.

Hamburger V, Hamilton HL (1951). A series of normal stages in the development of the chick embryo. J Morph 88:49-92.

Hay ED (1984). Cell-matrix interactions in the embryo: cell shape, cell surface, cell skeletons, and their roll in differentiation. In Trelstad RL (ed): "The Role of the Extracellular Matrix in Development," New York: Alan R. Liss, pp 1-31.

Little, CD, Chen W-T (1982). Masking of extracellular collagen and the co-distribution of collagen and fibronectin during matrix formation by cultured embryonic fibroblasts. J Cell Sci 55:35-50.

Merlino GT, McKeon C, deCrombrugghe B, Pastan I (1983). Regulation of the expression of genes encoding types I, II, and III collagen during chick embryonic development. J Biol Chem 258:10041-10048.

Mollenhauer J, von der Mark K (1983). Isolation and characterization of a collagen-binding glycoprotein from chondrocyte membranes. EMBO J 2:45-50.

Ogle RC, Little CD (1984). Isolation and characterization of collagen binding proteins from chicken embryonic cells. J Cell Biol 99:167a.

Pytela R, Pierschbacher MD, Ruoslahti E (1985). Identification and isolation of a 140kd cell surface glycoprotein with properties expected of a fibronectin receptor. Cell 40:191-198.

Wylie DE, Damsky CH, Buck CA (1979). Studies of the function of cell surface glycoproteins. I. Use of antisera to surface membranes in the identification of membrane components relevant to cell-substrate adhesion. J Cell Biol 80:385-402.

Yamada KM, Akiyama SK, Hasegawa T, Hasegawa E, Humphries MJ, Kennedy DW, Nagata K, Urushihara H, Olden K, Chen W-T (1985). Recent advances in research on fibronectin and other cell attachment proteins. J Cell Biochem 28:79-97.

Progress in Developmental Biology, Part B, pages 177–185

REGULATION OF TISSUE PATTERNING IN THE DEVELOPING HEART BY FIBRONECTIN

Peter B. Armstrong and Margaret T. Armstrong

Department of Zoology, University of California, Davis, California 95616

Many artists begin with the pig and make sausages. I begin with sausages from which I reconstitute a pig. - Jean Dubuffet

INTRODUCTION

The sciences of anatomy and histology present a picture of living organisms as precisely organized ensembles of cells, tissues and organs. Knowledge of the factors that govern the establishment and organization of tissues during development constitutes one of the fundamental goals of experimental biology. What is desired is an accounting of tissue organization based on properties and behavior of the constituent cells and molecules. In this essay, I will explore the utility of the phenomenon of cell sorting-out in artificially-constructed aggregates of cells for arriving at cellular and molecular explanations for tissue organization. The particular situation to be considered is the organization of mesenchymal and myocardial tissue in the chick embryo heart. The explanation will emphasize the importance of the extracellular matrix protein fibronectin in the organization of these two tissues.

TISSUE ORGANIZATION IN THE EMBRYONIC HEART

The principal sites of accumulation of large volumes of mesenchymal tissue in the 10-day chick embryonic heart are in the endocardial cushions (e.g., the tissue of the atrio-ventricular valves and of the outflow tracts) and in

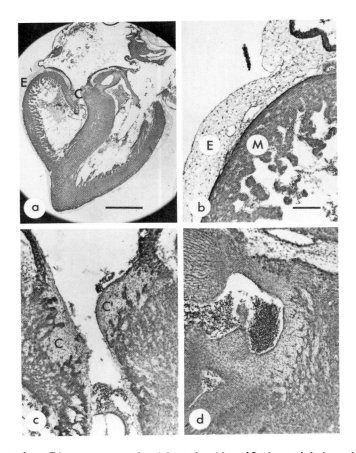

Figure 1. Tissue organization in the 10-day chick embryo
heart. The myocardium is identified by its intense
staining in these sections which have been stained by the
immunoperoxidase method for actin. The principal regions
consisting primarily of mesenchyme are the endocardial
cushions (C in Fig. 1a) and the epicardium-associated
mesenchyme (E in Fig. 1a). Epicardial mesenchyme (E) and
myocardium (M) are segregated, without tissue intermingling
(Fig. 1b), whereas intermingling of mesenchyme and
myocardium is evident in the right atrioventricular cushion
(Fig. 1c) and in the vicinity of the tricuspid valve of the
systemic aorta (Fig. 1d). Figure 1d is of a section at a
different level in the heart than the section photographed
in Figs. 1a, 1b, and 1c. Bar = 1 mm (Fig. 1a), 100 μm
(Figs. 1b, 1c, 1d).

the walls of the atria and ventricles, interposed between
epicardium and myocardium (Fig. 1a). The cushion
mesenchyme arises during development from cells that
migrate from the endocardium (Kinsella and Fitzharris,
1980; Manasek, 1970; Markwald et al., 1977). The origin of
the epicardium-associated mesenchyme has not been
established with certainty, but it may originate from the
epicardium itself (Manasek, 1969). In both regions,
myocardium and mesenchyme are in direct contact. In the
10-day heart prepared by conventional means for
transmission electron microscopy, a continuous basal lamina
is not present between mesenchyme and myocardium either in
the cushion tissue or in the epicardium (Armstrong, 1985).

The organization of the interface between muscle and
mesenchyme differs markedly in the two regions. The
epicardial mesenchyme-myocardium border is planar and
discrete, with complete segregation of the two tissues
(Fig. 1b). In contrast, significant intermingling of
mesenchyme and myocardium is evident at the cushion
mesenchyme border, especially in the right atrioventricular
valves (Fig. 1c) and in the vicinity of the tricuspid valve
of the systemic aorta (Fig. 1d) (Armstrong, 1985). Thus,
in the 10-day embryonic heart, we see the two tissue
arrangements that are possible: segregation of epicardial
mesenchyme and myocardium into discrete domains and
intermingling of myocardium and cushion mesenchyme. Our
goal is to provide an explanation at cellular and molecular
levels for these two distinct modes of tissue organization.

SORTING OUT OF CARDIAC MESENCHYME AND MYOCARDIUM

Cell sorting out occurs when two or more different
cell types are aggregated into randomly-organized cell
aggregates and the aggregates are then maintained for one
or more days in organ culture. During the sorting out
process, the cells move about within the aggregate to
segregate into relatively homogeneous domains of tissue.
These tissue domains are organized in a reproducible
pattern characteristic of the cell types included in the
aggregate. Almost any arbitrarily-chosen combination of
tissue cells will sort out in this fashion. When the cell
types are taken from tissues that normally are in
association in the body, the patterned array of tissues
formed following sorting out in many cases bears a
remarkable similarity to the normal histologic tissue

organization of the selected tissues seen <u>in</u> <u>vivo</u> (for
review see Armstrong, 1971). We have utilized the
phenomenon of cell sorting of cardiac mesenchyme/myocardium
aggregates to study the mechanisms governing tissue
patterning in the heart.

Cardiac mesenchymal and myocardial cells can be
separated following tissue dissociation by taking advantage
of differences in the rates of attachment to tissue culture
polystyrene surfaces: mesenchymal cells attach rapidly and

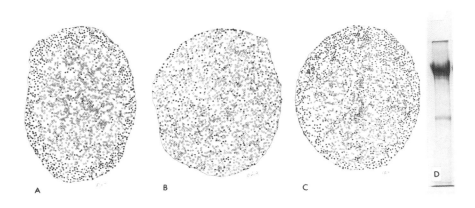

Figure 2. Camera lucida drawings of sections of heart
mesenchyme/myocardium aggregates maintained in organ
culture for 2 days. The open circles show the positions of
the nuclei of myocytes, the filled circles the positions of
the nuclei of mesenchymal cells. The culture medium was
Dulbecco-modified Eagles medium (DMEM) + 10% chicken serum
(Fig. 2a), DMEM + 1 mg/ml bovine serum albumin (BSA)
(Fig. 2b), and DMEM + 1 mg/ml BSA + cellular fibronectin
(Fig. 2c). Sorting out of mesenchyme to the surface of the
aggregate is evident in Fig. 2a and 2c, whereas sorting has
not occurred in the aggregate shown in Fig. 2b. A SDS
polyacrylamide gel electropherogram (reducing conditions)
of a fibronectin preparation similar to that used to
supplement the culture medium for the aggregate shown in
Fig. 2c is shown in Fig. 2d. The principal protein band
has a M_r = 235 x 10^3, a value consistent with that of
cellular fibronectin. Bar = 100 µm.

can be separated from the myocardial cells by removing the
culture medium containing the unattached myocardial cells
after 1.5 hr in culture (Armstrong, 1978). Random
reaggregates of myocardial and mesenchymal cells, when
cultured in serum-containing medium, sort out with the
mesenchyme occupying the surface layers of the aggregate
and the myocardium the interior (Fig. 2a). Our analysis of
sorting has emphasized the role of the extracellular matrix
protein fibronectin, which is produced by the mesenchyme
and co-localizes with it in the sorted out aggregate (Fig.
3) (Armstrong and Armstrong, 1984). The ability of the

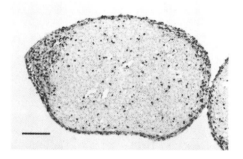

Figure 3. Section of a cardiac mesenchyme/myocardium
aggregate after 2 days of culture in serum-containing
medium. The mesenchymal cells were labeled prior to the
preparation of the aggregate with [^{3}H]-thymidine and
have been visualized by autoradiography. Fibronectin has
been stained by the immunoperoxidase technique and can be
seen to co-localize with the superficial mesenchymal
tissue. Bar = 100 μm.

cultured cardiac mesenchyme to deposit a fibronectin-rich
matrix is dependent on exposure to a factor present in the
serum component of the culture medium. In the absence of
serum, only small quantities of fibronectin are deposited
in the matrix and sorting out is minimal (Fig. 2b). If
cellular fibronectin isolated by extraction of cardiac
fibroblast monolayers with 1 $\underline{M}$ urea (method of Yamada et
al., 1975) is added to the serum-free medium, sorting out
occurs, producing aggregates similar to those observed
under permissive conditions for fibronectin synthesis
(e.g., aggregates cultured in the presence of serum) (Fig.
2c). Fibronectin is present in these aggregates and
co-localizes with the mesenchyme. Our interpretation of

these observations is that cell sorting in heart
mesenchyme/myocardium aggregates is a fibronectin-
dependent process. It is suggested that the mesenchymal
cells adhere better than the myocardial cells to the
fibronectin matrix and, thus, are able to out-compete and
exclude the myocardium from regions of the aggregate rich
in fibronectin. This vision of cell sorting obviates the
necessity for highly specific adhesive interactions and
emphasizes the possibility that quantitative differences in
the adhesive affinity for a broad-spectrum adhesive
protein, such as fibronectin, can lead to the segregation
of tissues into homogeneous domains.

Our hypothesis emphasizes the importance of components
of the extracellular matrix in cell sorting. In this
regard, it is important to remember that one of the tissues
under study is mesenchymal. Other studies that have
identified adhesive factors involved in sorting have used
epithelial tissues and have shown that integral membrane
proteins play important roles in tissue recognition
(Edelman, 1983; Lindner et al., 1983; Rutishauser et al.,
1978). The differences from our demonstration of a role
for matrix proteins may result from basic differences in
tissue organization: epithelial tissue is organized with
extensive contact between cell surfaces whereas mesenchymal
tissue is organized with the extracellular matrix forming
the continuous phase, in which are embedded the cells. It
can be proposed that whilst integral membrane proteins play
a regulatory role in the sorting out of epithelial tissues,
mesenchymal cells utilize molecules involved in cell-matrix
adhesion, which include both membrane receptors and, as
described above, matrix molecules such as fibronectin.

ROLE OF FIBRONECTIN IN ORGANIZATION IN SITU

Based on our analysis of the mechanisms of sorting out
of aggregates composed of cardiac mesenchyme and myocardium,
we suggest that fibronectin plays an important role in the
state of organization of these two tissues in situ.
Specifically, we suggest that the segregated arrangement of
epicardial mesenchyme and heart-wall myocardium is
stabilized by a fibronectin-rich matrix associated with the
epicardial mesenchyme, in a manner similar to the role
played by a fibronectin-rich matrix in the dynamic process
of tissue segregation seen during sorting out of the tissues
in vitro. It is to be remembered that in vivo these two

tissues do not intermingle across a common border that lacks a basal lamina. Furthermore, we suggest that the intermingling of tissue that occurs along the cushion mesenchyme-myocardium border is a consequence of low levels of fibronectin in the cushion mesenchyme. The apparent distribution of fibronectin in the 10-day heart, as detected by immunocytochemical staining, is consistent with this hypothesis. The epicardial mesenchyme shows significantly higher levels of immunocytochemically-detectable fibronectin than the cushion tissue (Fig. 4). When removed to culture, cushion mesenchyme will produce a fibronectin-rich matrix in

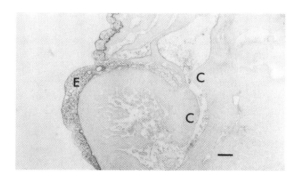

Figure 4. Section of a 10-day chick embryo heart stained using the immunoperoxidase technique for fibronectin. Dense staining is present in the epicardial mesenchyme (E); weak staining in the cushion mesenchyme (C). Bar = 100 μm.

the presence of serum. Under these conditions, a portion of the mesenchyme segregates to the surface as a homogeneous tissue layer. In summary, we suggest that the principal factor that determines whether cardiac mesenchyme and myocardium remain in a segregated state or engage in mutual invasion to generate an intermingled organization is the extracellular matrix protein fibronectin. Fibronectin is envisioned as stabilizing the segregated organization because the mesenchymal cells are more adhesive to the fibronectin matrix than to myocardial tissue, and, thus remain associated as a coherent mesenchyme rather than invading the myocardium. This notion is consistent with the oft-repeated suggestion that the invasive behavior of malignant sarcomas is dependent on a transformation-dependent loss of matrix fibronectin (for review see Akiyama and Yamada, 1983). To our knowledge, the relationship between low fibronectin levels and mesenchymal invasion is not well documented in situations of malignant invasion, but, as developed in the present report, the invasion of myocardium by mesenchyme that occurs during normal heart development may be dependent on the reduction in fibronectin levels that occurs during the development of cushion mesenchyme. Conversely, the maintenance of the segregated state of epicardial mesenchyme is suggested to depend on the abundance of fibronectin in this tissue.

An interesting parallel can be drawn between our hypothesis concerning the role of fibronectin in tissue organization in the heart and the suggestion of Lash et al. (1984) that the condensation of individual somites from segmental plate mesoderm in the chick embryo is a fibronectin-dependent process. There are numerous situations in development where homogeneous tissue sheets become subdivided into discrete organ rudiments. It will be of considerable interest to determine if fibronectin plays a role in situations other than somite segregation.

ACKNOWLEDGMENTS

This work was supported by NSF Grant No. PCM80-24181 and NIH Grant No. GM30062-01. Drs. K.M. Yamada and D.R. Garrod are thanked for providing anti-fibronectin antiserum.

REFERENCES

Akiyama SK, Yamada KM (1983). Fibronectin in disease. In Wagner B, Fleischmajer R, Kaufman N (eds): "Connective Tissue Diseases," Baltimore: Williams & Wilkens, pp. 55-96.

Armstrong PB (1971). Light and electron microscope studies of cell sorting in combinations of chick embryo neural retina and retinal pigment epithelium. Wilhelm Roux' Arch 168:125-141.

Armstrong PB (1978). Modulation of tissue affinities of cardiac myocyte aggregates by mesenchyme. Develop Biol 64:60-72.

Armstrong PB (1985). Stabilization of tissue architecture: Involvement of the extracellular matrix. In Lash JW, Saxen L (eds): "Developmental Mechanisms: Normal and Abnormal," (Prog Clin Biol Res Vol 171), New York: Alan R. Liss, pp. 87-107.

Armstrong PB, Armstrong MT (1984). A role for fibronectin in cell sorting. J Cell Sci 69:179-197.

Edelman GM (1983). Cell adhesion molecules. Science 219:450-457.

Kinsella MG, Fitzharris TP (1980). Origin of cushion mesenchyme in the development chick heart: cinematographic recordings of in situ formation. Science 207:1359-1360.

Lash JW, Seitz AW, Cheney CM, Ostrovsky D (1984). On the role of fibronectin during the compaction stage of somitogenesis in the chick embryo. J Exp Zool 232:197-206.

Lindner J, Rathjen FG, Schachner M (1983). L1 mono- and polyclonal antibodies modify cell migration in early postnatal mouse cerebellum. Nature (Lond) 305:427-430.

Manasek FJ (1969). Embryonic development of the heart II. Formation of the epicardium. J Embryol Exp Morph 22:333-348.

Manasek FJ (1970). Histogenesis of the embryonic myocardium. Amer J Cardiol 25:149-168.

Markwald RR, Fitzharris TP, Manasek FJ (1977). Structural development of endocardial cushions. Amer J Anat 148:85-120.

Rutishauser U, Thiery J-P, Brackenbury R, Edelman GM (1978). Adhesion among neural cells of the chick embryo. III. Relationships of the surface molecule CAM to cell adhesion and the development of histotypic patterns. J Cell Biol 79:371-381.

Yamada KM, Yamada S, Pastan I (1975). The major cell surface glycoprotein of chick embryo fibroblasts is a glycoprotein. Proc Natl Acad Sci USA 72:3158-3162.

Progress in Developmental Biology, Part B, pages 187–190
© 1986 Alan R. Liss, Inc.

NETWORK STRUCTURE IN THE BLASTOCOEL OF DEVELOPING SEA
URCHIN EMBRYOS.

Shonan Amemiya

Misaki Marine Biological Station, University of
Tokyo,
Miura, Kanagawa 238-02, Japan

INTRODUCTION

Endo and Noda (1977) originally demonstrated by a
scanning electron microscope a network structure in the
blastocoel of sea urchin embryos and this has been confirmed since then by the works of many other researchers (Katow
and Solursh, 1979; Akasaka et al., 1980; Kawabe et al.,
1981). However, such a structure may be an artificial
product resulting from the procedure for observation by
electron microscope, is a possibility that cannot be excluded.
In this study, an examination was made of blastocoelic
material subjected to two different fixation methods at
various developmental stages of sea urchin embryos from
early blastula to late gastrula using a scanning electron
microscope. At least three types of fibrillar matrices in
the blastocoel were found.

MATERIALS AND METHODS

Eggs and sperm were obtained from the sea urchin,
Hemicentrotus pulcherrimus, by the conventional KCl method.
Inseminated eggs were cultured in filtered sea water at 12
°C with gentle stirring. Embryos were collected by low-
speed centrifugation at various time intervals of culturing, from early blastula to midgastrula stages, and fixed
with two different fixatives for scanning electron microscopic observation. One fixative, the "Ca^{++}-rich fixative", consisted of 1 % OsO$_4$ in filtered sea water buffered
by 0.1M sodium cacodylate (pH 7.4). The other, "Ca^{++}-free

fixative", consisted of 1% OsO4 in 0.6M sucrose buffered by 0.1M sodium cacodylate (pH 7.4). The fixed embryos were dehydrated, dried by the critical point-drying method, glued to a stage and cut manually with a glass knife. The dissected embryos were then coated with gold and observed in a Hitachi HHS-2R SEM.

RESULTS AND DISCUSSION

1) Embryos fixed with the "Ca^{++}-rich fixative".
    Fig. 1 shows the inside of a blastocoel in an early blastula cultured for 21.5 h after insemination. It is filled with a rough-surfaced fibrillar matrix. Fibrils are attached to the inner surface of the ectodermal wall as indicated by arrows. In some cases, the fibrillar matrix is constricted in a certain part of the blastocoel as a small mass. The function of this fibrillar matrix in mor-

phogenesis is not understood but it may possibly be an artificial product produced during fixation for electron microscopic observation.

Fig. 1. Inside of blasto-coel in an early blastula cultured for 21.5 h after insemination and fixed with the Ca^{++}-rich fixative.   x 1300.

2) Embryos fixed with the "Ca^{++}-free fixative".
    Fig. 2A shows part of the dissected surface cut along the animal-vegetal axis in an early blastula cultured for 21.5 h following insemination. The rough-surfaced fibrillar matrix is absent from the middle part of the blasto-coel, indicating the matrix to possibly be composed of Ca^{++} -dependent material. In its place, a network structure of fine fibrils can be clearly seen on the inner surface of ectodermal wall in the vegetal hemisphere (Fig. 2A). This structure can be found only in the vegetal hemispere and is not formed in the animal pole region at this stage (Fig. 2B).
    It is well established (Okazaki, 1960) that primary mesenchyme cells formed from vegetal plate cells through ingression into the blastocoel at the mesenchyme blastula stage migrate along the inner surface of the ectodermal wall toward the animal pole to occupy their characteristic

place. The network structure shown in Fig. 2A may functions as the substratum by which primary mesenchyme cells
migrate along the inner surface of ectodermal wall.

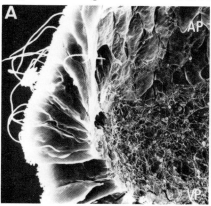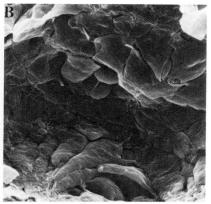

Fig. 2. Inside of a blastocoel in an early blastula cultured for 21.5 h after insemination and fixed with the Ca^{++}
-free fixative. A. A part of a dissected surface cut along
the animal-vegetal axis. AP. Animal pole; VP, Vegetal
pole; x 1350. B. Dissected surface of an animal pole
region cut along the equatorial zone. x 1700.

At the midgastrula stage, another type of fibrillar
structure appears between the invaginating archenteron and
ectodermal wall (Fig. 3). Its fibrils appear to be associated with the inner surface
of both the ectoderm and archenteron. The role of this
matrix in morphogenesis is
not clear, but possibly may
be to assist the archenteron
to indent.

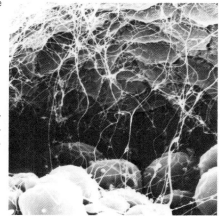

Fig. 3. Inside of a blastocoel in a midgastrula cultured for 33.5 h after insemination and fixed with the Ca^{++}-
free fixative. The cells in
the lower part of the figure
constitute a part of the
archenteron.   x 2400.

Data from the present study demonstrate the presence
of three types of network structures. Their characteristics are summarized in Table 1.

Table 1. Comparative characteristics of the three types of
network structures in sea urchin embryos.

	Type I	Type II	Type III
Stage of appearance	Early blastula	Early blastula	Mid gastrula
Requirement of Ca^{++} in fixative	Not needed	Needed	Not needed
Function	Possibly serves as substratum for primary mesenchyme cell migration.	Not clear	possibly guides archenteron to indent.
Locality	Inner surface of ectodermal wall	Middle part of blastocoel	Between ectodermal wall and archenteron

REFERENCES

Akasaka K, Amemiya S, Terayama H (1980). Scanning electron
  microscopical study of the inside of sea urchin embryos
  (Pseudocentrotus depressus). Effects of Aryl B-xyloside,
  Tunicamycin and deprivation of sulfate ions. Exp Cell
  Res 129:1-13.
Endo Y, Noda Y D (1977). Ultrastructure of the blastocoel
  of sea urchin embryos. Zool Mag 86: 309.
Katow H, Solursh M (1979). Ultrastructure of blastocoel
  material in blastula and gastrula of the sea urchin Lyte-
  chinus pictus. J Exp Zool 210: 561-567.
Kawabe T T, Armstrong P B, Pollock E G (1981). An extra-
  cellular fibrillar matrix in gastrulating sea urchin
  embryos. Develop. Biol. 85: 509-515.
Okazaki K (1960). Skeleton formation of sea urchin larvae.
  II. Organ matrix of the spicule. Embryologia 5: 283-320.

Progress in Developmental Biology, Part B, pages 191–194
© 1986 Alan R. Liss, Inc.

ENVIRONMENTAL CONTROL IN PIGMENT PATTERN
FORMATION OF THE AXOLOTL LARVA

Hans H. Epperlein, Roberto Perris[1] and
Jan Löfberg[1]
Anatomisches Institut, Universität Frei-
burg, Albertstr. 17, 7800 Freiburg, West
Germany; [1]Department of Zoology, Uppsala
University, Box 561, S-751 22 Uppsala,
Sweden

The pigment pattern of the axolotl (<u>Ambystoma
mexicanum</u>) larva (Fig. 1) consists of several alternating transverse bands or bars of black melanophores and yellow xanthophores along the dorsal
trunk. The pigment cells or chromatophores are derived from the neural crest and, since they localize under the epidermis, they are termed dermal
chromatophores. Several characteristics make the
pigment pattern of the axolotl larva an interesting
model for studies on differentiation, migration and
localization of neural crest derivatives in relation to environmental influences - particularly
from the epidermis and its subepidermal ECM. These
studies are facilitated by the easy way in which
melanophores and xanthophores, distinguished by
their natural markers melanin and pterin, can be
observed from outside. With special techniques these markers can be visualized even at early stages
of cell differentiation when chromatophores are not
yet visible from outside. These techniques include
DOPA incubation for demonstrating phenol oxidase in
melanophores and ammonia treatment for eliciting
pterin fluorescence in xanthophores (Epperlein and
Claviez, 1982; Epperlein and Löfberg, 1984).

Following DOPA incubation of stage 35/36 embryos, several DOPA-positive black melanophore
groups appeared along the trunk in the position of

the premigratory neural crest. In addition, single
melanophores were scattered over the entire dorso-
lateral flank. The position of the melanophore
groups suggests that they might be precursors of
the larval melanophore bars. Treatment of stage
35/36 embryos with dilute ammonia revealed several
pterin-fluorescing groups along the trunk, indicating xanthophores. Whether these xanthophore groups
were precursors of the later xanthophore bars (separate from or identical with the DOPA-positive
groups) could be decided by combining DOPA incubation and fluorescence analysis in the same embryo.
It follows that both groups have identical positions
and that melanophores and xanthophores occur in them
separately. The mixed chromatophore groups could be
correlated in the scanning electron microscope with
humps along the neural crest cell string. They are
not present at earlier or later stages. We assume
therefore that the barred pigment pattern of the
axolotl larva develops from a prepattern of mixed
chromatophore groups established along the premigratory trunk neural crest. Xanthophores determine
the site of the yellow bars, causing melanophores
in and around the groups to become invisible. Black
bars arise from melanophores in regions between the
mixed groups (Epperlein and Löfberg, 1984).

   The role of the epidermis and the subepidermal
ECM in pigment pattern formation was investigated
in several experiments. If the epidermis was removed from embryos at an early stage, several chromatophore groups from which the pigment cells could
not migrate out, developed at intervals along the
trunk. The chromatophore groups consisted of xanthophores or of both xanthophores and melanophores.
Hence the epidermis seems to have no effect on
group formation but on dispersion and migration of
chromatophores. If a piece of epidermis close to the
neural crest in a young dark embryo of premigratory
crest-stage is replaced by older epidermis taken
from a crest-free donor, the chromatophores migrate
precociously at the site of the graft. White axolotl
embryos have an abnormal subepidermal ECM which
Spieth and Keller (1984) have suggested prevents
chromatophore migration. Therefore, in these mutant
embryos chromatophore groups are maintained during

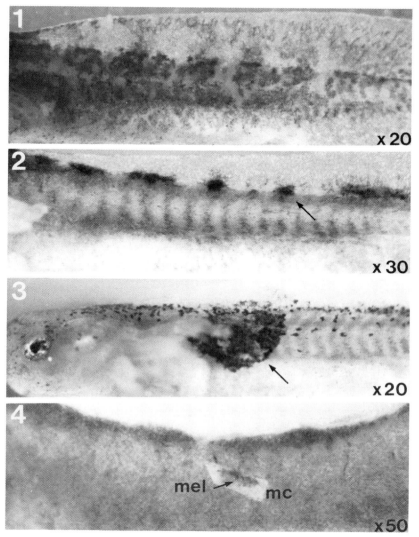

Fig. 1: The barred pigment pattern of the wild-
    type axolotl larva; head on the left (all figs.)
Fig. 2: Maintenance of chromatophore groups(arrow)
    in the white mutant larva; flank unpigmented.
Fig. 3: Local migration (arrow) of chromatophores
    in a white mutant larva, stimulated by a graft
    of wild-type epidermis.
Fig. 4: Local migration of melanophores (mel) in a
    white mutant larva stimulated by a microcarrier
    (mc) conditioned with wild-type subepidermal ECM

larval life (Fig. 2). Replacement of white by wild-
type epidermis in a flank position close to the
neural crest in early embryos of premigratory crest
stage stimulated melanophore and xanthophore migration locally (Fig. 3). When a microcarrier (Löfberg et al., 1985) conditioned with wild-type subepidermal ECM was implanted under the epidermis of
a white embryo in a position close to the neural
crest, melanophores migrated out and ended up on
the microcarrier on which they could be shown after DOPA incubation (Fig. 4). This experiment indicates that the wild-type ECM by itself can stimulate chromatophore migration from the crest. We
conclude that the barred pigment pattern of the
axolotl larva depends on a chromatophore prepattern, while the realization of this prepattern
(i.e. the migration and arrangement of chromatophores into bars) is under the control of the subepidermal ECM of the wild-type, which apparently
furnishes a suitable substrate for chromatophore
migration.

REFERENCES

Epperlein HH, Claviez M (1982) Changes in the distribution of melanophores and xanthophores in
Triturus alpestris embryos during their transition from the uniform to banded pattern. Roux'
Arch Dev Biol 191: 5 - 18
Epperlein HH, Löfberg J (1984) Xanthophores in
chromatophore groups of the premigratory neural
crest initiate the pigment pattern of the axolotl larva. Roux' Arch Dev Biol 193: 357 - 369
Löfberg J, Nynäs-McCoy A, Olsson C, Jönsson L,
Perris R (1985) Stimulation of initial neural
crest cell migration in the axolotl embryo by
tissue grafts and extracellular matrix transplanted on microcarriers. Dev Biol 107: 442 - 459
Spieth J, Keller RE (1984) Neural crest cell behaviour in white and dark larvae of Ambystoma
mexicanum: Differences in cell morphology, arrangement, and extracellular matrix as related
to migration. J Exp Zool 229: 91 - 107

Progress in Developmental Biology, Part B, pages 195–198

EXTRACELLULAR CARDIAC PROTEINS ACTIVATE CHICK ENDOTHELIAL
TRANSITION TO PREVALVULAR MESENCHYME

Edward L. Krug and Roger R. Markwald

Department of Anatomy and Cell Biology,
Medical College of Wisconsin,
Milwaukee, Wisconsin 53226

INTRODUCTION

Early embryonic cardiac endothelium undergoes an epithe-
lial/mesenchymal transformation to produce the primordia of
membranous septa and valves. The cellular events of the transformation sequence include endothelial (epithelial) cell separation, hypertrophy and polarization of the Golgi apparatus,
and formation of basal migratory appendages (Markwald et al.,
1984). A 3-dimensional collagen gel culture model has been
developed which retains the in vivo differentiation characteristics of cardiac endothelium (Bernanke and Markwald, 1982).
In this culture model, atrioventricular canal (AV) endothelial cells from embryos younger than stage 16–17 required
myocardial co-culture to initiate the transformation sequence
(Runyan and Markwald, 1983). This observation supports prior
in situ studies (Markwald and Funderburg, 1983) which showed
that an inductive interaction occurs between the myocardium
and AV endothelium resulting in mesenchyme formation. Our
working hypothesis is that this interaction is mediated by
extracellular molecules secreted by the myocardium and
assembled into an extended basement membrane, historically
termed "cardiac jelly" (Markwald et al., 1985). To test this
hypothesis we have selectively extracted the myocardial basement membrane (MBM) with EDTA and testicular hyaluronidase and
observed from 30 – 35 proteins by IEF/SDS-PAGE (Krug et al.,
1985). When this MBM extract was applied to cultured endothelium in the absence of myocardial tissue, it initiated the
transformation sequence, but failed to affect cell migration
into the collagen gel. This incomplete activation of the epithelium may result from the degradation of hyaluronic acid

in the MBM, which may be required for the maintenance of intermolecular interactions essential for mesenchyme formation. In this study, we have attempted to explore this possibility by extracting the MBM with EDTA alone. Preliminary results indicated that EDTA extracts of the MBM were able to "induce" complete transformation of AV endothelium into mesenchyme. It was significant that the proteins extracted (5 - 7 major proteins) included those found previously to be unique to the AV region (the site of endothelial transformation).

MATERIALS AND METHODS

The methods for culturing cardiac endothelium and assaying for endothelial activation have been previously described (Krug et al., 1985). Briefly, cardiac endothelial cultures from stage 14 chick embryos were established on hydrated collagen gels, then treated with various extracts of the MBM (cardiac jelly). Activation of the endothelial transformation sequence was based on the observation of mesenchymal cells seeded within the collagen gel lattice as confirmed by optical sectioning of living cultures or by histological sectioning of material fixed in 3% glutaraldehyde containing 1% tannic acid and embedded in plastic by standard procdures (Bernanke and Markwald, 1982). The MBM extract was prepared from stage 16 chick hearts by incubation in phosphate buffered saline containing 5 mM EDTA and 1 mM phenylmethylsulfonylfluoride, pH 7.2 at 4° for 45 minutes with shaking, then centrifugation at 200 x g. The resulting supernatant was incubated overnight with -20° acetone, the precipitate collected by centrifugation and washed with water-saturated ether, allowed to dry under nitrogen, then suspended in culture medium. MBM extract was radiolabelled with ^{3}H-KBH$_4$ (Kumarasamy and Symons, 1979).

RESULTS AND DISCUSSION

As shown in Table I, AV endothelium is incapable of transforming into mesenchyme without myocardial co-culture. However, complete activation ensued in the absence of myocardial tissue if MBM extracts were added (Figures 1 a-f). The timing of the transformation sequence following extract addition was virtually identical to myocardial co-culture in that mesenchymal cells were first observed after 24 hr. Thus, MBM extract seemingly initiates transformation without disrupting

the biological clock for this phenomenon.   The threshold for
activation appeared to be 0.3 ug/ml protein.   Although kinetic
studies have yet to be done, increasing the amount of protein
visibly augmented the number of cells seeded.   Heat (60°/10
min) inactivated the extracts.   Ventricular endothelium was
unresponsive to the extracts.

TABLE I. Standard Culture Assay For Endothelial Activation [1]

Protocol	Cell Separation	PAS Staining and Polarization	Mesenchyme Formation
Stage 14 AV Endothelium			
myocardial co-culture	+	+	+[3]
myocardium removed	-	-	-
EDTA/hyaluronidase extract[2] 50 - 400 ug protein/ml	+	+	-
EDTA extract 0.1 ug protein/ml	-	-	-
0.3 - 1.2 ug/ml	+	+	+[3]
Stage 14 Ventricular Endothelium			
myocardial co-culture	-	-	-
EDTA extract 0.1 - 1.2 ug protein/ml	-	-	-

(1) Endothelial cultures were established in the presence of myocardium for the first 18 hr as described previously (Krug et al., 1985).
The myocardium was then removed, unless otherwise indicated, and the
remaining endothelium treated with various extracts of stage 16
hearts. Cultures were terminated after a total of 72 hr.
(2) Prepared according to Krug et al. (1985).
(3) Complete transformation occurred as early as 24 hr in these
cultures.

Figure 2 shows the protein composition of MBM extracts
from stage 14 and 17 hearts. The small differences in mobility
of proteins between these two stages may reflect altered
glycosyltransferase, glycosidase, or protease activities.   The
material on the top of the gel may represent proteoglycan.

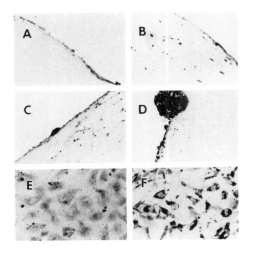

Figure 1. Standard AV Activation Assays.
A) AV endothelium (En) alone; B) AV En plus
EDTA extract; C) AV En with myocardial co-
culture; D) ventricular En with myocardium;
E) AV En alone, PAS; F) AV En plus extract,
PAS. A-D) 150X. E-F) 500X, en face.

Figure 2. SDS-
PAGE/fluoro-
graphy of MBM
extracted with
EDTA alone.

REFERENCES

Markwald, RR, Runyan, RB, Kitten, GT, Funderburg, FM,
    Bernanke, DH, and Brauer, PR (1984) In "The Role of
    Extracellular Matrix in Development," (R. Trelstad, ed.),
    pp. 323-350, Alan R. Liss, NY.

Bernanke, DH and Markwald, RR (1982) Dev. Biol. 91, 235-245.

Runyan, RB and Markwald, RR (1983) Dev. Biol. 95, 108-114.

Markwald, RR and Funderburg, FM (1983) Dev. Biol. 99, 395-407.

Markwald, RR, Krug, EL, Runyan, RB and Kitten, GT (1985) In
    "Cardiac Morphogenesis," (C. Weinstein, ed.), Elsevier, NY.

Krug, EL and Markwald, RR (1985) Dev. Biol. - in press.

Kumararasamy, R and Symons, RH (1979) Anal. Biochem. 95,
    359-363.

Progress in Developmental Biology, Part B, pages 199–202

MATRIX-DRIVEN TRANSLOCATION: POSSIBLE ROLE IN PRECARTILAGE
MESENCHYMAL CONDENSATION

Stuart A. Newman, Dorothy A. Frenz,
James J. Tomasek, and Douglas F. Paulsen

Departments of Anatomy, New York Medical
College, Valhalla, New York 10595 (S.A.N.,
D.A.F., J.J.T.), and Morehouse School of
Medicine, Atlanta, Georgia 30310 (D.F.P.)

INTRODUCTION

Several key steps in development involve translocation
of cells from one site in the embryo to another. Cell
translocation in vertebrate embryos occurs over relatively
long distances during gastrulation, migration of primordial
germ cells into the gonads, and dispersion of neural crest
cells to their sites of terminal differentiation. Translocation over shorter distances occurs during cell condensation events, such as those that lead to the formation of
feather germs in birds and the precartilaginous primordia
of the bones of vertebrate limbs (see Saunders, 1982, for
citations pertaining to these and related processes).

Morphogenetic events in general, and cell translocation in particular, are usually mediated by interactions
of cells with matrices consisting of extracellular macromolecules that they and their neighboring cells have
produced (Hay, 1981). In addition to well-documented cases
in which cells move by intrinsic motile mechanisms over
and through matrices that act as passive substrata
(Trinkaus, 1976) it has been suggested that the extracellular environment could play an active role in translocating
cells within embryos (Bronner-Fraser, 1982). We have
demonstrated that assembling, native, type I collagen
matrices containing nonuniformly distributed fibronectin
can indeed promote the translocation of certain types of
cells or certain types of inert particles from one region
to another (Newman et al., 1985). We call this effect

"matrix-driven translocation". Here we show that polystyrene latex beads with different surface coatings move
selectively into precartilage mesenchymal condensations in
culture. Moreover, the selectivity exhibited in the translocation of coated beads through tissue masses corresponds
to the capacity of such beads to be moved by matrix-driven
translocation in collagen gels.

METHODS

     Polystyrene latex beads were coated with dextran
sulfate or heparin, as described (Newman et al, 1985).
Drops of collagen containing beads or 25 µg/ml human
plasma fibronectin were simultaneously deposited on the
surface of a plastic petri dish and allowed to become
confluent (Fig. 1). Matrix-driven translocation was
assayed as previously described (Newman et al, 1985).

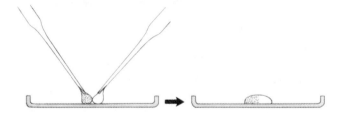

Fig. 1.   Placement of collagen drops containing beads
(stippled) and fibronectin (white) in preparation for
matrix-driven translocation assay.

     Precartilage mesenchymal cells were prepared from the
tips of 5 day chick wing buds (Newman, 1977). They were
mixed with polystyrene latex beads coated with dextran
sulfate or heparin, at a cell to bead ratio of 95:5, plated
at a density of 2.5×10^7 cells per ml in Ham's F-12
medium, and allowed to grow for 5 days. Under these
conditions cells aggregate into foci within 1-2 days and
form cartilage within 3-4 days.

RESULTS AND DISCUSSION

     Latex beads coated with dextran sulfate failed to move
into the fibronectin-rich region of a compositionally non-

uniform assembling collagen matrix (Fig. 2, left). In
contrast, beads coated with heparin moved 3 mm or more into
the fibronectin-rich region within 5 min (Fig. 2, right).

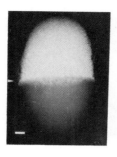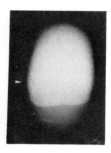

Fig. 2   Selective capacity of beads coated with different
sulfated polysaccharides to undergo matrix-driven translocation.   (Left) Beads were coated with dextran sulfate.
(Right) Beads were coated with heparin.   Arrowheads show
original position of interface between bead-containing and
fibronectin-containing gels.   Scale bar represents 1 mm.

In high density chondrogenic cultures dextran sulfate-
coated beads remained dispersed throughout the tissue mass
during the entire course of culture (Fig. 3, left).   In
contrast, beads coated with heparin were translocated over
distances of several cell diameters into sites of mesenchymal condensation during the first 2 days of culture.
By 4 days large aggregates of beads had accumulated at
these sites. (Fig. 3, right).

The movement of heparin-coated latex beads into precartilage condensations in high density chondrogenic
cultures suggests that the forces that drive cells into
these condensations may also be independent of cell motility.   Such condensations in developing limbs are rich in
fibronectin (Tomasek et al, 1982).   Heparin-coated latex
beads and precartilage mesenchymal cells are translocated
into fibronectin-rich regions of an artifical matrix by a
specific interaction with a defined domain of the fibronectin molecule (Newman et al, 1984).   We propose that
similar interactions can occur in developing mesenchyme
and may play a role in the formation of precartilage
condensations.

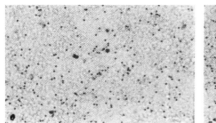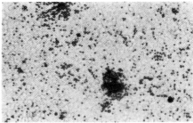

Fig. 3   Selective capacity of 6 µm latex beads coated
with different sulfated polysaccharides to undergo translocation into foci of cell condensation.   Cultures were
photographed after 4 days.   (Left) Beads were coated with
dextran sulfate.   (Right) Beads were coated with heparin.

REFERENCES

Bronner-Fraser, ME (1982).   Distribution of latex beads and
    retinal pigment epithelial cells along the ventral
    neural crest pathway.   Devel Biol 91:50.
Hay, ED, ed (1981).   "Cell Biology of Extracellular
    Matrix".   New York: Plenum Press.
Newman, SA (1977).   Lineage and pattern in the developing
    wing bud.   In Ede, DA, Hinchliffe, JR, Balls, M (eds):
    "Vertebrate Limb and Somite Morphogenesis",
    Cambridge: Cambridge Univ Press, p 181.
Newman, SA, Frenz, DA, Hasegawa, E, Akiyama, SK (1984).
    Matrix-driven translocation: Dependence on heparin-
    binding domain of fibronectin. J Cell Biol 99:167a.
Newman, SA, Frenz, DA, Tomasek, JJ, Rabuzzi, DD (1985).
    Matrix-driven translocation of cells and nonliving
    particles.   Science 228:885.
Saunders, JW, Jr (1982). "Developmental Biology."
    New York: Macmillan.
Tomasek, JJ, Mazurkiewicz, JE, Newman, SA (1982).
    Nonuniform distribution of fibronectin during avian
    limb development.   Develop Biol 90:118.
Trinkaus, JP (1976).   On the mechanism of metazoan cell
    movements.   In Post, G, Nicolson, GL (eds): "The Cell
    Surface in Animal Embryogenesis and Development."
    New York: North-Holland, p 225.

Progress in Developmental Biology, Part B, pages 203–206
© 1986 Alan R. Liss, Inc.

MECHANISMS OF EXTRACELLULAR MATRIX TURNOVER IN NORMAL AND
NEOPLASTIC CELLS.

Jelena Gavrilovic and Gillian Murphy

Department of Cell Physiology, Strangeways
Research Laboratory, Cambridge, U.K.

INTRODUCTION

The degradation of extracellular matrix components may
be of great importance in both morphogenesis and in
pathological conditions such as rheumatoid arthritis and
tumour invasion. For example, during involution of the
mammary gland, disappearance of components of the basement
membrane has been shown histologically (Martinez-Hernandez
et al, 1976). Connective tissue cells, tumour cells and
other cell types can synthesize and secrete
metalloproteinases capable of degrading different types of
collagens and other extracellular matrix components
(Trechsel et al 1982, Liotta et al 1981).
     In order to investigate the mechanisms involved in
extracellular collagen degradation we have established a
model system involving rabbit VX2 carcinoma cells or normal
articular chondrocytes plated in direct contact with type I
collagen films. We have investigated the ability of these
cells to degrade collagen films and the action of specific
agents capable of inhibiting collagenase activity.

METHODS

     VX2 cells were teased out from pieces of the primary
VX2 carcinoma (carried by serial transplantation in the
thigh muscle of New Zealand White rabbits) and grown in
Dulbecco's Modification of Eagle's Medium (DMEM)

supplemented with 10% foetal calf serum. After 1 week
cells were passaged to washed ^{14}C-labelled type I collagen
films at 5 x 10[4] cells/cm[2]. Once the cells had adhered
the medium was changed to DMEM supplemented with 2% rabbit
serum which contained very low levels of proteinase
inhibitors. After 3 days medium was collected and
radioactivity released estimated by scintillation
counting. An aliquot of the medium collected was assayed
for collagenase in the reconstituted collagen fibril assay
as previously described (Sellers and Reynolds 1977). One
unit degrades one ug of collagen per minute at 35°C.
Bacterial collagenase was added to all wells for 24 hours
to determine the total radioactivity in each well.

Rabbit articular chondrocytes were cultured as
previously described (Trechsel et al 1982) and passaged to
collagen films. Chondrocytes were stimulated with pig
monocyte conditioned medium prepared as previously
described (Trechsel et al 1982) and 5ug human plasminogen
was added to some wells after 24 hours stimulation.
Medium was collected and analysed as above.

Sheep anti-rabbit collagenase IgG (Hembry, R.H,
Murphy, G, Cawston, T.E., Dingle, J.T. and Reynolds, J.J.
submitted) was added to some wells (460 ug/well) with
control wells receiving normal sheep serum. Purified TIMP
from human amniotic fluid (Murphy et al 1981) was added to
other wells (2 units/well) with control wells receiving the
buffer only. One unit of TIMP inhibits two units of
collagenase by 50% at 35°C.

RESULTS AND DISCUSSION

VX2 cells spontaneously degraded type I collagen
films. Low levels of collagenase were detected in the
medium, some of which was in the active form (Table 1).
In marked contrast rabbit articular chondrocytes were
unable to degrade the films spontaneously even when
stimulated to make high levels of latent collagenase.
Degradation was effected only after the addition of
plasminogen to the cultures. Active enzyme was then
detected in the medium. (Table 1).

TABLE 1

% lysis collagen film over 3 days	Collagenase (Units/well)	
	Latent	Active
VX2 tumour cells 61 ± 0.4	0.42± .07	0.24-±.05
Chondrocytes + MCM 0	4.25± .27	-
Chondrocytes + MCM + plasminogen 43 ± 0.8	4.11± .30	0.11± .04

These results are similar to those of Werb et al (1977) who showed that collagenase-producing rheumatoid synovial cells required activation with plasmin to effect degradation of ^{3}H collagen films.

The degradation of type I collagen films by VX2 cells was inhibited by 74% with anti-collagenase antibody and by 87% with purified TIMP (Table 2).

TABLE 2

	% lysis collagen film
VX2 cells + Normal sheep serum IgG	80 ± 0.1
VX2 cells + anti-collagenase IgG	21 ± 0.2
VX2 Cells + Control buffer	61 ± 0.3
VX2 cells + TIMP	8 ± 0.2

These results are consistent with the observations of Thorgeirsson et al (1982) who demonstrated inhibition with TIMP of invasion of amnion basement membrane and stroma by metalloproteinase-producing tumour cells.

Our results suggest that degradation by VX2 cells of type I collagen films is largely mediated by the metalloproteinase, collagenase.

REFERENCES

Liotta LA, Tryggvason K, Garbisa S, Robey PG and Abe S (1981). Partial purification and characterization of a neutral protease which cleaves type IV collagen. Biochemistry 20 100-104.

Martinez-Hernandez A, Fink IM, and Pierce G (1976). Removal of basement membrane in the involuting breast. Lab. Invest. 34, 455-462.

Murphy G, Cawston TE and Reynolds JJ (1981). An inhibitor of collagenase from human amniotic fluid. Biochem. J. 195, 167-170.

Sellers A and Reynolds JJ (1977). Identification and partial characterization of an inhibitor of collagenase from rabbit bone. Biochem. J. 195 167-170.

Thorgeirsson UP, Liotta LA, Kalebic T, Marguiles IM, Thomas K, Rios-Candelore M and Russo RG (1982). Effect of natural protease inhibitors and a chemo attractant on tumour cell invasion in vitro. J. Natl. Cancer Inst. 69 1049-1054.

Trechsel U, Dew G, Murphy G and Reynolds JJ (1982). Effects of products from macrophages, blood mononuclear cells and of retinol on collagenase secretion and collagen synthesis in chondrocyte culture. Biochem. Biophys. Acta 720 364-370.

Werb Z, Mainardi CL, Vater CA and Harris ED (1977). Endogenous activation of latent collagenase by rheumatoid synovial cells. Evidence for a role of plasminogen activator. New Engl. J. Med. 296 1017-1023.

Progress in Developmental Biology, Part B, pages 207–210

LOCALIZATION OF SURFACE ASSOCIATED ANTIGENS BEFORE AND AFTER TUMOR CELL INVASION THROUGH A BASEMENT MEMBRANE

Mary J.C. Hendrix, Kurt R. Gehlsen and Jacqueline L. Brailey

Department of Anatomy, College of Medicine, University of Arizona, Tucson, Arizona 85724

INTRODUCTION

The incidence of melanoma has rapidly increased over the past decade, specifically in the Southwest region of the United States. At the present time, metastatic melanoma is considered to be incurable due to the rapid dissemination of this disease through the body. An important consideration in the invasive movement of malignant cells is the role of cell adhesion and extracellular matrix (ECM) proteins – fibronectin (FN), laminin (LAM), and collagens (COL) IV and V (Ruoslahti, 1984; McCarthy et al., 1985; Barsky et al., 1984). Interactions between the cell surface and the ECM are vital for cell recognition, cell adhesion, and metastasis (Nicolson, 1984).

Our laboratory has been interested in the biological processes involved in the invasion and metastasis of melanoma tumor cells. Our focus has been two-fold: (1) to develop an in vitro model that would allow us to study tumor cell invasion, and (2) to study the localization of specific cell surface associated antigens – FN, LAM, and COL IV and V – which have been shown to be dramatically altered during metastasis. Understanding the role of these molecules would undoubtedly lead to a better understanding of the invasion process.

MATERIALS AND METHODS

Tumor cell surface associated antigens were studied <u>in vitro</u> before and after invasion through a basement membrane (BM) using the human amnion model (Liotta et al., 1980) in combination with indirect immunofluorescence microscopy. Aliquots of high (A375M) and low (A375P) metastatic variants of the human melanoma cell line A375 (donated by Dr. Fidler, M.D. Anderson, Houston TX) were sampled at the time of initial seeding (before invasion) on the BM, and 24 hr later the cells that completely traversed the BM (after invasion) were also collected in Membrane Invasion Culture System (MICS) chambers (developed by our laboratory). Cells in suspension were treated with polyclonal antibodies to LAM and COL IV and V (gifts from Dr. C. Little, University of Charlottesville, VA), and FN (Cappel Labs, PA) following cell surface fixation with 2% paraformaldehyde in PBS, pH 7.4.

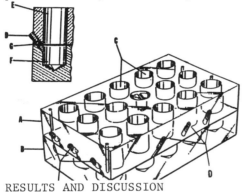

MICS: (A) Top Plate, (B) Bottom Plate, (C) Experimental Wells, (D) Sampling Ports, (E) Upper Well, (F) Lower Well, (G) Human Amniotic Basement Membrane with Underlying Stroma. The human BM is interposed between the two plates.

RESULTS AND DISCUSSION

Immunofluorescence microscopy show no significant staining for COL IV and V before or after invasion. These data are not unexpected since tumor cells have been shown to produce specific basement membrane collagenases for degradation (Liotta et al., 1983).

Figures 1,2: A375P cells (P) stained with anti-COL IV. Before invasion (BI), after invasion (AI). X200

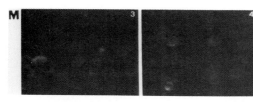

Figures 3,4:   A375M
cells (M) stained
with COL V anti-
bodies. X 300.

        More staining for FN is shown associated with the
A375P cells than the higher metastatic variant A375M before
and after invasion. The brightly stained extracellular
material associated with both cell lines after invasion
appears to have been carried with them from the amnion.
Previous reports have shown reduced amounts of FN in highly
metastatic cell lines (Ruoslahti, 1984; McCarthy et al.,
1985).

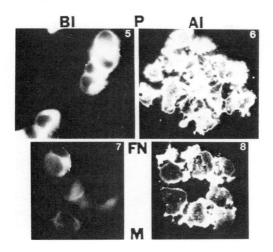

Figures 5,6:   A375P
cells stained with FN
BI and AI. X260.

Figures 7,8:   A375M
cells stained with FN
BI and AI. X260.

        A very distinctive staining pattern for LAM is shown
in both cell lines. Select cells have cell surface
staining before invasion; however, all cells that invaded
the BM stain for LAM after invasion. Previous reports
implicating the role of LAM in metastasis have shown that
tumor cells with increased receptor sites for LAM
demonstrate higher pulmonary metastatic potential than
cells from the same population with fewer LAM receptors
(Terranova et al., 1983; Barsky et al., 1984). In our
study, we may be observing LAM staining after invasion on
only those cells which expressed it before invasion. In
any event, these results suggest the importance of LAM in
the metastatic process of melanoma tumor cells.

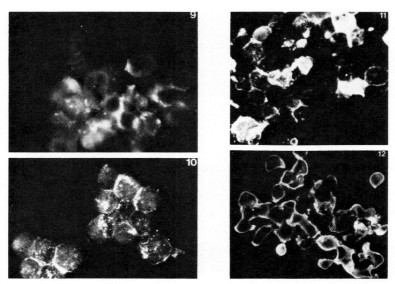

Figures 9,10: A375P cells stained with LAM BI (top) and AI (bottom). X270. Figures 11,12: A375M cells stained with LAM BI (top) and AI (bottom). X220.

REFERENCES

Barsky SH, Rao CN, Williams JE, Liotta LA (1984). Laminin molecular domains which alter metastasis in a murine model. J. Clin Invest 74:843-848.
Liotta LA (1980). New method for preparing large surfaces of intact human basement membrane for tumor invasion. Cancer Lett 11:141-152.
Liotta LA, Rao CN, Barsky SH (1983). Tumor invasion and the extracellular matrix. Lab Invest 49:636-649.
McCarthy JB, Basara ML, Palm SL, Sas DF, Furcht LT (1985). The role of cell adhesion proteins-laminin and fibronectin-in the movement of malignant and metastatic cells. Cancer Metas Rev 4:125-152.
Nicolson GL (1984). Cell surface molecules and tumor metastasis: Regulation of metastatic phenotypic diversity. Exp Cell Res 150:3-22.
Ruoslahti E (1984). Fibronectin in cell adhesion and invasion. Cancer Metas. Rev 3:43-51.
Terranova VP, Liotta LA, Russo RG, Martin GR (1982). Role of laminin in the attachment and metastasis of murine tumor cells. Cancer Res 42:2265-2269.

Progress in Developmental Biology, Part B, pages 211-214
© 1986 Alan R. Liss, Inc.

A Ca²⁺-BINDING PROTEIN AND AN ENDOGENOUS LECTIN FROM SEA URCHIN EMBRYOS.

Yasuto Tonegawa, Takeshi Doi and Takashi Suzuki

Department of Regulation Biology, Saitama University, Urawa 338, JAPAN.

INTRODUCTION

Since the discovery of cell aggregation factor from chicken embryos, lots of cell adhesion-related macromolecules have been isolated and characterized(Moscona,1979; Edelman,1983). Studies on sponge cell adhesion pointed out Ca^{2+} dependent cell adhesion mechanism, and similar mechanisms have been reported also on vertebrate embryos. On the other hand, cell-cell interaction of sugar-lectin type has been shown to play essential roles in several organisms (Barondes 1981).

Sea urchin embryos dissociate into constituent cells in $Ca^{2+}-$,Mg^{2+}-free sea water (CMF-SW) and reconstitute normal embryos by the addition of Ca^{2+}(Guidice, 1973).

In the supernatant of cell dissociation, one of the authors found a factor capable of promoting cell aggregation (Tonegawa, 1973). It was a gigantic sugar-protein complex (aggregation factor complex, AFX) and very unstable. Recently, we have isolated a Ca^{2+}-binding protein from AFX and found significant quantities of γ-carboxyglutamic acid (Gla) in it(Tonegawa, 1984). The possible role of Gla in Ca^{2+}-dependent cell adhesion will be discussed.

In addition, we isolated another cell adhesion-related macromolecule(Tonegawa and Doi, 1983). It was a hydrophobic protein with hemagglutinating activity and recognized α-mannosyl residues on a cell surface glycoprotein. The involvement of sugar-lectin type interaction in the cell adhesion will be demonstrated.

MATERIALS AND METHODS

A Japanese sea urchin, <u>Hemicentrotus pulcherrimus,</u> was used for most of the experiments and some other species were used for comparison.

<u>Isolation of Ca^{2+}binding protein.</u>   Sea urchin blastulae were washed quickly with two changes of cold CMF-SW and extracted in the same medium with gentle stirring. After 60 min, dissociated cells were collected by centrifugation and the supernatant was used as crude AFX. After concentration (Amicon PM-30) and dialysis, the extract was fractionated on DEAE-cellulose(50 mM NaCl, 50 mM Tris-acetate, pH 8.0) and cell aggregating activity was recovered in 0.5 M NaCl eluate. It was further purified on Sephalose 4B and by isoelectric focusing(pI 3).

<u>Isolation of the endogenous lectin.</u>   Acetone powder of dissociated cells was extracted with buffered saline(0.15 M NaCl, 10 mM Tris-HCl, pH 8.0) and then with the same buffer containing 1% Triton X-100. Hemagglutinating activity recovered in Triton extract, was precipitated with 40% ammonium sulfate and was fractionated on DEAE-cellulose(50 mM NaCl, 10 mM Tris-HCl, 0.1% Triton, pH 8.0). The activity was eluted by 0.15 M NaCl, and further purified on Sepharose 4B and by isoelectric focusing(pI 6.4).

The procedures for cell aggregation and Ca^{2+}-binding assay have been reported before(Tonegawa, 1973,1984).

RESULTS AND DISCUSSION

I. Ca^{2+}-BINDING PROTEIN

<u>Physicochemical properties.</u>   The active substance did not penetrate into 7.5% gel on SDS-PAGE, but it gave a single band around dye-front in 3% gel containing 8M urea. Its molecular mass was estimated on Sepharose CL-4B to be 1,500K. It was an acidic glycoprotein(pI 3) containing 2.5% neutral sugar, 5.0% amino sugar and 1.6% sialic acid.

<u>Cell aggregating actibvity.</u>   The isolated protien induced cell aggregation of dissociated cells in a similar manner as the intact AFX. Its activity was dependent on Ca^{2+} and also on pH. Cell aggregation was maximal at pH 8, decreased gradually with lowering pH and vanished below pH 4. It was readily inactivated by heat(60 C, 10 min) and trypsin.

<u>Ca^{2+}binding activity.</u>   The same protein bound ^{45}Ca^{2+} quantitatively and its dissociation constant was in the order of 10^{-4}M. The Ca^{2+}-binding was also affected by pH and showed almost identical pH profile as the cell aggregating

activity. These results suggest that the binding of Ca^{2+} to this protein constitutes an essential link in cell adhesion. In addition, relatively low affinity and characteristic pH profile suggested the involvement of Gla in this system.
Involvement of Gla in cell adhesion.   Amino acid analysis of this protein detected 0.5% of Gla, which corresponded to 39 residues per molecule. In addition, cell aggregation induced by this protein was inhibited by 0.1 mM of Cd^{2+}, which is known to block the binding of Ca^{2+} to Gla. Also, the addition of Warfarin to the culture medium of developing embryos resulted in the disorder of their cell association. Warfarin is well known antagonist of vitamine K which is needed for γ-carboxylation. These results suggest strongly that Gla-Ca^{2+} linkage constitutes an essential part of Ca^{2+}-dependent cell adhesion in sea urchin embryos.

II. ENDOGENOUS LECTIN

Physichochemical properties.   The active substance gave a single band in chloral hydrate-containing polyacrylamide gel, but separated into two upon SDS-PAGE. The apparent molecular masses were 290K and 300K. It was hydrophobic glycoprotein containing 21.6% neutral sugars and 8.1% amino sugar. The activity was destroyed with heat and trypsin.
Characterization of the lectin.   The purified substance agglutinated formalin-fixed human RBC and also horse, sheep and rabbit RBC. This hemagglutination was not inhibited by authentic neutral sugars, amino sugars, glycosaminoglycans and glycopeptides. The activity was inhibited significantly only by a glycopeptide released from sea urchin cells with trypsin. Its inhibitory activity was specifically destroyed by α-mannosidase. So, this active substance is assumed to be an endogenous lectin recognizing α-mannosyl residues on glycoprotein exposed on sea urchin cell surfaces.
Localization of the lectin.   The antibody against this lectin agglutinated dissociated cells. On sectioned embryos, immunofluorescent staining visualized the lectin to be localized on the cell membranes. These results indicate that the lectin is exposed on the cell surface in dissociated cells as well as in intact embryos.

On the other hand, the lectin aggregated formalin-fixed blalstula cells. This aggregation was reduced when cells had been treated with trypsin, and this supernatant contained a glycopeptide inhibiting the lectin activity. Accordingly, the receptor for this lectin is also exposed on the cell surfaces.

Participation of the lectin in cell association.   When
Fab fragment of the antibody was added to the embryos, it
loosened cell association and finally dissociated embryos.
Immunofluorescent staining revealed that the Fab penetrated
into the embryos and bound to whole cell surfaces. The cell-
dissociating effect of Fab was shown to be species-specific.
Also, Fab inhibited the spontaneous reaggregation of
dissociated cells, usually seen at room temperature within
several hours. These results indicate that this endogenous
lectin participates actually in the cell association of sea
urchin embryos.

As has been shown above, we have two sets of cell
adhesion-related macromolecules in sea urchin embryos.
Their relative roles in developing embryo is not yet
clarified. However, low specificity of Ca^{2+}-binding protein
with cells of other species and larger dimension of AFX
suggest that it might be mostly involved in the initial
long-range reaction among blastomeres. On the contrary,
endogenous lectin is assumed to be related to more specific
and close-range interaction, because membrane located lectin
reacts directly with membrane glycoprotein and it is highly
specific. Further reserch is in progress on the mechanism of
interaction and roles in development of these macromolecules.

REFERENCES

Barondes SH (1981). Lectins: Their multiple endogenous
    cellular functions. Ann Rev Biochem 50:207-231.
Edelman GM (1983). Cell adhesion molecules. Science 219:
    450-457.
Giudice G (1973). Reaggregation of dissociated cells of sea
    urchin embryos. Advan Morphogenesis. 8:115-158.
Moscona AA (1979). Cell aggregation. In Monroy A and Moscona
    AA (eds): "Introductory Concepts in Developmental Biology,"
    Chicago: The University of Chicago Press, pp 155-205.
Tonegawa Y (1973). Isolation and characterization of a
    particulate cell-aggregation factor from sea urchin
    embryos. Dev Growth Differ 14:337-352.
Tonegawa Y, Doi T (1983). An endogenous lectin participates
    in cell adhesion of sea urchin embryo. Proc 7th Int Symp
    Glycoconjugates 608-609.
Tonegawa Y (1984). A Ca-binding protein responsible for Ca-
    dependent cell association of sea urchin embryos. Dev
    Growth Differ 27:181-182.

Progress in Developmental Biology, Part B, pages 215–218
© 1986 Alan R. Liss, Inc.

ENERGY LOSS SPECTROSCOPIC IMAGING OF RAT AMELOBLASTS

A. Zaki, D. Eisenmann, S. Ashrafi, R. Leapman
and C. Fiori

Department of Histology, College of Dentistry,
University of Illinois at Chicago, IL 60612
(A.Z., D.E., A.S.) and Biomedical Engineering
and Instrumentation Branch, National Institutes
of Health, Bethesda, MD 20205 (R.L., C.F.)

INTRODUCTION

The overall objective of our research is to clarify
the role of the ameloblasts in controlling calcium availability at the enamel mineralization front.

To achieve this aim a model system has been developed
in which enamel mineralization is temporarily inhibited
by injecting rats with either fluoride or cobalt. The
rat incisor is utilized since all stages of amelogenesis
are present in the same tooth. A multi-method approach
has been employed to localize calcium in ameloblasts as
well as analyze the cell role in controlling calcium transport to the mineralizing enamel (Eisenmann, et al., 1982
and 1984). The methods employed included: Transmission
Electron Microscopy (TEM) and Pyroantimonate cytochemistry,
Energy-dispersive X-ray Emission Microanalysis of chemically fixed and freeze-dried specimens. The present paper
describes the additional use of a new technique of Elemental
Imaging based on Electron Energy Loss Spectroscopy (EELS)
combined with Scanning Transmission Electron Microscopy
(STEM) which we applied to rat secretory ameloblasts.
This method has an intrinsically higher resolution as
well as a higher sensitivity for low atomic number elements
which cannot be normally detected with EDS (Leapman, et al.,
1984). In EELS microanalysis we measure the characteristic
energy loss "edges" in a beam of fast electrons when inner
shell levels of atoms in the sample are excited or ionized.

Moreover, the new technique of EELS imaging produces quantitative elemental distributions with a resolution capable of distinguishing different intracellular and extracellular sites. Further digital and computer assisted processing provides direct and simultaneous visualization of several elements over the entire electron image. Calcium distribution in and around ameloblasts was investigated during normal as well as in experimentally altered enamel mineralization. We used potassium pyroantimonate (PPA) in the preparation of some specimens for analysis to help retain loosely bound calcium which otherwise might be lost during processing. Although there are limitations to pyroantimonate cytochemistry, our previous work (Eisenmann, et al., 1979) as well as that of other investigators has demonstrated that with adequate controls, this procedure is a useful probe for cellular calcium distribution (Wick and Hepler, 1982). In our investigations, PPA is used for comparative purposes and is complemented by analyses of frozen strips of the amelo-blastic layer. The former allows precipitation of calcium in specific sites while the latter gives insight into the calcium content across the cell layer without chemical fixation.

MATERIALS AND METHODS

For EELS and spectroscopic elemental imaging, samples were used from rats perfused with 2% glutaraldehyde. Mid-sagittal slices of the rat incisor were cut and post-fixed in 1% osmium tetroxide (Weber, et al., 1982). Some animals were fixed in the same manner but with the addition of 50 mM PPA to both fixatives. An additional group of rats was injected subcutaneously with either 5 mg sodium fluoride/100 g body weight or 12 mg cobalt chloride/100 g body weight, killed one hour later (fluoride injected) and 8 or 16 hours later (cobalt injected) and fixed in the same manner with or without PPA. Stained and unstained araldite-embedded thin sections less than 100 nm thick were prepared. EELS spectra were recorded at 100 KeV beam energy using a Hitachi H 700H transmission electron microscope equipped with a magnetic sector electron spec-trometer and a STEM capability. A probe current of 1 nA and a probe diameter of about 10-15 nm provided by a conventional thermal tungsten source were used in STEM analysis and imaging.

RESULTS

Spatial distribution of calcium, nitrogen and carbon was visualized during normal and temporarily inhibited enamel mineralization. Figure 1 is a TEM micrograph showing an example of the areas analyzed and imaged.

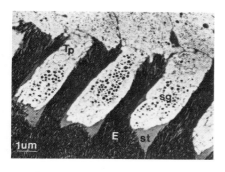

Figure 1. Tome's processes (Tp) of secretory ameloblasts from a fluoride injected specimen. Note the numerous secretory granules (sg) and the abundant stippled material (st) at the enamel surface (E).

Spectra of secretory granules with PPA deposits in unstained samples showed a strong Ca L_{23} edge at 348 eV as well as oxygen K and antimony M_{45} edges which overlap at approximately 530 eV.

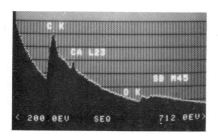

Figure 2. EELS spectrum of a secretory granule with PPA deposit, showing separate edges for calcium and antimony.

The application of STEM-EELS mapping demonstrated the presence of calcium in secretory granules (Fig. 3).

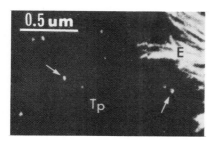

Figure 3. Ca L_{23} image of part of Tomes' process (Tp) showing calcium deposits in secretory granules (arrows). Immature enamel (E) shows calcium in its hydroxyapatite crystals.

It is believed that calcium plays a role in regulating
the extracellular release of secretion product (Douglas,
1974). Such a role is feasible in the case of the secretory
ameloblasts. In addition, since these cells are forming
a highly mineralized tissue another possible role for
calcium in their secretory granules is that of a
hydroxyapatite crystal seeding component within the organic
matrix when it is secreted by the cell.

Electron spectroscopic imaging in STEM has been demonstrated as a useful technique for the study of mineralized
tissues with an accuracy superior to that of energy dispers-
ive x-ray microanalysis.

REFERENCES

Douglas WW (1974). Involvement of calcium in exocytosis
    and the exocytosis-vesiculation sequence. Biochem Soc
    Symp 39:1-28.
Eisenmann DR, Ashrafi SH, Neiman A (1979). Calcium trans-
    port and the secretory ameloblasts. Anat Rec 193:403-422.
Eisenmann DR, Ashrafi SH, Zaki AE (1982). Multi-method
    analysis of calcium localization in the secretory amelo-
    blasts. J Dent Res 16(Sp Iss):1555-1561.
Eisenmann DR, Ashrafi SH, Zaki AE (1984). Calcium distri-
    bution in freeze-dried enamel organ tissue during normal
    and altered enamel mineralization. Calcif Tissue Int
    36:596-603.
Leapman RD, Fiori CE, Gorlen KE, Gibson CC, Swyt CR (1984).
    Combined elemental and STEM imaging under computer con-
    trol. Ultramicroscopy 12:281-292.
Weber DF, Eisenmann DR, Zaki AE (1982). A grinding method
    for producing sections of large areas of plastic embedded
    tissues. J Microscopy 127:271-176.
Wick SM, Hepler PK (1982). Selective localization of
    intracellular Ca^{2+} with potassium pyroantimonate. J
    Histochem Cytochem 30:1190-1204.

Supported in part by NIDR grant #DE05323.

Progress in Developmental Biology, Part B, pages 219-222
© 1986 Alan R. Liss, Inc.

COLOCALIZATION OF ACETYLCHOLINE RECEPTORS AND BASAL LAMINA
PROTEOGLYCAN

Diana Card Linden and Susan M. Jerian
Department of Biology, Occidental College
Los Angeles, California 90041

These experiments were done to determine the in vivo
colocalized distribution of acetylcholine receptors (AChR)
and a heparan sulfate proteoglycan (PG) in innervated and
denervated Xenopus laevis sartorius muscles, and in developing Rana catesbeiana cutaneous pectoris muscles. AChR were
visualized by fluorescence microscopy after rhodamine α-bun-
garotoxin labeling; PG was localized by a fluorescein-labeled
monoclonal antibody (2AC2, a gift from M. John Anderson).
The PG was located in the basal lamina of the muscle and was
concentrated at least fivefold in the synaptic region (Anderson & Fambrough, 1983). PG was also present in the nerve
sheath and the endothelial cells of capillaries. Experiments
using primary cell cultures of Xenopus or chick muscles have
shown that the distribution of PG was congruent with AChR
(Anderson et al, 1984; Bayne et al, 1984). The observation
that PG and AChR were present on the muscle surface in the
same areas both in vivo and in vitro led to the pursuit of
two main areas of investigation: 1) How extensive are areas
of colocalization of the AChR and PG molecules in innervated,
denervated, and immature muscles? If they are colocalized
in the presence and in the absence of the nerve, then their
synthesis and placement in the cell may be coregulated. 2)
If junctional PG is present after prolonged periods of denervation, then it may be a chemotactic agent for a regenerating
nerve (Sanes et al, 1978).

The areas of colocalization of AChR and PG were determined by measuring the areas of rhodamine and fluorescein
fluorescence from negatives projected on graph paper. The
areas were quantified using a Hipad digitizing tablet and

Bioquant software with an IBM PC microcomputer.

Colocalized molecules in innervated muscle were organized in a railroad track pattern in the postsynaptic membrane. There was perfect overlap of AChR and PG staining in the junctional folds at 98% of normal and at 96% of denervated Xenopus neuromuscular junctions. Note the similar pattern of staining in Figure 1A and 1B. Up to 9 weeks after denervation, the junctional staining pattern remained largely unchanged, however colocalized accumulations of PG and AChR appeared in membrane areas not associated with junctional folds.

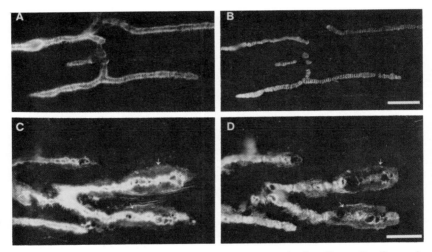

Figure 1. A. Innervated PG, B. Innervated AChR, C. 8 week denervated PG, D. 8 week denervated AChR. Scale = 20 µm.

Intrajunctional staining is defined as the staining within the synaptic area of the muscle fiber that is not associated with junctional folds (arrows in Figure 1C,D). After 5 weeks of denervation the area of intrajunctional staining increased to more than 60 times that of innervated junctions. Intrajunctional AChR/PG staining was colocalized at 97% of the denervated junctions that were studied and it made up approximately 51% of the total intrajunctional staining area. PG occurred by itself at 100% of the junctions, occupying on the average, 45% of the intrajunctional stained area. In about 65% of the denervated junctions, AChR were found in areas not colocalized with PG, these areas averaged 4% of the intrajunctional stained area. Therefore, the PG composed most of the intrajunctional staining whether it was or was not colocalized with AChR. AChR staining occurred by itself much less frequently than either PG by itself or colocalized AChR/PG. In addition, the total membrane area covered solely by AChR was a small fraction of that containing PG alone or AChR/PG.

Extrajunctional aggregations of AChR and PG were present in the denervated muscle membrane far from the nearest neuromuscular junction (Figure 2). The extrajunctional clusters were seen most frequently 5 weeks after denervation and were never observed in innervated muscle fibers. Between 56-70% of the area of each cluster was colocalized. Occasionally, a cluster was composed only of PG. Clusters containing only AChR were never seen.

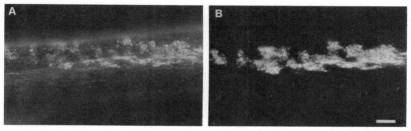

Figure 2. Extrajunctional cluster from a 4 week denervated muscle. A. PG, B. AChR. Scale = 20μm.

Development of PG and AChR was examined in muscles from Stage XVII and older bullfrog tadpoles. By Stage XVII the muscle responded to nerve stimulation, contained 30% of the adult number of muscle fibers, and had been contacted by 60% of the adult number of myelinated nerve fibers (Linden & Letinsky, 1983). As shown in Figure 3, AChR and PG were colocalized in a diffuse staining pattern. Note that one area of staining (indicated by arrows in Figure 3) had condensations of AChR/PG resembling stripes. Later in development, the AChR/PG were more frequently organized into the adult striped pattern. In developing animals, although the muscle and neuromuscular junctions were not mature, the AChR and PG were colocalized. These results are similar to those found in vitro by Anderson et al (1984).

In summary, because PG and AChR were colocalized in membranes of immature, adult, and denervated muscles they may be coregulated. After denervation, PG and colocalized AChR/PG

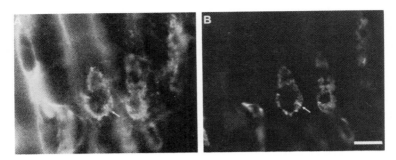

Figure 3.   Stage XVII tadpole neuromuscular junctions.
A. PG, PG outlines muscle fibers, B. AChR.   Scale = 10μm.

occurred with about equal frequency intrajunctionally.   AChR
rarely were present in clusters that did not contain PG.   This
suggests that after denervation PG precedes the placement of
AChR in the intrajunctional and extrajunctional aggregations.
Additionally, the distribution of PG and AChR seems to depend
on neural influence.

     This research was supported by grants from Muscular
Dystrophy Association and Research Corporation.   We are grateful to Gilbert Pineda for his expert technical assistance.

REFERENCES

Anderson MJ, Fambrough, DM (1983).   Aggregates of acetylcho-
    line receptors are associated with plaques of a basal lamina
    heparan sulfate proteoglycan on the surface of skeletal
    muscle fibers.   J Cell Biol 97:1396-1411.
Anderson MJ, Klier FG, Tanguay KE (1984).   Acetylcholine re-
    ceptor aggregation parallels the deposition of a basal la-
    mina proteoglycan during development of the neuromuscular
    junction.   J Cell Biol 99:1769-1784.
Bayne EK, Anderson MJ, Fambrough DM (1984).   Extracellular
    matrix organization in developing muscle: correlation with
    acetylcholine receptor aggregates. J Cell Biol 99:1486-1501.
Linden DC, Letinsky MS (1983).   Correlated nerve and muscle
    differentiation in the bullfrog cutaneous pectoris.   In
    Grinnell AD, Moody Jr WJ (eds): "Physiology of Excitable
    Cells," New York: Alan R. Liss, pp 423-433.
Sanes JR, Marshall LM, McMahan UJ (1978).   Reinnervation of
    muscle fiber basal lamina after removal of muscle fibers.
    J Cell Biol 78:176-198.

Neural Crest Cells

Progress in Developmental Biology, Part B, pages 225–228
© 1986 Alan R. Liss, Inc.

CONTROL OF NEURAL CREST CELL MIGRATORY PATHWAYS AND
DIRECTIONALITY

Carol A. Erickson and Richard P. Tucker

Department of Zoology, University of California,
Davis, California 95616

The neural crest is a population of cells that
separates from the neural epithelium and begins an
extensive migration through the embryo along precise
pathways. Our research concentrates on the factors that
control the patterns of migration of chick and amphibian
neural crest cells. Specifically we will address: 1) what
environmental elements determine the precise pathways taken
by the neural crest, 2) what directs crest cells to
disperse from the neural tube, and 3) what are the cues
that provide directionality along that pathway?

RESULTS

The role of the extracellular matrix (ECM) in
controlling neural crest migration has been studied in a
variety of species. Recently we have examined the
migratory pathways of neural crest-derived pigment cells in
two anurans, Xenopus laevis and Discoglossus pictus, and
correlated them with the distribution of glycosaminoglycans
(GAG) in the ECM of these pathways. In X. laevis, most of
the melanophores in the trunk reach the dermis by migrating
ventrally, between the neural tube and somites, and then by
migrating through the somites to reach the subectodermal
space. In D. pictus pigment cells migrate laterally over
the dorsal margin of the somites to reach the dermis. GAG
was identified in the light microscope using Alcian blue
staining and in the electron microscope using Ruthenium red
staining. The ECM at the dorsal entrance to the lateral
pathway in X. laevis and in young D. pictus (at a stage

prior to invasion by pigment cells) is filled with 25-50 nm chondroitin sulfate (CS) proteoglycan aggregates. When this ECM in X. laevis is digested in vivo with chondroitinase ABC, melanophores enter the lateral pathway. In older D. pictus embryos, the migration of pigment cells into the lateral pathway is correlated with increases in the space between the ectoderm and somites and in the number of hyaluronate (HA) microfibrils. These observations suggest that CS proteoglycan in the subectodermal ECM restricts the migration of pigment cells into the lateral pathway by limiting the amount of space for migration and possibly by acting as a less adhesive migratory substratum than the ventral pathway, and that in D. pictus HA opens spaces permitting the migration of pigment cells directly over the dorsal margin of the somites.

Such correlations between ECM and pathways taken by neural crest cells have also been observed in chick and mouse. To test directly the role of the ECM in providing a substratum for neural crest cells we have constructed artificial ECM in culture using hydrated collagen lattices to which various ECM components have been added (Turley et al., 1985). These matrices morphologically resemble their counterparts in vivo. Quail neural crest cells were cultured in such matrices in vitro and their behavior, morphology and speed of movement examined (Tucker and Erickson, 1984). From such studies the following conclusions were drawn. 1) Both collagen and fibronectin can act as preferred substrata for migration. 2) CS and CS proteoglycan increase speed of movement, but probably do so by decreasing adhesiveness and thereby producing more frequent detachment. Such a decrease in adhesiveness was also noted when crest cells were cultured on a planar substratum of CS (Erickson and Turley, 1983). In the embryo, crest cells would most likely avoid regions containing high concentrations of CS. 3) HA cannot act as a substratum for migration (see also Erickson and Turley, 1983), but in low concentrations it can open space in the matrix and consequently may stimulate movement.

From such studies we and others propose that fibronectin and collagen act as substrata for migration, whereas CS acts to inhibit migration into certain regions. Finally HA stimulates movement by opening up spaces in the matrix fibers. Other molecules, such as laminin, undoubtedly play a role in determining the pathways of

migration but these cannot be considered here. Thus the pathways of migration appear to be determined by:
1) extracellular spaces that offer pathways of least resistance, 2) an adhesive substratum on which the crest cells prefer to migrate, and 3) boundaries provided by basal laminae (Erickson, unpublished data) which are impenetrable and extracellular matrix that is relatively nonadhesive.

Although the macromolecules that define the neural crest pathways and their boundaries have been described, the forces that direct the dispersion of the neural crest away from the neural tube are not well understood. There are many mechanisms that can impose directional movement on cells. These include positive and negative chemotaxis, haptotaxis, galvanotaxis and contact inhibition. We have tested the role of each of these with a series of grafting and tissue culture experiments.

When either pigmented neural crest derivatives or freshly isolated neural crest cells are grafted into the neural crest pathway, either lateral to the somites or in the ventral pathway adjacent to the dorsal aorta, the cells in both positions disperse radially and migrate on the crest pathways toward the dorsal neural tube or along the dorsal aorta (Fig. 1). This medial or dorsal migration of the grafted cells stops when they are confronted with a stream of host crest migrating in the opposite direction. Since crest cells can move in the reverse direction along the crest migratory pathways, these experiments indicate that neither a preestablished chemotactic nor haptotactic (adhesive) gradient exists in the embryo. These results also suggest that crest cells are capable of active migration in the embryo and do not disperse primarily by passive mechanisms, since they are capable of defying these passive influences in our experiments.

The primary mechanism that can account for the dispersal of crest cells away from the neural tube is contact inhibition. We have made time-lapse films of neural crest cells in culture using high resolution, differential interference optics. Such studies unequivocally demonstrate that crest cells display contact paralysis. We are presently developing methods to film the migration of neural crest cells in the embryo during their earliest stages of migration.

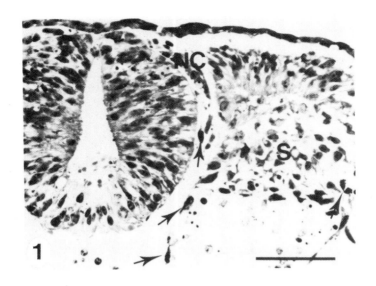

Figure 1. A cross-section of a chick embryo 18 hr after
receiving a graft in the ventral pathway at the level of
the last somite. The grafted cells (arrowheads) have moved
laterally along the dorsal aorta and dorsally along the
surface of the somite. The extent of dorsal migration of
the grafted cells coincides with the ventral distribution
of the host crest cells (NC). X470. Scale bars = 50 μm.

REFERENCES

Erickson CA, Turley EA (1983). Substrata formed by
  combinations of extracellular matrix components alter
  neural crest cell motility in vitro. J Cell Sci
  61:299-323.
Tucker RP, Erickson CA (1984). Morphology and behavior of
  quail neural crest cells in artificial three-dimensional
  extracellular matrices. Dev Biol 104:390-405.
Turley EA, Erickson CA, Tucker RP (1985). The retention
  and ultrastructural appearances of various extracellular
  matrix molecules incorporated into three-dimensional
  hydrated collagen lattices. Dev Biol 109:347-369.

Progress in Developmental Biology, Part B, pages 229–233
© 1986 Alan R. Liss, Inc.

MAPPING OF NEURAL CREST PATHWAYS IN <u>XENOPUS</u> <u>LAEVIS</u>

Danuta M. Krotoski and Marianne Bronner-Fraser

Developmental Biology Center, University of California
Irvine, California 92717

Cell migration is one of the major processes that shapes the embryo during morphogenesis. The neural crest provides a particularly suitable paradigm for studying this process since these cells migrate extensively throughout the embryo and differentiate into a wide variety of derivatives. We have chosen to use amphibians for studying neural crest migration since they offer several advantages for studying early morphogenetic events due to their external development, large size, and the availability of mutants. The migration of pigment cells in amphibians, for instance, has served as a model system for studying pattern development for many years. However, little has been known about the early migration of other neural crest cells due to the lack of suitable cell markers.

Two cell markers have recently been described in <u>Xenopus</u>: the <u>X. borealis</u> nuclear marker (Thiebaud, 1983) and lysinated fluorescein dextran, a fixable fluorescent vital dye (Gimlich and Braun, 1985). Here we have used these markers to graft labelled neural crest cells into unlabelled hosts. Grafted cells were easily identified in the unlabelled hosts and the distribution of donor neural crest cells was used as a basis of defining migratory pathways. We controlled for grafting artifacts by using both an inter- and an intra-specific marker. After examining neural crest pathways, we have investigated the relationship between fibronectin and neural crest cells as a first step in exploring the role of extracelular matrix molecules in neural crest migration.

MATERIALS AND METHODS

X. borealis embryos were obtained by natural spawnings. X. laevis eggs were fertilized in vitro. Lysinated fluorescein dextran (LFD) donors were prepared by injecting LFD into fertilized eggs prior to first cleavage. Trunk neural folds from stage 16 neurulae containing either the X. borealis nuclear marker or LFD were grafted orthotopically into stage 16-17 hosts. Larvae were allowed to develop to stages 26-32 during which time neural crest cells are actively migrating.

Borealis-laevis chimerae were fixed in Carnoy's fixative and were dehydrated and embedded in Historesin (LKB). 4 micron sections were stained in quinacrine (Thiebaud, 1983). LFD chimerae were fixed in 4% paraformaldehyde, embedded in Historesin and sectioned at 4 microns. Labelled cells were visualized by epifluorescence.

For immunofluorescence, Xenopus embryos were fixed in 4% paraformaldehyde and embedded in polyacrylamide. Embryos were frozen in liquid nitrogen and sectioned at 15u. Sections were incubated with anti-Xenopus fibronectin (kindly provided by Dr. Richard Hynes) and then visualized with a fluorescein-conjugated second antibody.

RESULTS AND DISCUSSION

Migration of Trunk Neural Crest Cells

Lysinated fluorescein dextran or Xenopus borealis labelled neural crest cells were grafted into unlabelled hosts. Labelled cells were easily distinguished from unlabelled host cells either by the freckled appearance of the borealis nuclei (Figure 1A) or the intense green fluorescence of LFD labelled cells (Figure 1B). Using both cell markers, the majority of neural crest cells were distributed in equivalent positions. The results suggested that these techniques placed neural crest cells onto normal pathways. Furthermore, when grafted chimerae were allowed to develop to stage 52, by which time neural crest cells have condensed to form recognizable derivatives, labelled cells were observed in host dorsal root ganglia, sympathetic ganglia, chromaffin cells and melanocytes. Thus labelled neural crest cells not only migrated to their appropriate locations but could also differentiate into normal structures.

Dorsoventral Distribution. The analysis of grafted chimerae indicated that neural crest cells follow at least two primary pathways and possibly one minor pathway in the Xenopus laevis trunk. This is schematically diagramed in Figure 1C. Using both cell markers, neural crest cells were seen primarily along the narrow spaces around the neural tube and the notochord, between these structures and the somites (Figure 1A-B). This we have defined as the *ventral route*. These ventrally migrating cells probably contribute to the formation of the dorsal root ganglia and the sympathetic ganglia. Some cells continue to migrate ventrally along the dorsal mesentery and beneath the flank ectoderm (Figure 1B), probably differentiating into the chromaffin cells of the adrenal medulla and skin melanocytes. Labelled neural crest cells were also located in the dorsal fin, defining a second pathway, the *dorsal route*, which populates the dorsal fin with melanocytes. Finally, a few cells of X. borealis origin appear between the dermomyotome and ectoderm which in other species has been defined as the lateral route, along which trunk melanocytes migrate. Since this lateral distribution is seen only in interspecific grafts, it points to the usefulness of performing more than one marker to control for grafting artifacts.

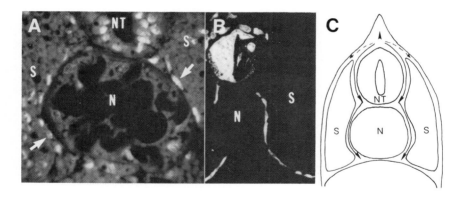

Figure 1. Sections through the trunk of grafted X. laevis embryos. A. X. borealis-laevis chimera with neural crest cells containing freckled grafted nuclei located around the notochord (500X). B. LFD chimera in which the neural crest and parts of the neural tube are labelled. Neural crest cells are localized around the notochord, along the dorsal mesentery and along the flank under the ectoderm (120X). C. Composite diagram of the distribution of labelled neural crest cells in unlabelled hosts (NT, neural tube; N, notochord; S, somite).

Anterior-Posterior Distribution. Neural crest cells in avians exhibit a periodic pattern of migration in the trunk, only moving through the anterior half of each somite. By examining grafted Xenopus chimerae in longitudinal sections, we found that neural crest cells also exhibited a metameric pattern of localization. Labelled cells were observed in the spaces between the posterior half of the somite and the neural tube or the notochord, illustrated in camera lucida tracings (Figure 2A). This periodicity was also evident in serial transverse sections. Labelled neural crest cells appeared in 25 serial sections (100u), were absent for about 20-25 (80-100u) including the intersomitic cleft, and then reappeared for another 25 sections (100u).

Distribution of Fibronectin.

Newgreen and Thiery (1980) have identified fibronectin (FN) in avian embryos during neural crest migration and have proposed that FN may play a role in avian neural crest migration. As a first step in determining whether FN affects neural crest migration in amphibians, we have examined the distribution of fibronectin along the pathways followed by neural crest cells in Xenopus.

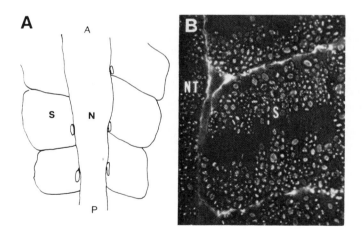

Figure 2. Longitudinal sections through the trunk of Xenopus embryos. A. Camera lucida tracing of a section through the level of the notochord. Labelled neural crest cells are located between the notochord and the posterior somite. B. Fibronectin staining of a single somite seen as fluorescence on bright field. FN fluorescence is evenly

distributed around the somite and the neural tube. (N, notochord; S, somite, NT, neural tube)

During neural crest migration, fibronectin staining is present around the neural tube, the somites, notochord, along the dorsal mesentery, under the ectoderm and in the fin. Thus in the transverse plane, FN colocalizes with neural crest cells. In longitudinal sections, FN is uniformly distributed around the neural tube, the notochord and around the entire somite (Figure 2B). Neural crest cells, however, are seen only adjacent to the posterior somite in this plane of section. This lack of correlation indicates that fibronectin cannot play the sole guiding role in neural crest migration. Rather, it may act as a permissive substrate in cooperation with other factors that pattern the anterior/posterior distribution.

CONCLUSION

Using two new cell marking techniques we have described three pathways along which neural crest cells are observed in Xenopus: a ventral route around the neural tube and notochord, a dorsal route into the fin and, in interspecific grafts, a lateral route under the ectoderm. Neural crest cells exhibit a metameric pattern of localization along the ventral route. They migrate facing the posterior portion of the somite. We have examined the distribution of fibronectin along neural crest pathway. Although FN codistributes with neural crest cells and may be permissive for migration, it does not exhibit the selective distribution that would suggest a role in the guidance of neural crest migration.

REFERENCES

Gimlich, R. and J. Braun (1985) Improved fluorescent compounds for tracing cell lineage. Dev. Biol. 109:509-514.
Newgreen, J. and J-P. Thiery (1980) Fibronectin in early avian embryos: synthesis and distribution along the migration pathways of neural crest cells. Cell Tissue Res. 211:269-291
Thiebaud, Ch.H. (1983) A reliable new cell marker in Xenopus. Dev. Biol. 98:245-249

Progress in Developmental Biology, Part B, pages 235–238

ANTIBODIES AND A SYNTHETIC PEPTIDE THAT BLOCK CELL–FIBRONECTIN
ADHESION ARREST NEURAL CREST CELL MIGRATION IN VIVO

Thomas J. Poole and Jean Paul Thiery

Department of Anatomy and Cell Biology, State
University of New York Upstate Medical Center,
Syracuse, New York 13210 and Institut d'Embry-
ologie du CNRS, 94130 Nogent–Sur–Marne, France

INTRODUCTION

The cephalic neural crest cells are the first to
segregate from the neural tube. They migrate as a large,
loosely connected mass between the ectoderm and the mesenchyme. The routes and derivatives of these cells are well
characterized. It is also clear that the local environment plays an important role in directing this migration.
In the cephalic region crest cells migrate into a large
hyaluronate-rich cell-free space bordered by fibronectin-
rich basement membranes (Newgreen and Thiery, 1980; Duband
and Thiery, 1982). Neural crest cells adhere preferentially to fibronectin (FN) in vitro (Newgreen et al.,
1982) and this adhesion can be blocked by Fab' fragments
of antibody to a 160 kilodalton fragment of fibronectin
containing the cell-binding region (Rovasio et al., 1983).
These results strongly suggest a role for exogenous fibronectin in the attachment and migration of neural crest
cells.

The demonstration of a causal role for fibronectin in
the migration of neural crest cells in vivo requires a
more direct approach. Monovalent antibodies have previously been used to show the effects of interrupting cell-
to-cell or cell-to-substrate adhesion. We have recently
introduced with others another technique for interrupting
cell to fibronectin adhesion using synthetic peptides
(Boucaut et al., 1984). The synthetic peptide with the
sequence Arg-Gly-Asp-Ser-Pro-Ala-Ser-Ser-Lys-Pro contains
the cell recognition site of the fibronectin molecule and

it is able to arrest amphibian gastrulae and inhibit
neural crest cell adhesion and migration on fibronectin
substrata in vitro. It also blocks mesencephalic neural
crest cell migration in vivo. Here we describe more fully
the effect of the injection of this peptide and the lack
of perturbation produced by several related peptides. In
addition, we describe the results of injection of monovalent antibodies to the 160 kd cell-binding fragment of
fibronectin.

MATERIALS AND METHODS

The synthetic peptides Arg-Gly-Asp-Ser-Pro-Ala-Ser-
Lys-Pro (peptide I, cell binding region), Cys-Gln-Asp-Ser-
Glu-Thr-Arg-Thr-Phe-Tyr (peptide III, collagen-binding
region) and Gly-Arg-Gly-Asp-Ser (GRGDS) were obtained from
Dr. Kenneth M. Yamada who purchased them from Peninsula
Laboratories, Inc. (Belmont, CA) and further purified them
(Yamada and Kennedy, 1984). The preparation of rabbit
antibodies against the 160 kd cell-binding fragment produced by limited chymotryptic proteolysis of chick embryo
fibroblast cellular fibronectin has been previously
described (Rovasio et al., 1983). The sera could be
diluted a thousandfold or more for visualization of fibronectin in fibroblast extracellular matrix. Fab' fragments
were prepared, lyophilized and stored at −70°C. Embryos
of 5 somites were injected at the level of the mesencephalon in the cell free space into which crest cells will
shortly thereafter begin to migrate. Approximately 2–5 nl
was injected through a window into embryos visualized by
subblastodermal Indian ink injection. The window was
covered with cellophane tape and the eggs were replaced
into a humidified incubator (37–38°C.) for an additional
8–9 hours. The embryos were cut from the yolk and fixed
in Bouin's fixative before embedding in paraffin. Sections cut at 6.5 microns were deparaffinized by brief (2
minute) exposure to toluene, passed through a graded
ethanol series to PBS and stained for 1 hour with a 1:400
dilution in 3% BSA-PBS of a 5 mg/ml solution of NC-1
directly coupled to FITC. After a 15 min PBS wash, sections were mounted in 90% glycerol in PBS supplemented
with p-phenylene diamine (1 mg/ml) to prevent bleaching
and photographed in a Leitz Orthoplan microscope.

RESULTS

The injection of peptide I into the cell-free space on one side before neural crest (NC) migration has commenced results in bilateral inhibition of NC emigration from the neural tube (Boucaut et al., 1984). This results in a "uvula-shaped" tissue profile extending into the neural tube when embryos are sectioned transversely. A portion of this tissue is stained with the monoclonal antibody NC-1 which stains neural crest after they leave the dorsal neural tube (Vincent and Thiery, 1984). Neural tube defects and inhibition of NC migration was observed in all 16 embryos injected at the level of the mesencephalon with a 10 mg/ml solution of peptide I. The collagen region decapeptide (peptide III) had no effect on mesencephalic NC emmigration at 10 mg/ml (5 cases). The pentapeptide GRGDS which blocks cell to fibronectin adhesion in vitro at a molar concentration less than half that of peptide I (Yamada and Kennedy 1984, 1985) fails to block mesencephalic NC migration in the embryo at 6.6 mg/ml (9 cases). The injection of Fab' fragments of antibodies to the 160 kd cell-binding fragment of fibronectin (50 mg/ml) blocks NC migration unilaterally. Fab' fragments of pre-immune serum (50 mg/ml) had no effect on NC emigration. There is also a unilateral defect in the dorsal aspect of the neural tube resembling that seen bilaterally with peptide I injection (Boucaut et al., 1984).

DISCUSSION

The results show that two reagents capable of blocking cell to fibronectin adhesion in vitro (e.g. Rovasio et al., 1983; Yamada and Kennedy, 1984) are able to inhibit mesencephalic NC emmigration within the embryo as well. Preliminary studies indicate that the minimal recognition sequence for in vitro cell to fibronectin adhesion (GRGDS Piershbacher et al, 1985 and Yamada and Kennedy, 1985) does not display this same capacity in vivo. Perhaps the binding requirements to block cell migration in embryos are more stringent than those for blocking cell to fibronectin adhesion in short term dish assays. The minimum sequence generating complete recognition of cell to fibronectin adhesion in vivo remains to be investigated.

ACKNOWLEDGEMENTS

T.J.P. was a fellow of the U.S.-France Exchange of Scientists Program of the NSF and CNRS and recipient of a travel grant from the Philippe Foundation of New York City. JPT was supported by grants from CNRS, INSERM and the Lique Nationale Francaise Contre le Cancer. We thank Kenneth M. Yamada for peptides and advice.

REFERENCES

Boucaut JC, Darribere T, Poole TJ, Aoyama H, Yamada KM, Thiery JP (1984). Biologically active synthetic peptides as probes of embryonic development: A competitive peptide inhibitor of fibronectin function inhibits gastrulation in amphibian embryos and neural crest cell migration in avian embryos. J Cell Biol 99:1822–1830.

Duband JL, Thiery JP (1982). Distribution of fibronectin in the early phase of avian cephalic neural crest cell migration. Devel Biol 93:308–323.

Newgreen DF, Gibbins IL, Sauter J, Wallenfels B, Wütz R (1982). Ultrastructural and tissue culture studies on the role of fibronectin, collagen and glycosaminoglycans in the migration of neural crest cells in the fowl embryo. Cell Tissue Res 221:521–549.

Newgreen DF, Thiery JP (1980). Fibronectin in early avian embryos: Synthesis and distribution along the migratory pathways of neural crest cells. Cell Tissue Res 211:269–291.

Piershbacher MD, Hayman EG, Ruoslahti (1985). The cell attachment determinant in fibronectin. J Cellular Biochem 28:115–126.

Rovasio RA, Delouvee A, Yamada KM, Timple R, Thiery JP (1983). Neural crest cell migration: Requirements for exogenous fibronectin and high cell density. J Cell Biol 96:462–473.

Yamada KM, Kennedy DW (1984). Dualistic nature of adhesive protein function: Fibronectin and its biologically active peptide fragments can autoinhibit fibronectin function. J Cell Biol 99:29–36.

Yamada KM, Kennedy DW (1985). Amino acid sequence specificities of an adhesive recognition sequence. J Cellular Biochem 28:99–104.

Progress in Developmental Biology, Part B, pages 239-242
© 1986 Alan R. Liss, Inc.

CHANGES IN THE UTILIZATION OF CELL SURFACE CARBOHYDRATES
ARE IMPLICATED IN THE ADHESION OF *XENOPUS LAEVIS* MELANO-
PHORES *IN VITRO*.

Nadine C. Milos and H. Christopher Wilson

Department of Anatomy, University of Alberta,
Edmonton, Alberta, Canada. T6G 2H7

INTRODUCTION

The migration of neural crest cells through the embryo
and their arrangement into specific types of differentiated
cellular patterns is dependent on adhesive interactions between the surfaces of the cells and their extracellular environment. One of the surface-associated components that may
be involved are carbohydrates. These molecules are good candidates for involvement in adhesive events because of their
peripheral location and structural complexity. The latter
may encode information relative to cellular adhesion and recognition via the different arrangements of saccharides present (Cook and Stoddart, 1973; Lackie, 1980; Zalik and Milos,
1985).

To investigate the role of specific cell surface saccharides, we have cultured neural crest tissue of *X. laevis*,
in vitro, on collagen-coated substrates in serum-containing
medium. Cell outgrowths develop from these explants consisting of unpigmented, migratory cells which subsequently differentiate into migratory and later, epithelial-like melanophores. The latter cells cease active cell migration (Milos
and Wilson, 1985). Cultures were washed in saline and treated
with dialyzed jack bean α-mannosidase (Sigma, 0.1 U/ml) to
remove mannose residues from the cell surface.

RESULTS AND DISCUSSION

When cells in 24 h cultures were stained with fluores-

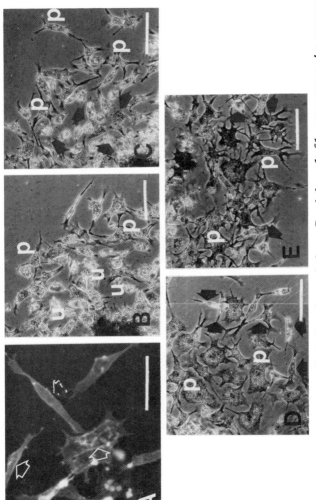

Figure 1A. 24 h culture after FITC-Con A staining. Peripheral fluorescence is present (arrows). B. 24 h culture before α-mannosidase addition, (P) pigmented and (U) unpigmented migratory cells. C. Culture in (B), T= 1 h. Unpigmented cells (arrows) are rounded compared to pigmented cells (P) which have continued to disperse. D. 24 h culture after neuraminidase addition, T= 1 h. Migratory unpigmented and pigmented cells have a normal morphology (arrows) while pigmented cells (P) are extensively spread on the substrate. E. 24 h culture after β-galactosidase addition, T= 1 h. Unpigmented cells (arrows) are migratory while pigmented cells (P) are spidery with irregular outlines. Bar= 100 μm.

cently-labelled Concanavalin A (which binds to mannose residues) peripheral fluorescence was obtained (Fig. 1A).
This indicates that mannose residues are present at the cell
surface.

The presence of α-mannosidase in the medium was correlated with the rounding up of unpigmented cells on the substrate. This effect was visible as early as 5 min after enzyme addition and was pronounced by 1 h (Fig. 1B and C). In
contrast, migratory pigmented cells (either with few melano-
somes or with heavy melanization) were unaffected and continued their migration away from the explant; epithelial-
like melanophores were also unaffected.

When media from enzyme-treated cultures were tested
using a glucose-mannose test kit (Boehringer-Mannheim), free
mannose could be detected (7.2×10^{-11} moles/cell). No free
mannose was released from substrates which received a prior
incubation in serum-containing medium before enzyme treatment. In addition, staining with fluorescently-labelled Concanavalin A was greatly reduced at the surfaces of enzyme-
treated cells. Finally, in a third series of experiments,
addition of heat-inactivated enzyme (100°C for 1 h) to cell
cultures had no effects on cellular morphology. These results
suggest that the effect of the enzyme on the cells is not due
to nonspecific effects of enzyme addition; rather, adhesion
of the unpigmented cell population is affected by the removal of mannose from the cell surface.

Other experiments have used neuraminidase and β-galactosidase (0.1 U/ml) to remove terminal sialic acid and galactose residues respectively from the cell surface. Removal of
sialic acid exposes more galactose groups. With both enzymes,
pigmented cells were more responsive than unpigmented cells.
With neuraminidase, epithelial-like melanophores became more
well spread; unpigmented and pigmented migratory cells were
not affected (Fig. 1D). With removal of galactose, pigmented
cell-substrate adhesion decreased and cells either detached
or became spidery (Fig. 1E). Unpigmented cells either detached more slowly or underwent transitory retraction before
recovery (Fig. 1E). The magnitude of the response depended on
the enzyme's lot number (from Sigma). Effects of other concentrations of these enzymes are shown in Milos and Wilson (1985).

These results suggest that X. laevis neural crest cells
developing along the pigment pathway in vitro, utilize cell

surface mannose in cell-substrate adhesion early in migration. After they begin to synthesize melanin, they increasingly rely on cell surface galactose, thus changing saccharide dependencies as they differentiate. This change may reflect a carbohydrate-involved alteration at the surfaces of melanophores early in development. Mannose (Grabel et al., 1979; Roberson and Armstrong, 1980) and galactose (Milos and Zalik, 1983) have previously been suggested to play roles in cellular adhesion in other embryonic vertebrate cells. It has been suggested that they may function in conjunction with endogenous mannose or galactose-binding proteins (lectins). Whether similar lectins are present and involved in functioning of the mannose and galactose-bearing receptors detected by us, are subjects under current investigation in our laboratory.

REFERENCES

Cook GMW, Stoddart RW (1973). "Surface Carbohydrates of the Eukaryotic Cell." New York: Academic.

Grabel LB, Rosen SD, Martin G (1979). Teratocarcinoma stem cells have a cell surface carbohydrate-binding component implicated in cell-cell adhesion. Cell 17: 477-484.

Lackie JM (1980). The structure and organization of the cell surface. In Bittar EE (ed): "Membrane Structure and Function." Vol. 1 New York: John Wiley and Sons, pp 73-102.

Milos NC, Wilson HC (1985). Cell surface carbohydrate involvement in controlling the adhesion of neural crest cells and melanophores of Xenopus laevis. Submitted.

Milos NC, Zalik SE (1983). Calcium independent adhesion of extraembryonic endoderm cells from the early chick blastoderm is inhibited by the β-D-galactoside-binding lectin and by β-galactosidase. Cell Diff'n 12: 341-347.

Roberson MM, Barondes SH (1980). Carbohydrate-binding component of amphibian embryo cell surfaces: restriction to surface regions capable of cell adhesion. PNAS 77: 3460-3463.

Zalik SE, Milos NC (1985). Endogenous lectins and cell adhesion in embryonic cells. In Browder L (ed): "Developmental Biology: A Comprehensive Synthesis." New York: Plenum, In Press.

Support: Scholarship, Establishment and Major Equipment Grants from the Alberta Heritage Foundation for Medical Research (Canada) to NCM.

Progress in Developmental Biology, Part B, pages 243–248
© 1986 Alan R. Liss, Inc.

IN VITRO DIFFERENTIATION OF QUAIL NEURAL CREST CELLS
INTO SENSORY NEURONS

Maya Sieber-Blum* and Sanjiv R. Patel

Department of Cell Biology and Anatomy,
The Johns Hopkins University School of
Medicine, Baltimore, Maryland 21205.

*)Current address: Department of Anatomy and
Cellular Biology, Medical College of Wisconsin,
Milwaukee, Wisconsin 53226.

INTRODUCTION

The neural crest is a transient tissue of the
vertebrate embryo that originates from the dorsal neural
tube. It gives rise to most neurons and to the nerve
supporting cells of the peripheral nervous system, to
endocrine cells, to melanocytes and to the cranial
mesectoderm (reviewed by Weston, 1970, 1982; Noden 1980; Le
Douarin, 1982). The mechanisms that govern neural crest
cell determination and differentiation are not fully
understood. Recent data show that neural crest cells are
already a heterogeneous population at the onset of
migration. They contain "pluripotent" cells, the progeny of
which can differentiate into both adrenergic neurons and
melanocytes, and cells that are already committed to the
melanogenic or neuronal lineages (Sieber-Blum and Cohen,
1980). Photosensitization experiments with the lipophilic
membrane probe merocyanine 540 indicated that the three
types of progenitor cells differ in the composition and/or
arrangement of their plasma membrane lipids (Sieber-Blum and
Sieber 1984). Subpopulations of neural crest cells have
also been identified with monoclonal antibodies raised
against autonomic neurons, sensory neurons, or gangliosides
(Barald, 1982; Ciment and Weston, 1983; Weston et al., 1984;
Marusich et al., 1985).

One key issue in current neural crest research is the question of the origin of the sensory and autonomic neuronal lineages. Is there a common progenitor cell, whose progeny gives rise to both sensory and autonomic neurons, or are sensory and autonomic progenitor cells already two separate populations at the onset of neural crest cell migration? Grafting experiments by Schweitzer et al. (1983) showed that young embryonic dorsal root ganglia contain cells that are capable of differentiating into autonomic neurons when injected into young host embryos, or when cultured in vitro (Xue et al., 1985). However, when autonomic ganglia were injected, no cells homed in sensory ganglia. The results indicated that in addition to sensory neuron precursors, young dorsal root ganglia also contain precursor cells capable of differentiating into autonomic neurons. In vitro clonal analysis is one way to distinguish between common progenitor cell and separate presumptive autonomic and sensory neurons. The in vitro clonal approach offers several advantages: a) Every individual progenitor cell can be accounted for, thus enabling us to distinguish between selection of a subpopulation of committed cells and induction of uncommitted cells (Sieber-Blum and Cohen, 1980). b) The effect of exogenous regulators can be described in quantitative terms (Sieber-Blum and Cohen, 1980; Sieber-Blum and Sieber, 1985). c) We may eventually be able to perform such experiments under controlled conditions in a defined culture medium (Sieber-Blum and Chokshi, 1985).

So far only three classes of differentiated cells have been identified in primary culture: pigment cells, autonomic neurons, and endocrine cells (Cohen and Konigsberg, 1975; Cohen, 1977; Greenberg and Schrier, 1977; Sieber-Blum, 1984). We here describe the differentiation of neural crest cells into a fourth cell type, sensory neuroblasts. The sensory neurons are characterized by their morphology, neurotransmitter content, cytochemical characteristics, and their sensitivity to nerve growth factor and fibronectin.

SENSORY NEUROBLAST DIFFERENTIATION IN PRIMARY NEURAL CREST CELL CULTURES

Sensory neuroblasts were identified in 5 to 7 day old primary cultures as rounded cells with straight processes of

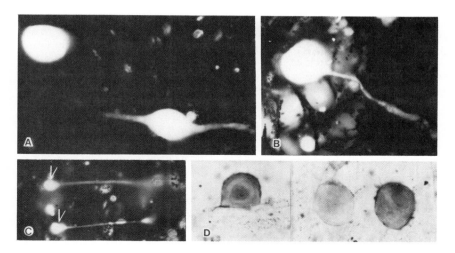

Figure 1: Neural crest cell primary cultures were prepared according to the method of Cohen and Konigsberg (1975). After 2 weeks in culture rounded, SP-like immunoreactive cells were observed. They had either no processes or were dipolar (A) or unipolar (B). Neuronal processes ended with bulb-like specializations (C). Rounded cells that stained for carbonic anhydrase were also observed in these cultures (D). Magnifications: 500 x (A-C), 232 x (D).

rather high caliber. As early as on day 7 of culture such cells reacted with antibodies against vasoactive intestinal polypeptide (VIP) or substance P (SP; Fig. 1 A,B). The peptide transmitters VIP and SP are characteristic for (although not limited to) some sensory neurons in many species (Burnstock et al., 1979). Very often we observed endings of SP-like immunoreactive neuronal processes with bulb-like swellings (Fig. 1C). Smaller, flattened multipolar cells with varicose processes of the autonomic type that stained with VIP- or SP- antibodies were also detected in the cultures. No staining was observed in control experiments where the primary antibody was preincubated overnight with 5 mM antigen (in 100 ug/ml collagen and 1 mM dithiothreitol at pH 6.5), or when the primary antibody was replaced by an irrelevant antibody.

Carbonic anhydrase is accumulated in some sensory neurons (Riley et al., 1984). When the cultures were stained for carbonic anhydrase (Hansson, 1968), we noticed darkly stained rounded cells that were similar to the VIP- or SP-like immunoreactive neurons (Fig. 1D). All other cells in the dense multilayer were negative.

Addition of fibronectin or nerve growth factor to the culture medium caused an increase in the number of SP-like immunoreactive neurons. The NGF-mediated increase in the number of SP-like immunoreactive neurons confirms earlier findings by other investigators (Kessler and Black 1980, 1981). A positive regulatory role of fibronectin on in vitro neuron differentiation was previously reported for neural crest derived adrenergic neurons (Sieber-Blum et al., 1981) and met-enkephalin- and somatostatin-like immunoreactive cells (Sieber-Blum, 1984).

The newly detected VIP- and SP-like immunoreactive neurons differentiating in quail neural crest cell cultures should prove useful for future clonal analyses of the autonomic and sensory neuronal lineages.

ACKNOWLEDGMENT

This project was supported by NIH grant HD15311 and by a grant from the Dysautonomia Foundation.

REFERENCES

Barald K F (1982). Monoclonal antibodies to embryonic neurons. In: N C Spitzer (ed) Neuronal Development, New York: Plenum Press, p 101.
Burnstock C, Hökfelt T, Gershon M D, Iversen L L, Kosterlitz H W, Szurszewski J H (eds), (1979). Non-adrenergic, non-cholinergic autonomic neurotransmission mechanisms. Neurosci Res Progr Bull 17, Boston: MIT Press.
Ciment G, Weston J A (1983). Enteric neurogenesis by neural crest-derived branchial arch mesenchymal cells. Nature (London) 305:424.
Cohen A M (1977). Independent expression of the adrenergic phenotype by neural crest in vitro. PNAS 74:2899.

Cohen A M, Konigsberg I R (1975). A clonal approach to the problem of neural crest determination. Dev Biol 46:262.

Greenberg T H, Schrier B K (1977). Development of choline acetyltransferase activity in chick cranial neural crest cells in culture. Dev Biol 61:86.

Hansson H P J (1968). Histochemical demonstration of carbonic anhydrase activity in some epithelia noted for active transport. Acta Physiol Scand 73:427.

Kessler, J A and Black, I B (1980). Nerve growth factor stimulates the development of substance P in sensory ganglia. PNAS 77:699.

Kessler J A, Black I B (1981). Nerve growth factor stimulates development of substance P in the embryonic spinal cord. Brain Res 208:135.

Le Douarin N (1982). The neural crest. Cambridge University Press, Cambridge.

Marusich M F, Pourmehr K, Weston J A (1985). Subpopulations of neural crest cells and non-neuronal dorsal root ganglion cells express a sensory neuron specific epitope. Cell Diff 16:113S.

Noden D M (1980). The migration and cytodifferentiation of cranial neural crest cells. In Pratt R M, Christiansen R L (eds): "Current Research Trends in Prenatal Craniofacial Development," New York: Elsevier North Holland, p 3.

Riley D A, Ellis S, Lang D H, Bain J L W (1984). Examination of carbonic anhydrase activities in the peripheral nervous systems of humans, Rhesus monkeys, cats and rats. In: Biology and Chemistry of the Carbonic Anhydrases. 429:408. Annals of the New York Academy of Sciences.

Schweitzer G, Ayer-LeLièvre C and Le Douarin N (1983). Restrictions of developmental capacities in the dorsal root ganglia during the course of development. Cell Diff 13:191.

Sieber-Blum M (1984). Differentiation of quail neural crest cells in vitro into somatostatin- and met-enkephalin-immunoreactive neurons. Neuropeptides 4:457.

Sieber-Blum M, Chokeshi H R (1985). In vitro proliferation and terminal differentiation of quail neural crest cells in a defined culture medium. Exp Cell Res 158:267.

Sieber-Blum M, and Cohen A M (1980). Clonal analysis of quail neural crest cells: they are pluripotent and differentiate in vitro in the absence of noncrest cells. Develop Biol 80:96.

Sieber-Blum M, Sieber F (1984). Membrane heterogeneity among early quail neural crest cells. Develop Brain Research 14:241.

248 / Sieber-Blum and Patel

Sieber-Blum M, Sieber F (1985). In vitro analysis
  of quail neural crest cell differentiation.   In
  Bottenstein J Sato G (eds)" Cell Culture in the
  Neurosciences", New York: Plenum Press, p 193.
Sieber-Blum M, Sieber F, Yamada K M (1981). Cellular
  fibronectin promotes development of quail neural crest
  cells in vitro.   Exp Cell Res 133:285.
Weston, J A (1970).   The migration and differentiation of
  neural crest cells.   Advan Morphogen 8:41.
Weston J A (1982).   Regulation of Neural Crest Cell
  Migration and Differentiation.   In Yamada K M (ed): "Cell
  Interactions and Development.   Molecular Mechanisms", New
  York: John Wiley & Sons, p 153.
Xue Z O, Smith J, Le Douarin N M (1985). Sympathetic
  precursor cells in dorsal root ganglia of the avian
  embryo.   Cell diff 16:136S.

Progress in Developmental Biology, Part B, pages 249-253
© 1986 Alan R. Liss, Inc.

SUBPOPULATIONS OF MORPHOLOGICALLY NON-NEURONAL NEURAL CREST
AND DORSAL ROOT GANGLION (DRG) CELLS EXPRESS A SENSORY
NEURON SPECIFIC EPITOPE

Michael F. Marusich, Keyvan Pourmehr, and James A.
Weston

Department of Biology, University of Oregon
Eugene, Oregon 97403

The process by which phenotypic heterogeneity is
established among cells of a developing embryo can be
characterized by studying the differentiation of neural
crest derivatives. The vertebrate neural crest contains
cells that migrate throughout the embryo and give rise to a
wide variety of cell types, including all the neurons and
support cells of the peripheral nervous system, various
endocrine and paracrine cells, pigment cells, and connective
tissues of the face and neck (Weston, 1982; Le Douarin,
1982). Although neural crest cells (NCC) are
morphologically indistinguishable at the time of migration,
the developmental status of individual cells has not been
established. Thus, the neural crest may be either a
homogeneous population of pluripotent cells that
differentiate in response to local environmental cues, or a
mixture of covertly determined subpopulations that are
capable of selective expansion or regression in response to
such cues.

In order to characterize the sequence of events that
occur during diversification of the crest cell population,
markers that can specifically identify each of the crest
derivatives are being developed (Ciment and Weston, 1982;
Barald, 1982). We recently characterized a monoclonal
antibody (McAb), designated SN1, that binds to a cell
surface epitope expressed on a subpopulation of avian
sensory neurons, and no other neurons of the peripheral or
central nervous systems (Marusich, et al., 1985a). The
proportions of SN1(+) neurons in DRG depend on axial level,
and appear to be regulated by interactions with the
periphery. Moreover, experimental alteration of peripheral

fields can change the proportion of SN1(+) neurons within individual DRG (Marusich and Weston, 1985). On the basis of their central and peripheral projections, we have tentatively designated SN1(+) neurons as cutaneous afferents.

SN1 also binds to a minor subpopulation of flattened cells in cultures of DRG, and cultures of NCC. If the SN1(+) NCC and DRG cells lacking neuronal morphology were sensory neuronal presursors, this McAb might be useful to follow the process and control of sensory neuron differentiation in vitro. Although these SN1(+) cells lack neuronal morphology, crest cells that lack neuronal morphology have been reported to exhibit a variety of other neuronal traits both in vivo and in vitro. These include neurofilament (Payette et al., 1984) and tyrosine hydroxylase (TH; Vogel and Weston, 1985) immunoreactivities, formaldehyde-induced fluorescence (Loring et al., 1982), the binding of several putatively neuron-specific McAbs (Ciment and Weston, 1982; Girdlestone and Weston, 1985), and the ability to bind nerve growth factor (NGF; P. Bernd, personal communication).

In order to establish the degree of similarity between the DRG and NCC SN1(+) flattened cells, and to determine whether they expressed other neuronal traits, we tested them with a battery of neuronal markers. DRG from 12 day embryonic quail were dissociated and cultured for 20 hours (Marusich et al., 1985a), and then double-labeled as described by Marusich et al. (1985b) with SN1 and one of the following markers: 1) E/C8, a McAb that binds to a neurofilament-associated protein (Ciment and Weston, 1982); 2) ^{125}I-NGF (courtesy of P. Bernd); or 3) HNK-1, a McAb that can be used to identify crest cells and their neural tissue derivatives (Tucker et al., 1984). The results are summarized in Table 1.

Table 1. CHARACTERISTICS OF SN1(+) DRG CELLS IN VITRO

Morphology Label	flattened	neuronal
^{125}I-NGF	(-)	(+,-)
E/ C8	(-)	(+)
HNK-1	(+)	(+)

As described by Ciment and Weston (1982), only those DRG cells that exhibited a neuronal morphology were labeled by E' C8. We also found, as previously reported by Rohrer and Barde (1982) and Zimmerman and Sutter (1983), that subpopulations of cells with both neuronal and non-neuronal morphology specifically bound ^{125}I-NGF (i.e., binding could be blocked by addition of an excess of unlabeled NGF). All of the morphologically neuronal SN1(+) cells expressed E/C8 immunoreactivity, but only a subpopulation of them also bound ^{125}I-NGF. In contrast, none of the SN1(+) flattened cells expressed E/C8 immunoreactivity or NGF binding. Finally, HNK-1 labeled all of the SN1(+) and SN1(-) morphologically neuronal cells, all of the SN1(+) flattened cells, and most of the SN1(-) flattened cells. This HNK-1 immunoreactivity is consistant with the neural crest origin of DRG neurons and support cells, and the mesodermal origin for HNK-1(-) fibroblasts. These results suggest that the SN1(+) flattened DRG cells are of neural crest origin, and that they do not express other neuronal traits.

Similar double-label experiments were performed using NCC that were cultured as described by Loring et al., (1982) for 2-7 days. In these cultures, as shown in Table 2, SN1 only labeled cells that lacked neuronal morphology. Again, E/C8 bound only to cells with neuronal morphology, and all of the SN1(+) flattened cells lacked E/C8 immunoreactivity. Similarly, although some morphologically non-neuronal crest cells specifically bound ^{125}I-NGF, and similar cells expressed TH immunoreactivity (anti-TH kindly provided by T. Joh), no SN1(+) cells were labeled with either of these markers. Finally, some, but not all, of the SN1(+) flattened cells expressed HNK-1 immunoreactivity, consistant with their identification as neural crest cells. Also consistant with this designation are our observations that SN1(+)cells never appear in cultures of ectoderm, notocord or unsegmented somitic mesoderm. The reason why only some of the SN1(+) flattened cells are HNK-1(+) is not clear.

Table 2. CHARACTERISTICS OF SN1(+) CELLS IN NCC CULTURES

Morphology	flattened
^{125}I-NGF binding	(-)
E/C8 immunoreactivity	(-)
tyrosine hydroxylase immunoreactivity	(-)
HNK-1 immunoreactivity	(+,-)

Our results indicate that the SN1(+) NCC and the SN1(+) flattened DRG cells have similar phenotypes. These SN1(+) crest and crest-derived cells do not exhibit neuronal morphology and fail to express any of the neuronal markers that we have tested. Although they do not exhibit neuronal traits, it is possible that they are neuronal precursors that fail to fully differentiate in the present in vitro conditions. Alternatively, they may be a previously unrecognized subpopulation of support cells. Since SN1 binds to a cell surface determinant, it should be possible to use it to either mark live cells or to isolate the immunoreactive cells and assess their functional properties and differentiative abilities.

ACKNOWLEDGEMENTS

This work was supported by NSF Grant PCM-8218899, NIH Grant DE-04316, NIH Postdoctoral Fellowship HD-06292 to M. M., and a grant from the National Neurofibromatosis Foundation, Inc. We would also like to thank Patti Olsen for her expert technical assistance.

REFERENCES

Barald, KF (1982). Monoclonal antibodies to embryonic neurons: Cell specific markers for chick ciliary ganglion. In Spitzer N (ed): "Neuronal Development," New York: Plenum.
Ciment G, Weston JA (1982). Early appearance in neural crest and crest-derived cells of an antigenic determinant present in avian embryos. Dev Biol 93: 355-367.
Girdlestone J, Weston JA (1985). Identification of early neuronal subpopulations in avian neural crest cell cultures. Dev Biol 109: 274-287.
Le Douarin N (1982). The Neural Crest. Cambridge Univ. Press, Cambridge.
Loring J, Glimelius B, Weston JA (1982). Extracellular matrix materials influence quail neural crest cell differentiation in vitro. Dev Biol 90: 165-174.
Marusich MF, Pourmehr K, Weston JA (1985a). Immunocytochemical identification of a subpopulation of cutaneous sensory neurons in embryonic avian dorsal root ganglia. Submitted.

Marusich MF, Pourmehr K, Weston JA (1985b). Phenotypic similarities between a subpopulation of cultured neural crest cells and a subpopulation of cultured dorsal root ganglion cells. In preparation.

Marusich MF, Weston JA (1985). The development of an identified subpopulation of avian sensory neurons is regulated by interaction with the periphery. Submitted.

Payette RF, Bennett GS, Gershon MD (1984). Neurofilament expression in vagal neural crest-derived precursors of enteric neurons. Dev Biol 105: 273-287.

Rohrer H, Barde Y-A (1982). Presence and disappearance of nerve growth factor receptors on sensory neurons in culture. Develop Biol 89: 309-315.

Tucker GC, Aoyama H, Lipinski M, Tursz T, Thiery JP (1984). Identical reactivity of monoclonal antibodies HNK-1 and NC-1: conservation in vertebrates on cells derived from the neural primordium and on some leukocytes. Cell Diff 14: 223-230.

Vogel K, Weston JA (1985). Multiple subpopulations of avian neural crest cells arising in culture. Cell Diff 16: 188s.

Weston, JA (1982). Motile and social behavior of neural crest cells. In Bellairs R, Curtis A, Dunn G (eds): "Cell Behavior," Cambridge: Cambridge Univ Press.

Zimmermann A, Sutter A (1983). β-Nerve growth factor (βNGF) receptors on glial cells. Cell-cell interaction between neurones and Schwann cells in cultures of chick sensory ganglia. EMBO J 2: 879-885.

Progress in Developmental Biology, Part B, pages 255-258
© 1986 Alan R. Liss, Inc.

ORIGIN OF THE THYMIC MYOID CELLS IN BIRDS

Harukazu Nakamura,   Kenji Watanabe,   Christiane
Ayer-Le Lievre   and Nicole Le Douarin

Department   of   Anatomy,   Hiroshima   University
School of medicine, Hiroshima 734 (H.N.), Department of   Anatomy,   Fukui   Medical   School,   Fukui
910-11 (K.W.), Japan,   Institut   d'Embryologie du
CNRS   et du College   de   France,   94130   Nogent-
sur-Marne,   France (C.A-L.L.,   N.L.D.),   Present
address   of   C.A-L.L.,   Department of   Histolgy,
Karolinska Institute, S-10401 Stockholm,   Sweden

INTRODUCTION

     In   the   vertebrate thymus,   myoid cells   which   share
common   morphological and functional characteristics   with
skelertal   muscle,   are found in the medulla   (Raviola   and
Raviola,   1967;   Ito et al.,   1969; Kao and Drachman, 1977).
The   myoid   cells have called a special   attention   because
they   are   thought to be related with   autoimmune   disease,
'myasthenia gravis' (Van de Velde and Friedman,   1970;   Kao
and Drachman,   1977;   Cooper and Tochinai, 1982). As to the
origin   of   the thymic myoid cells,   two alternative   hypotheses   have been proposed.   One is that the   myoid   cells
occur   from thymic endodermal epithelial cells (Raviola and
Raviola,   1967; Ito et al.,   1969).   The other is that myoid
cells   originate   from   surrounding   tissues   (Cooper   and
Tochinai,   1982).   As the connective tissue cells come from
the   rhombencephalic neural crest,   we thought that   thymic
myoid   cells   come   from neural crest   (Le   Lievre   and   Le
Douarin,   1975),   and we transplanted rhombencephalic quail
neural crest into a chick embryo.

MATERIALS AND METHODS

     Quail (Coturnix   coturnix   japonica) and chick (Gallus
gallus   domesticus) embryos obtained from local farms   were

incubated in a humidified atmosphere at 37° C. At 7-10 somite stages (stages 9-10 of Hamburger & Hamilton, 1951), right hand side of the neural tube at the level of myelencephalon down to the 4th somite was excised from a chick embryo and exchanged by that of a quail embryo.

The thymus from the operated embryos on the 20th day of incubation (just before hatching) was processed for electron microscopy and for immunohistochemistry. For immunohistochemistry, the thymus was first cut at 100 µm by a Microslicer (Dosaka E. M., Kyoto) in 0.1M phosphate buffer, and fixed by a fluid of a mixture of ethanol (10 volume), formalin (2 volume) and acetic acid (1 volume) for 5 minutes, and We employed the peroxidase-antiperoxidase method (Sternberger, 1979) to identify myoid cells. Anticreatine kinase antibody which reacts specifically to striated muscle was used as a primary antibody. After the slices were incubated in a H_2O_2-diaminobenzidine medium (DAB), they were dehydrated, embedded in paraffin and cut at 5 µm. Then the sections were stained with Feulgen's (1924) method which made it possible to distinguish quail and chick cells (Le Douarin, 1973).

RESULTS

It is possible to apply Feulgen's staining on the specimen which has been immunohistochemically processed. In this way we can distinguish myoid cells and quail cells at a same time. Thymic myoid cells are localized in the medulla, but were rarely found in the cortex where lymphoid cells were predominant.

Figure 1 is a micrograph from a specimen which was stained by Feulgen's method after immunohistochemical process. This figure shows a myoid cell with faint cross striations and with a quail nucleus.

Electron microscopically, a quail nucleus have a large mass of heterochromatin associated with nucleolar RNA while heterochromatic DNA is scattered in the nucleus of the chick (Le Douarin, 1973). An electron micrograph in which a myoid cell had a large mass of heterochromatin was obtained from a chimeric embryo (data not shown here).

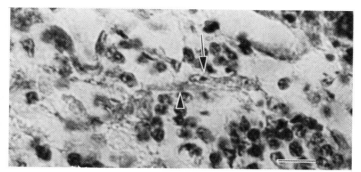

Fig. 1   Thymus from a chimeric embryo on the 20th day   of
incubation.   Note an elengated cell with faint   striations
(arrow head) and with quail nuclei (arrow).   Bar=10 μm

DISCUSSION

As   myoid cells are very small in number,   it is   very
difficult   to obtain an electron micrograph of a cell   with
both myofilaments and a quail type nuclei.   This is why we
adopted   immunohistochemistry to pursue the origin   of   the
thymic myoid cells.

The   anti-creatin kinase antibody which we used in this
experiment react specifically to the skeletal muscle cells.
In   the   thymus   this antibody   stained   only   myoid   cells
(Nakamura and Ayer-Le Lievre, 1985).

It has been proposed that the thymic myoid cells arise
from   the thymic epithelial cells because the   myoid   cells
are   connected   with   the epithelial   cells   by   desmosomes
(Raviola   and Raviola,   1967;   Ito et al.,   1969).   On the
other hand,   Cooper and Tochinai (1982) cultured the thymus
of Xenopus embryos at various stages.   They found that only
epithelial   cells differentiated in cultures of young   thy-
muses, but that myoid cells, lymphoid cells, and epithelial
cells differentiated in cultures of older embryos.   Cooper
and   Tochinai   proposed that the thymic   myoid   cells   were
extrinsic in origin.

Figure   1 of the present study clearly shows that   the
cell which has reacted to the anti-creatin kinase   antibody
in the chimeric thymus has a quail type nucleus.   Electron
microscopy also showed that the myoid cells of the chimeric

thymus had quail type nuclei (Nakamura and Ayer-Le Lievre, 1985). These results indicate that the thymic myoid cells originate from the rhombencephalic neural crest.

This study was supported by a grant 83-01-33 from NCMMD of the ministry of Health and Welfare and by Grant-in-Aid for Special Project Research from the Ministry of Education, Sciences and Culture, No. 59212011

REFERENCES

Cooper EL, Tochinai S (1982). Myasthenia gravis and thymic myoid cells. In Cooper EL, Bazier MAB (eds): "Developmental Immunology: Clinical Problems and Aging," New York: Academic Press, pp209-213

Feulgen R, Rossenbeck H (1924). Mikroskopisch-Chemisher Nachweis einer Nucleinsäure vom Typus der Thymonuclein-säure und die darauf beruhende elective Färbung von Zell-kernen der microskopischen Präparaten. Hoppe-Seyler's Z Physiol Chem 135: 203-248

Hamcurger V, Hamilton H (1951). A series of normal stages in the development of the chick embryo. J Morphol 88: 49-92

Ito T, Hoshino T, Abe K (1969). The fine structure of myoid cells in human thymus. Arch Histol Jap 30: 207-215

Kao I, Drachman DB (1977). Thymic muscle cells bear acetylcholine receptors: possible relation to myasthenia gravis. Science 195: 74-75

Le Douarin NM (1973). A biological cell labelling tenique and its use in experimental embryology. Develop Biol 30: 217-222

Le Lievre CS, Le Douarin NM (1975). Mesenchymal derivatives of the neural crest: analysis of chimeric quail and chick embryo. J Embryol Exp Morphol 34: 124-154

Nakamura H, Ayer-Le Lievre C (1985). Neural crest and thymic myoid cells. Curr Topics Develop Biol 20: in press.

Raviola E, Raviola G (1967). Striated muscle cells in the thymus of reptiles and birds: an electron microscopic study Am J Anat 121: 623-646

Sternberger LA (1979). Immunocytochemistry, 2nd ed. New York: John Wiley and Sons

Van de Velde RL, Friedman NB (1970). Thymic myoid cells and myasthenia gravis. Am J Pathol 59: 347-368

Progress in Developmental Biology, Part B, pages 259–262

REVERSAL OF A DEVELOPMENTAL RESTRICTION IN NEURAL
CREST-DERIVED DORSAL ROOT GANGLION CELLS OF AVIAN EMBRYOS BY
THE TUMOR-PROMOTING DRUG 12-O-TETRADECANOYLPHORBOL-
13-ACETATE (TPA).

Gary Ciment, Bengt Glimelius*,
Diane M. Nelson and James A. Weston
Department of Biology, University of Oregon,
Eugene, Oregon 97403; *Department of Oncology,
Akademiska Sjukhuset, Uppsala, Sweden.

INTRODUCTION

Neural crest cells (Dorris, 1938; Loring et al, 1981)
and some of the crest-derived cells of the dorsal root
ganglia (DRG) (Cowell and Weston, 1970; Nichols and Weston,
1977) of early avian embryos undergo pigmentation when
placed in a suitable tissue culture environment. DRG from
older embryos, on the other hand, do not produce such
adventitious melanocytes (Nichols and Weston, 1977). This
loss of melanogenic capability by DRG cells may be caused
either by developmental restrictions occuring after crest
cell localization, or by the programmed death of a
subpopulation of crest cells committed to melanogenesis.
One way to eliminate the latter possibility would be to
identify DRG cells with latent melanogenic properties in
ganglia from older embryos. Since TPA had been shown to
increase the incidence of pigmentation in cultures of neural
crest cells (Sieber-Blum and Sieber, 1981; c.f., Glimelius
and Weston, 1981), we tested the possibility that this drug
might reveal such latent cells.

RESULTS AND DISCUSSION

DRG from quail embryos (Coturnix coturnix japonica) of
various ages were cultured for 10 days in the absence or
presence of 0.1 uM TPA and then examined for the presence of
pigmented cells. Figure 1 shows that TPA dramatically
extends the embryonic age when pigment cells can arise in
these explant cultures. Whereas DRG from 5-day old quail
embryos or older rarely gave rise to pigmented cells when

cultured in control medium, in the presence of TPA, DRG from
embryos as old as 9 days produced pigmented cells. Phorbol
alcohol, a non-tumour promoting analog of TPA, did not
induce pigmentation in DRG cultures (not shown). These data
suggest that cells with latent melanogenic capabilities are
present in the DRG from older embryos, and that the tumour
promoting properties of TPA serve to reveal these latent
cells.

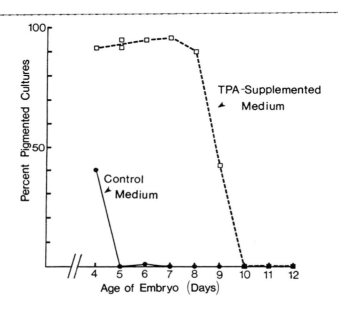

Figure 1. TPA extends the embryonic period in which pigment
cells arise in cultures of quail DRG cells. Individual DRG
were cultured in 96-wells using the medium of Loring et al.
(1981) in the absence or presence of 0.1 uM TPA. Live
cultures were examined on the tenth day under bright field
illumination and scored for the presence of pigmented cells.

Although pigmentation in culture is a convenient test
for melanogenic capability, it does not test for other
properties of avian melanocytes, such as their ability to
invade feather primordia. To determine whether
adventitious, DRG-derived pigment cells would display such
morphogenetic properties, an in vivo test of melanogenic
capability was used (Ciment and Weston, 1983). Table 1

lists the results of two such experiments and shows that
when 7-day embryonic quail DRG were cultured in the presence
of TPA for 5 days and then grafted into the right wing bud
of 4 day White Leghorn chicken embryos (an unpigmented
strain), pigmented feather follicles could be seen at the
graft site in host embryos. In contrast, when TPA was
absent from the culture medium, similar 7-day DRG grafts
failed to give rise to pigment cells. As a control in these
experiments, 4-day embryonic quail DRG were cultured in the
absence of TPA and then grafted into host chicken embryos.
As expected, since cultured 4 day embryonic quail DRG were
able to produce pigmented cells in the absence of TPA
(Fig.1), most of these grafted 4-day DRG resulted in
pigmented feathers.

Table 1. Pigmentation of Quail DRG Cells in Chimeric
Embryos*

Graft	Culture	Pigmented Feathers
4 day DRG	5 days	7/10 = 70%
7 day DRG	5 days	0/14 = 0%
7 day DRG	5 days with TPA	4/8 = 50%

*DRG were dissected from either 4-day or 7-day quail
  embryos and cultured for 5 days in the presence or
  absence of 0.1uM TPA. At the end of the culture
  period, the explants were washed and then grafted into
  the base of the right wing buds of 4-day White Leghorn
  chicken embryos in ovo. The host embryos were then
  allowed to develop normally for an additional 14 days
  and then the right wings were examined for the presence
  of pigmented feather germs.

In summary, TPA causes some DRG cells of older quail embryos to undergo metaplasia into functional melanoblasts both in culture as well as in vivo. It seems likely that TPA produces this effect by reversing a developmental restriction of melanogenesis that normally occurs between days 4 and 5 of embryogenesis in quails. It remains to be determined to what extent TPA can reverse developmental restrictions among other neural crest-derived cells. In any case, analysis of the mechanisms by which tumour promoting drugs affect developmental restrictions may shed light on the mechanisms by which stable developmental changes occur.

This work was supported by NSF grant PCM-8218899 and NIH grant DE-04316 to J.A.W.

REFERENCES

Ciment G, Weston JA (1983). Enteric neurogenesis by neural crest-derived branchial arch mesenchymal cells. Nature 305: 424-427.
Cowell LA, Weston JA (1970). An analysis of melanogenesis in cultured chick spinal ganglia. Devel. Biol. 22: 670-697.
Dorris F (1938). The production of pigment in vitro by chick neural crest. Arch. Entwicklungsmech. Organismen. 138: 323-334.
Glimelius B, Weston JA (1981). Analysis of developmentally homogeneous neural crest cell populations in vitro. II. A tumor-promoter (TPA) delays differentiation and promotes cell proliferation. Devel. Biol. 82: 95-101.
Loring J, Glimelius B, Erickson C, Weston JA (1981). Analysis of developmentally homogeneous neural crest cell populations in vitro. I. Formation, morphology, and differentiative behavior. Devel. Biol. 82: 86-94.
Nichols DH, Weston JA (1977). Melanogenesis in cultures of peripheral nervous tissue. I. The origin and prospective fate of cells giving rise to melanocytes. Devel. Biol. 60: 217-225.
Sieber-Blum M, Sieber F (1981). Tumor-promoting phorbol esters promote melanogenesis and prevent expression of the adrenergic phenotype in quail neural crest cells. Diffn. 20: 117-123.

Progress in Developmental Biology, Part B, pages 263–266
© 1986 Alan R. Liss, Inc.

EVIDENCE OF CRANIAL NEURAL CREST CONTRIBUTION TO THE
SKELETON OF THE SEA LAMPREY, PETROMYZON MARINUS.

Robert M. Langille and Brian K. Hall
Department of Biology
Dalhousie University
Halifax, Nova Scotia Canada
B3H 4J1

INTRODUCTION, MATERIALS AND METHODS

The neural crest has been implicated in the evolutionary origin of the vertebrate cranial and visceral skeleton
primarily on the basis of the significant contribution the
crest makes to these structures in higher vertebrates as
well as the phylogenetic coincidence of the crest and these
structures (Northcutt and Gans, 1983). Evidence of neural
crest involvement in the skeletons of lower vertebrates is
restricted to two studies on Lampetra spp. by Damas (1944)
and Newth (1956) which suggest crest involvement in branchial arch development, but are in conflict as to whether
other skeletal elements require neural crest contribution.

The study presented herein was undertaken to map out
more precisely, the neural crest contribution to the skeleton of lampreys, in this case Petromyzon marinus. Because
lamprey embryos are obtainable for only a few short weeks
each year, this initial study employed the simple, reproducible technique of neural crest ablation.

Lamprey, matured in the lab, were stripped of gametes.
These gametes were then mixed, fertilization occurred and
the resultant embryos grown at 18°C for 6d to reach stage
12 (Piavis, 1971) which is when the neural crest first appears. The neural crest was then removed from the embryos
with tungsten needles from one of seven 250 μm regions along
the anterior half of the neural rod (fig. 1). As the rod is
slightly raised above the rest of the embryo, crest could be
removed with little or no mesodermal damage. Controls con-

sisted of sham operations in which the surface ectoderm was
merely reflected and intact embryos. All embryos were then
incubated a further 14d at 21°C to reach stage 17 (Piavis,
1971) at which time the unoperated controls displayed significant skeletal development (fig. 2). The animals were
then processed for light microscopy by standard techniques.

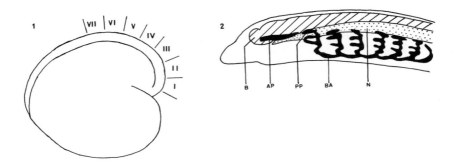

Figure 1. Diagram of a stage 12 lamprey embryo showing div--
isions I-VII of the anterior neural rod from which neural
crest was removed. Side view, anterior to the right.
Figure 2. Diagram of the skeleton of a stage 17 lamprey
embryo. (ap) anterior parachordals, (pp) posterior parachordals (ba) branchial arches, (b) brain, (n) notochord.
(Redrawn from deBeer, 1985).

RESULTS AND DISCUSSION

    Of the 50 stage 12 embryos which were operated on, 24
survived the operation, reached stage 17 and were recovered.
Deletions or reductions in skeletal elements were observed
in 11 (46%) of these animals. Five control and 10 sham operated individuals displayed no skeletal abnormalities.
Neural crest removal appeared to primarily affect elements
in two skeletal regions, the branchial arches and possibly
also the anterior parachordals (fig. 2). Other tissues examined appeared normal (dorsal ganglia and aortic arches
and related structures were not evaluated).

    Removal of neural crest from the most anterior region
(I) had no effect on skeletal elements (table 1). This is
consistent with results reported for amphibians (Chibon,
1967). Likewise the removal of neural crest from the most
posterior region (VII) had no effect, suggesting that reg-

ion VI to VII marks the transition between cranial and
trunk neural crest.

TABLE 1. The effect of neural crest ablations on the development of the branchial arches and anterior parachordals
from the 24 embryos which survived to stage 17.

	Position[a]	No. of ablations	No. deletions/ reductions	As % of Total
Branchial Arches	I-II	6	0	0%
	III-VI	13	9	70%
	VII	5	0	0%
Anterior Parachordals	I	4	0	0%
	II-V	9	4	45%
	VI-VII	11	0	0%

[a]See figure 1 for location of positions I-VII.

Defects to the branchial arch skeleton were observed
after the removal of crest cells from regions III to VI.
Such neural crest involvement in branchial arch production
confirms the findings of Damas (1944) and Newth (1956). We
have further localized the region of neural crest cells
which contribute to these structures to the posterior half
(regions III-VI) of the cranial neural crest. To pinpoint
the specific origin of each arch however, will require further data from ongoing studies.

Deletions or reductions in the anterior parachordals
occurred in 45% of those animals where the neural crest was
removed from regions II to V, which suggests the possibility of neural crest contribution to these basicranial elements. Similar assertions of crest involvement in the
production of these structures were made by Damas (1944) but
not by Newth (1956). The evidence presented in this study
(table 1) indicate that the neural crest cells which appear
to be involved in anterior parachordal development are derived in part from more anterior regions of the crest than
those which contribute to the branchial arches, which is in
keeping with the more cranial placement of the anterior
parachordals in the skeleton (fig. 2). As the absolute number of positive results in the present initial study is low,

266 / Langille and Hall

further ongoing investigation is required to firmly establish the role the neural crest plays in the production of basicranial elements in this primitive vertebrate and to confirm the regionalization of the cranial neural crest.

The evidence for neural crest contributions to the branchial arch skeleton of lampreys confirmed in this report and similar evidence in amphibians and birds (Hall, 1980) establishes a homology within this wide range of both agnathan and gnathostome vertebrates with respect to the developmental origins of the branchial arches. The evidence of possible neural crest contributions to the basicranium in lampreys requires further investigation, but if borne out, will substantiate the claims by Damas (1944) and will demonstrate a homology of cranial development within the vertebrates. Such findings would further reinforce the role of the neural crest in the evolutionary origins of the vertebrates.

REFERENCES

Chibon P (1967) Marquage nucléaire par la thymidine tritée des dérivés de la crête neurale chez l'Amphibian Urodèle Pleurodeles waltlii Michah. J. Embryol exp Morph 18: 343-358.
Damas H (1944) Recherches sur le developpment de Lampetra fluviatilis L. Contribution à l'étude de la cephalogenese des Vertebrés. Arch Biol Paris 55: 1-284.
deBeer GR (1985) "The Development of the Vertebrate Skull". Chicago: Univ Chicago Press, plate 9.
Hall BK (1980) Chondrogenesis and osteogenesis of cranial neural crest cells. In Pratt RM, Christiansen RL (eds): "Current Trends in Prenatal Craniofacial Development", New York: Elsevier/North-Holland p 48-49.
Newth DR (1956) On the neural crest of lamprey embryos. J Embryol exp Morph 4: 358-375.
Northcutt RG, Gans C (1983) The genesis of neural crest and epidermal placodes: A reinterpretation of vertebrate origins. Quart Rev Biol 58: 1-27.
Piavis GW (1971) Embryology. In Hardisty MW, Potter IC (eds): "The Biology of Lampreys", New York: Academic Press p 363-386.

Progress in Developmental Biology, Part B, pages 267–272
© 1986 Alan R. Liss, Inc.

NEURAL CREST CELL DIFFERENTIATION <u>IN VITRO</u>:   FACTORS
AFFECTING EXPRESSION OF THE ADRENERGIC PHENOTYPE

Marthe J. Howard
Division of Pharmacology M-013H
University of California, San Diego
La Jolla, CA 92095

INTRODUCTION

The neural crest is a migratory population of progenitor cells that gives rise to a remarkable and varied array
of cell types including neurons, melanocytes, and glia.
(rev. Weston, 1970; Le Douarin, 1984).   The variety of
derivatives exemplifies the developmental potential of the
neural crest and demonstrates its usefullness as a model
system in which to determine factors that might affect or
influence embryonic cell lineage decisions.

The embryonic environment may have an influence,
either by selection or induction, on the lineage followed
by a multipotent precursor. Some neural crest cells have
been shown to be at least bipotent (Cohen and Konigsberg,
1975; Bronner-Fraser et al., 1980; Sieber-Blum and Cohen,
1980) indicating that the cells may be capable of recognizing and responding to more than one developmental signal.
For example, the induction of cholinergic properties in
sympathetic neurons by non-neuronal cell derived factors
(Patterson and Chun, 1974; 1977 a,b,; Reichardt and
Patterson, 1977) suggests that the microenvironment can
affect neuronal phenotypic properties. Tissue interactions
appear to restrict, select, or promote the expression of
one phenotype over another under certain circumstances.
When presumptive cholinergic neurons are transplanted to
sites where adrenergic neurons would normally differentiate, the cholinergic precursors express adrenergic
properties; these cells differentiate according to their
new environment (Le Douarin et al., 1975). The present

investigation was undertaken to determine whether the environment can provide permissive or inductive cues that specifically influence the expression of the adrenergic phenotype by neural crest cells in tissue culture. The results demonstrate that a factor present in chick embryo extract and in medium conditioned by neural tube cells can promote the differentiation of some neural crest cells into adrenergic neurons.

METHODS

Neural crest cell cultures were prepared from Japanese quail embryos (Coturnix| coturnix| japonica) as previously described (Howard and Bronner-Fraser, 1985). The cells were grown in Eagle's Minimal Essential Medium (MEM) containing 15% horse serum and 11-day chick embryo extract at concentrations of 2%, 5%, or 10%. Neural tube, somite, or notochord cells were used to "condition" medium containing 2% embryo extract and 15% horse serum.

Catecholamine production was examined by formaldehyde-induced fluorescense (Falk et al., 1962). As a quantitative measure of adrenergic and cholinergic expression, choline acetyltransferase and dopamine-B-hydroxylase levels were measured according to the methods of Fonum et al., (1974) and Molinoff et al., (1971) respectively. Embryo extract, extract lacking in central neural elements and neural extract were prepared as previously described (Howard and Bronner-Fraser, 1985).

RESULTS

The concentration of embryo extract (EE) in the growth medium influences the differentiation of both cranial and trunk neural crest cells. In medium supplemented with either 5% or 10% EE, both adrenergic neurons and melano-cytes differentiate. In contrast, if the EE concentration is reduced to 2%, adrenergic expression is not observed but melanocytes differentiate normally. This finding suggested that EE contains some factor required for adrenergic ex-pression and that tissue culture conditions can permit the expression of one phenotype (melanocyte) while restricting the expression of another (adrenergic cells). EE prepared from chicks in which the brain and spinal cord were removed was unable to support adrenergic expression at any concentration tested (2% and 10%) indicating that central nervous system components may contribute the appropriate factor(s) present in whole EE. This idea was confirmed by using an extract of 11-day chick brain and spinal cord; adrenergic expression occurred in the presence of this extract even at a concentration of 2%. These results suggest that a factor or set of factors produced by the central nervous system is required for adrenergic expression.

Tissues encountered by migrating neural crest cells were used to condition growth medium containing 2% EE (where adrenergic expression does not take place) in order to determine if these tissues synthesize and secrete soluble substances that might affect adrenergic expression. Catecholamine containing cells were detected in cultures of cells grown in neural tube conditioned medium (NTCM) while neither somite or notochord conditioned medium was able to support expression. In all cases and regardless of the axial level of origin of the neural crest cells, melanocytes always differentiated.

These results demonstrate that chick embryo extract and NTCM contain a factor or factors required for some neural crest cells to express the adrenergic phenotype. The results do not indicate whether cells which might follow the cholinergic lineage are affected or why cells grown in low concentrations of EE are apparently restricted in their ability to express adrenergic traits. These questions were addressed in a second series of experiments.

Neural crest cells from the trunk neural fold were maintained in tissue culture for from 0 to 10 days in medium supplemented with 2% or 10% EE or NTCM. The cells were explanted without neural tube making it possible to distinguish between neural tube effects and embryo extract effects; the development of choline acetyltransferase activity (ChAT) and dopamine-B-hydroxylase (DBH) activity were measured. Both DBH and ChAT activities were detectable at 2 days in culture (Howard and Bronner-Fraser, 1985). DBH activity increased between 4 and 6 days in both 10% EE and NTCM; peak activity was at 6 days at levels of 620 ± 186 pmols/min/mg protein (values $\pm$ S.E.M.) and 171 ± 62 pmols/min/mg protein respectively. The values are not significantly different indicating that the two conditions provide analogous developmental signals. In contrast, cells grown in 2% EE develop very low levels of DBH over the 10 day period examined. Peak activity of 17 ± 4.9 pmoles/min/mg protein was reached at 6 days; this value is significantly lower than that obtained in either 10% (P<.01) EE or NTCM (P<.05); the lack of catecholamine histofluorescense in cells grown in 2% EE therefore reflects the very low levels of DBH. The pattern of development of ChAT activity under these conditions was quite different. ChAT activity developed in cells grown in both 10% and 2% EE; this result shows that ChAT and DBH are independently regulated. In cells grown in 10% EE, ChAT activity peaked at 8 days at a level of 511 ± 30 pmols/min/mg protein. Cells grown in 2% EE developed lower (250 ± 40 pmols/min/mg protein) but not significantly different levels than cells grown in 10% EE. Throughout the ten day period examined, cells grown in neural tube conditioned medium developed significantly lower levels of ChAT activity than cells grown in either 10% or 2% EE. A peak in enzyme activity was never attained and the level reached by 10 days was still significantly lower than either of the other two conditions. The neural tube conditioned medium clearly suppressed or delayed the development of choline acetyltransferase.

CONCLUSIONS

The source and concentration of EE has several effects on the development of neuronal properties IN VITRO. A factor or factors present in EE is required for some cells to follow the adrenergic lineage. The development of cholinergic traits is independently regulated and not affected by lowering the EE concentration to 2%.

The biochemical differentiation observed when cells were grown in 10% or 2% EE and NTCM demonstrate that both adrenergic and cholinergic cells develop under several conditions. In addition, the very low levels of DBH observed in cells grown in 2% EE provides a clear basis for the lack of histochemically detectable catecholamines under these growth conditions. The neural tube derived factor supports expression of the adrenergic phenotype while suppressing expression of cholinergic properties. The environmental factors that regulate or affect these neuronal phenotypes may be different; this is supported by the finding that 10% EE and NTCM have opposite effects on the development of ChAT activity while they have the same effect on the development of DBH. Melanogenesis occurred under all of the conditions examined indicating that this lineage is affected by yet another set of factors. The mechanisms responsible for the observed effects are not understood as yet. However, it is clear that cell lineage decisions can be affected by environmental conditions and it may be that the soluble factor produced by neural tube cells in tissue culture might effect some migrating neural crest cells <u>IN</u> <u>VIVO</u>.

REFERENCES

Bronner-Fraser M, Sieber-Blum M, Cohen AM (1980). Clonal analysis of the avian neural crest: Migration and maturation of mixed neural crest clones into host chicken enbryos. J. Comp. Neurol. 193:423-4321
Cohen AM, Konigsberg IR (1975). A clonal approach to the problem of neural crest determination. Dev. Biol. 46:262-280.
Falck B, Hillarp NA, Thieme G, Torp A (1962). Fluorescence of catecholamines and related compounds with formaldehyde. J. Histochem. Cytochem. 10:348-354
Fonum F (1974). A rapid radiochemical method for the determination of choline acetyltransferase. J. Neurochem. 24:407-409
Howard MJ, Bronner-Fraser M (1985). The influence of neural tube derived factors in differentiation of neural crest cells <u>IN</u> <u>VITRO</u>: Histochemical study on the appearance of adrenergic cells. J. Neurosci., in press
Howard MJ, Bronner-Fraser M (1985). Neural tube derived factors influence differentiation of neural crest cells <u>IN</u> <u>VITRO</u>: Effects on activity of neurotransmitter biosynthetic enzymes. Submitted for publication.
Le Douarin NM, Renaud D, Teillet MA, Le Douarin, G (1975). Cholinergic differentiation of presumptive adrenergic neuroblasts in interspecific chimeras after heterospecific transplantations. Proc. Natl. Acad. Sci. 72:728-732
Le Douarin NM (1982). The Neural Crest. Cambridge University Press, New York
Molinoff PB, Weinshibaum, Axelrod J (1971). A sensitive enzymatic assay for dopame-B-hydroxylase. J. Pharm. Exp. Ther. 178:425-451
Patterson DH, Chun LLY (1977a). The induction of acetylcholine synthesis in primary cultures of dissociated rat

sympathetic neurons. 1. Effects of conditioned medium. Dev. Biol. 60:473-481

Patterson DH, Chun LLY (1977b). The induction of acetyl-choline synthesis in primary cultures of dissociated rat sympathetic neurons. II. Developmental aspects. Dev. Biol. 60:473-481

Reichardt LF, Patterson DH (1977). Neurotransmitter synthesis and uptake by individual rat sympathetic neurons developing in microcultures. Nature 270:147-151

Weston JA (1970). The migration and differentiation of neural crest cells. Adv. Morphogen. 8:41-114

Development and Genetic Interventions in the Human Species

Progress in Developmental Biology, Part B, pages 275–288
© 1986 Alan R. Liss, Inc.

STATUS OF BASIC EXTERNAL HUMAN FERTILIZATION

Howard W. Jones, Jr., M.D.

The Institute for Reproductive Medicine, Department of
Obstetrics and Gynecology, Eastern Virginia Medical
School, Norfolk, Virginia 23507

My assignment for this symposium is to present the current
status of what might be referred to as basic in vitro fertilization. I
shall do this by presenting the total experience of the Norfok
program since the inception of its stimulating regime in early 1981
through March 30, 1985 (Series 1-18) supplemented by an analysis
of a subset of these data of the last year ending March 30, 1985
(Series 14-18). In addition, I shall discuss three unexplored areas of
biological knowledge, the opening up and elucidation of which seem
critical to the improved efficiency of the clinical application of
the in vitro process.

The results to be presented are those obtained by using
stimulation of the natural cycle with menopausal gonadotropin
either hMG (Pergonal, Serono) or FSH (Metrodin, Serono), singly or
in combination. The details of stimulation and monitoring have
been previously presented as have the methodology of aspiration,
oocyte culture, and the technique of transfer (Garcia et al, 1983;
Garcia et al, 1983; Jones et al, 1982; Veeck et al, 1983; Jones et al,
1983). The definition of a pregnancy has also been previously
discussed (Jones et al, 1983).

In this paper the term "pre-embryo" will be used to
designate the post-zygotic state prior to transfer.

Since the beginning of the program, 1,222 cycles of
follicular stimulation have been initiated. One thousand fifty-
seven of these cycles in 575 patients have come to laparoscopy.
Transfers of pre-embryos have occurred 776 times with
preovulatory eggs and 99 additional times with immature eggs

matured in vitro. There were 216 pregnancies with the mature eggs and an additional eight pregnancies with the immature eggs.

The gross pregnancy rate has been 224/1228 (18.3%) based on attempts of stimulation, 224/1057 (21.2%) based on laparoscopic cycles of aspiration, 224/875 (25.0%) based on transfers, and 224/595 (37.6%) based on patients.

Results in programs of in vitro fertilization are usually expressed in terms of transfers of pre-embryos from mature eggs. Thus, our pregnancy rate so expressed is 216/775, (27.8%).

If results only of the last year are considered, there were 109 pregnancies after 513 attempts at stimulation (21.2%), after 413 laparoscopies (26.4%), after 397 total transfers (27.5%) and after 371 transfers from preovulatory eggs (29.1%).

If results are considered including only those cases stimulated with the standard hMG regime supplemented by 2 ampules of FSH on days 3 and 4 of the menstrual cycle, there were 63 pregnancies after 264 attempts at stimulation (23.9 %), after 228 laparoscopies (27.6%), after 210 total transfers (30.0%), and after 197 transfers from preovulatory eggs (32.0%).

If with this stimulation regime only new patients are considered, there were 40 pregnancies after 165 attempts at stimulation (24.2 %), after 136 laparoscopies (29.4%), after 124 total transfers (32.3%), and after 116 transfers from preovulatory eggs (34.5%) (Table 1).

TABLE 1. PREGNANCIES BY EVENTS - NORFOLK

SERIES	ATTEMPTS STIMULATION %	ASPIRATIONS %	TOTAL TRANSFERS %	PREOV TRANSFERS %	PATIENTS %
1-18 4/1/81-3/30/85	224/1222(18.3)	224/1057(21.2)	224/875(25.6)	216/776(27.8)	224/595(37.6)
14-18 4/1/84-3/30/85	106/513(20.7)	106/413(25.7)	106/373(28.4)	105/351(29.9)	106/321(33.0)
14-18 HMG-FSH 4/1/84-3/30/85	63/264(23.9)	63/228(27.6)	63/210(30.0)	63/197(32.0)	63/207(30.4)
14-18 HMG-FSH-OLD 4/1/84-3/30/85	23/99(23.2)	23/92(25.0)	23/86(26.7)	23/81(28.4)	23/83(27.7)
14-18 HMG-FSH-NEW 4/1/84-3/30/85	40/165(24.2)	40/136(29.4)	40/124(32.3)	40/116(34.5)	40/136(29.4)

As of June 30, 1985, there were 126 viable births, 64 boys and 62 girls. These included 15 sets of twins and one set of triplets.

It needs to be emphasized that these are gross data without regard to diagnosis and include difficult cases with oligospermia, immunological problems, etc. A previous study analyzed the relation of diagnosis to pregnancy rate and found that the pregnancy rate was greatly influenced by the patient mix with respect to diagnosis. The worst pregnancy rate was among those with tubal disease which comprises over 80% of the material reported herein (Jones, 1985).

The cumulative pregnancy rate calculated for patients becoming pregnant shows a 54% cumulative pregnancy rate through the third attempt (Table 2). This is very similar to the natural cumulative pregnancy rate (Wilkes et al,In Press).

TABLE 2. CUMULATIVE PREGNANCY RATE BY TRY
NORFOLK (SERIES 1-18)

TRY	PTS	PREG	PREG RATE %	CUM RATE %
1	575	115	20	20
2	255	50	20	36
3	117	33	28	54
4	56	13	23	65
5	26	4	15	70
6	13	3	23	77
7	8	4	50	88
8	5	0	0	88
9	2	2	100	100

The pregnancy rate by number of pre-embryos transferred shows the importance of transfers up to four but indicates that transfers above three are of doubtful value. The improvement seen in the pregnancy rate in Series 14-18 as compared to the total material is apparently explained entirely by the enhanced ability to achieve multiple transfers during the last year (Table 3).

The risk of multiple pregnancies with multiple transfers is a point of concern. For this analysis Series 18 necessarily had to be excluded because the multiple pregnancy status could not yet be determined in this recent group. Furthermore, only pregnancies continuing beyond eight weeks are informative for this purpose, since the data are based on the ultrasonographic status at eight weeks or thereafter. With the transfer of two pre-embryos, the risk of twins in our material is 4.3% based on transfers and 18.2%

TABLE 3. PREGNANCIES BY CONCEPTI TRANSFERRED - NORFOLK

CONCEPTI TRANSFERRED	SERIES 1-18 776 TRANSFERS				SERIES 14-18 351 TRANSFERS			
	# TR	# PREG	% CYCLES TR	% PREG	# TR	# PREG	% CYCLES TR	% PREG
1	309	64	39.8	20.7	90	18	25.6	20.0
2	263	78	33.9	29.7	116	36	33.0	31.0
3	99	39	12.8	39.4	63	23	17.9	36.5
4	59	18	7.6	30.5	44	13	12.5	29.5
⁵5	46	17	5.9	40.0	38	15	10.8	39.5

based on pregnancies. The risk increases somewhat with the transfer of three pre-embryos but does not seem to rise appreciably above that (Table 4.).

TABLE 4-A. MULTIPLE PREGNANCIES BY CONCEPTI TRANSFERRED. NORFOLK (SERIES 1-17) 671 TRANSFERS

# CONCEPTI TR	# TR	# PREG (>8 WKS)	#* MULTIPLE PREG (>8 WKS)	% PREG (>8 WKS)	% MULTIPLE PREG/PG (>8 WKS)	% MULTIPLE PREG/TR (>8 WKS)
1	282	46	-	16.3	-	-
2	232	55	10	23.7	18.2	4.3
3	79	29	6	36.7	20.7	7.6
4	45	11	5	24.4	45.5	11.1
⁵5	33	11	4	33.3	36.4	12.1

* = 4/25 (16%) SACS DISAPPEARED

TABLE 4-B. MULTIPLE PREGNANCIES BY CONCEPTI TRANSFERRED
NORFOLK (SERIES 14-17) 189 TRANSFERS

# CONCEPTI TR	# TR	# PREG (>8 WKS)	#O MULTIPLE PREG (>8 WKS)	% PREG (>8 WKS)	% MULTIPLE PREG/PG (>8 WKS)	% MULTIPLE PREG/TR (>8 WKS)
1	52	5	-	9.6	-	-
2	64	18	3	28.1	16.6	4.7
3	28	9	4	32.1	44.4	14.3
4	22	6	3	27.3	50.0	13.6
≥5	23	9	4	39.1	44.4	17.4

O = 0/14 (0%) SACS DISAPPEARED

The data from Series 1-17 can also be used to calculate the preclinical abortion rate. Overall, it was 17.8% and varied little with the number of concepti transferred (Table 5). The clinical abortion rate is about 10% overall.

TABLE 5. CONTINUING PREGNANCY RATE BY
CONCEPTI TRANSFERRED
NORFOLK (SERIES 1-17)

CONCEPTI TR	# TR	# PREG	# PREG >8 WKS	% CONTINUING PREG
1	282	56	46	82.2
2	232	71	55	77.5
3	79	30	29	96.7
4	45	14	11	78.6
≥5	33	14	11	78.6
TOTAL	671	185	152	82.2

THREE AREAS UNEXPLORED IN DEVELOPMENTAL BIOLOGY

At the present state of knowledge, an improvement in the clinical pregnancy rate would seem to depend on our ability to accomplish several goals, three of which singly or in combination seem of special importance. To achieve each of these three goals requires a further understanding of the pertinent basic biological mechanisms in question. I shall attempt to point out the special significance of these three unknown areas for programs of in vitro fertilization and to point out some observations from the in vitro experience which must be taken into account in designing a methodology to overcome our ignorance: indeed, which might be of help in suggesting an avenue of approach to that end.

The three special goals are:

1.   To achieve the ability consistently to recruit more mature oocytes.

2.   To achieve the ability totally to mature in vitro oocytes harvested while immature.

3.   To achieve the ability to identify while in vitro the pregnancy potential of a given pre-embryo.

THE ABILITY TO CONSISTENLY TO RECRUIT MORE MATURE OOCYTES

The pregnancy rate is clearly influenced by the maturation of the egg at harvest. In earlier work, maturity was based largely on the status of the cumulus. Thus, eggs were classified as mature or immature (Veeck et al, 1983). The mature eggs were fertilized after no more than six hours of preincubation, whereas the immature eggs were fertilized after germinal vesicle breakdown and ejection of the polar body by preincubation over a span of up to 36 hours. With the transfer of a single fertilized mature egg, the pregnancy rate was 20.7% (Table 3), but with the transfer of a single immature egg the rate was 4/52 (8.7%).

It is therefore clear that the ability to recruit an adequate number of preovulatory eggs to assure the transfer of pre-embryos from a mature egg is important for success.

The fact that it is possible to recruit more than a single mature egg with stimulation indicates that it is possible to some extent with stimulation to override the normal process which selects a single dominant egg.

However, it seems possible only minimally to influence the maturational status of the eggs at harvest by the exogenous use of gonadotropins, be they FSH alone or in combination with LH. Thus, at the time eggs are collected, there seems to be a spectrum of maturational status. For example, during Series 14-18 (April 1, 1984-March 30, 1985) among the 413 cases coming to laparoscopy, the average number of eggs collected per cycle was 6.1, of which 2.85 were preovulatory and 2.1 were immature; the remaining were being atretic. For the 373 transfer cycles, an average of 3.37 pre-embryos were transferred.

According to Ross, it takes about 85 days, i.e. about the span of three menstrual cycles, for a primary follicle to mature to ovulation (Ross, 1974). Such follicles seem to respond to endogenous or exogenous gonadotropins only during the last 14 to about 20 days of their maturational process. It is unknown whether gonadotropins are required for the pre-gonadotropin sensitivity maturational process. However, even if gonadotropins are required—and they are certainly available to the follicle—the follicle clearly must acquire sensitivity through an additional mechanism.

The follicles seem to acquire sensitivity to gonadotropins seriatim. If this were not so, they would all respond simultaneously with the use of exogenous gonadotropins. Indeed, the serial acquisition of gonadotropin sensitivity is consistent with information available about the selection of the dominant follicle.

There are two observations from in vitro fertilization which bear on the question of the acquisition of gonadotropin sensitivity. It is possible to recruit essentially the same number of eggs of comparable maturational status from patients who have only one ovary as from patients who have two. Furthermore, the pregnancy rate is comparable (Jones, 1985). These data would seem to suggest that there is flexibility in the acquisition of gonadotropin sensitivity. The second observation concerns the distribution throughout the ovary or ovaries of responding follicles. The distribution is clearly random. For example, one never observes all responding follicles localized in one pole of one ovary. It is true, however, that one ovary sometimes seems to respond better than the other. These observations would seem to indicate that there is intraovarian follicular communication with respect to the acquisition of gonadotropin sensitivity.

Here our information on the acquisition of gonadotropin sensitivity stops. We badly need help in elucidating the mechanism of the acquisition of gonadotropin sensitivity in order to be able to modify it to allow the synchronization of oocyte maturation at recruitment.

THE ABILITY TOTALLY TO MATURE IN VITRO EGGS HARVESTED WHILE IMMATURE

It has been noted that immature eggs do not eventuate in pregnancies at the same rate as mature eggs.

As mentioned in the previous section, our original work on the maturational state of the egg was based on microscopic observation of the cumulus. This is not always reliable. For example, it is possible to have a very mature expanded cumulus containing an egg with a germinal vesicle.

It has been possible to refine the definition of the maturational stage of the egg at aspiration by observing directly in most cases the state of nuclear maturation at aspiration as will be noted.

The fallout due to immaturity occurs at three recognizable levels. For fertilization, cleavage, and viability the egg is best fertilized at meiosis II (Zenzes et al, 1985). The first fallout occurs in eggs harvested in the germinal vesicle stage, since only 86.5% will exhibit nuclear maturation to meiosis II. Thus, only 86.5% of germinal vesicle eggs are available for insemination in contrast to 100% of preovulatory eggs. At a second level, of germinal vesicle eggs matured to meiosis II in vitro, 69% fertilize and cleave in contrast to 76% of eggs which are mature at harvest (Veeck et al, 1983). At a third level, when immature eggs matured in vitro are fertilized and cleave, the pregnancy rate is approximately half of that achievable by the fertilization of eggs which are preovulatory when harvested, as has been previously noted.

These data indicate that nuclear maturation per se is an inadequate and inexact index of pregnancy potential. To account for the variable biological behavior of eggs which seem to be in the same state of nuclear maturation, it is sometimes said that the difficulty has to do with cytoplasmic maturation, although the details of this latter biological phenomenon are only incompletely described.

It would be of tremendous help to understand the factors which control total oocyte maturation in order to be able to control it in vitro and raise the pregnancy potential of immaturely harvested eggs to at least that of eggs harvested when in meiosis II.

THE ABILITIY TO EVALUATE THE PREGNANCY POTENTIAL OF A PRE-EMBRYO

Even eggs which seem to be at an optimum stage of nuclear maturation for fertilization at harvest and which do cleave at a normal rate have only one chance in five of producing a pregnancy.

With the transfer of multiple pre-embryos derived from preovulatory eggs at harvest in the same environment, there is a progressive diminution in the potential for pregnancy. This may be seen if one compares the theoretical expectancy of single and multiple pregnancies on the assumption that all fertilized eggs are equal with the actual experience (Jones et al, 1984).

This diminution in pre-embryo quality with multiple pre-embryos is further suggested by the flattening of the rise of the rate of pregnancy transfers above three.

This variable pregnancy potential observed by programs of in vitro fertilization is consistent with the same tendency observed by grosser methods in normal reproduction. For example, Edmonds et al observed that the expectancy of a pregnancy which will carry to term in any one cycle of exposure is no more than 23% (Edmonds et al, 1982). A possible explanation for this reproductive inefficiency observed in natural reproduction lies in the possible variation and quality of the singly ovulated egg in the normal menstrual cycle.

In harvesting pre-embryos by irrigation of the uterus after natural fertilization, Bustillo found that many had degenerated, and pregnancies could be obtained only from those which had developed to the blastocyst stage. One possible explanation for this observation is a variation in oocyte and/or pre-embryo quality (Bustillo et al, 1984).

In the above discussion, pre-embryo quality has been related to oocyte quality. This is to oversimplify the matter. There is reason to believe that there is considerable variability in quality among sperm. In semen considered normal, up to one-half of the sperm may be grossly deformed—bent heads, pin heads, etc. Furthermore, if 40% or more of normally formed sperm are actively motile, normalacy is considered to exist. In addition, the chromosomes of normally formed sperm have been found to be grossly abnormal in a small percent of cases (Martin et al, 1983).

Thus, the variable quality of the pre-embryo is surely the result of variability of male and female gametes.

However, there may also be a third and perhaps a most important variable. It is, of course, well-known that there is genetic heterogeneity among male and female gametes. What is not known is whether there is a zygotic requirement for minimum gametic genetic compatibility, if not actual homogeneity for pre-embryo viability.

Thus, oocyte A might well form a viable pre-embryo with spermatocyte Y, but a non-viable one with spermatocyte Z. On the other hand, oocyte B might be viable with spermatocyte Z, but not viable with Y.

Indeed, the concept of viability by genetic compatibility may also be operational at the gametic level during the prophase of meiosis I and may account in some measure—and perhaps in large measure—for the very high rejection rate of oocytes and spermatocytes during the maturational process.

To take this speculation one step further, it is possible that the concept of genetic compatibility at the gametic and zygotic level is related to the evolutionary process. There are very few data on the gametic or zygotic rejection rate by species.

An understanding of these matters, including an identification of viability at the pre-embryo stage prior to transfer, would be of tremendous practical application for programs of in vitro fertilization. The dilemma is not knowing the optimum number of pre-embryos to transfer, as there is no abilitiy to estimate their individual viability. It appears that the pregnancy rate is not greatly increased by transfer above three, but which three does one transfer? If three are selected at random, there is a chance that those rejected are in fact the best.

To transfer all risks the obstetrical and social misfortuntes associated with multiple births, especially of triplets and above.

Unfortunately, preservation of untransferred pre-embryos, specifically cryopreservation of pre-embryos as it now exists, is not the answer to this problem, as many pre-embryos are destroyed in the process.

What is needed at the practical level is a method other than microscopy to determine pre-embryo viability.

There is a possible clue from the in vitro experience.

An increased value of serum progesterone (P) soon after transfer has been a constant observation on conception cycles as compared to non-conception cycles in the data at Norfolk (Jones et al, 1984). Other investigators, however, have not observed this (Edwards and Steptoe, 1983). Nevertheless, published data from several other programs of in vitro fertilization have confirmed this (Dlugi et al, 1984; Gronow et al, 1985). Furthermore, data from natural conception cycles are in agreement (Rodgers and Oshea, 1982).

While the possibility exists that pregnancies occur preferentially in cycles with P values exceeding values in non-conception cycles, an alternative interpretation of the data is consistent with the notion that the conceptus which is going to survive emits a signal which promptly results in extra progesterone production.

The nature of such a putative signal is completely unknown. However, the concept of an early signal may have relevance to the renewed interest in the diverse origin of the two cells which comprise a mature corpus luteum.

The data are not inconsistent with the concept that the theca lutein cells which account for the augmentation of serum P in the conception cycles and for the rescue of the corpus luteum of pregnancy (Alila, 1983).

The National Institutes of Health have recently recognized this need by inviting grant requests for a study of this problem.

Developmental biologists can be of great assistance in pursuing this and other leads.

FURTHER CONSIDERATIONS

This discussion of these three areas of unexplored regions in developmental biology is by no means to imply that advances cannot be made in other areas. We need to know more about the optimum conditions for culture in the human - it is difficult to experiment in this area. We need to know more about the optimum time for transfer; i.e., what is the width of the transfer window? would we do better by waiting to morula or blastocyst? I suspect so, but at what cost in the percent of patients who would come to transfer? We need to know more about implantation and the mechanics of transfer. What is the explanation for the troublesome ectopic pregnancy rate which seems to plague some programs of in vitro fertilization? There are other areas of importance which have not been mentioned.

The selection of the three areas for emphasis is an expression of the bias of this observer that the principal inefficiency of in vitro fertilization is related to the quality of the pre-embryo and that this quality is in large measure an expression of the innate inefficiency of human reproduction. While improvements in in vitro fertilization will stem from an understanding of the ancillary points just mentioned and others, it is my current belief that the greatest improvement will come from a better understanding of the cause for variation in embryo quality.

There is a final point. The three unexplored areas of biology address critical issues in reproductive biology. A further understanding of these areas might well lead to an enhanced and easily applicable ability to suppress the reproductive process when desired. An ability and will to control reproduction will preserve and enhance our standard of living and therefore contribute to the preservation of peace and tranquility for the macrocosmos which is our general society. At the same time, further understanding will provide fulfillment for many couples plagued with infertility and so contribute to the stability of society by the enhancement of the individual family.

REFERENCES

Alila HW (1983). Origin of different cell types in the bovine corpus luteum as characterized by specific monoclonal antibodies. Biol of Reprod 28:Suppl#1.

Bustillo M, Buster JE, Cohen SW, et al (1984). Transfer as a treatment in infertile women. JAMA 251:1171.

Dlugi AM, Laufer N, DeCherney AH, et al (1984). The periovulatory and luteal phase of conception cycles following in vitro fertilization and embryo transfer. Fertil Steril 41:530.

Edmonds DK, Lindsay KS, Miller JF, Williamson E, Wood PJ (1982). Early embryonic mortality in women. Fertil Steril 38:447.

Edwards RG, Steptoe Pc (1983). Current status of in vitro fertilization and implantation of human embryos. Lancet 2:2165.

Garcia JE, Jones GS, Acosta, AA, Wright GL (1983). Hmg/hcg follicle maturation for oocyte aspiration: Phase I, 1981. Fertil Steril 39:167

Garcia JE, Jones GS, Acosta AA, Wright GL (1983). Hmg/hcg follicle maturation for oocyte aspiration: Phase III, 1982. Fertil Steril 39:194.

Gronow MJ, Martin MJ, Hay D, Moro D, Brown, JB (1985) The Luteal Phase often Hyperstimulative for In Vitro Fertilization. In In Vitro Fertilization & Embryo Transfer, p 391, New York Academy of Science, New York

Jones HW, Jr Acosta AA, Garcia JE(1982). A technique for the aspiration of oocytes from human ovarian follicles. Fertil Steril 37:26.

Jones, Jr Acosta AA, Garcia JE, Sandow BA, Veek LL (1983). On the transfer of concepti from oocytes fertilized in vitro. Fertil Steril 39:241.

Jones HW, Jr, Acosta AA, Anderws, MC, Garcia, JE, Jones GS, Mantzavinos T, McDowell J, Sandow BA, Beeck LL, Whibley TW, Wilkes CA, Wright GL (1983). What is a pregnancy? A question from programs of in vitro fertilization. Fertil Steril 40:728.

Jones HW, Jr, Acosta AA, Andrews C, Garcia JE, Jones GS, Mayer J, McDowell JS, Rosenwaks Z, Sandow BA, Veek LL, Wilkes CA (1984). Three years of in vitro fertilization at Norfolk. Fertil Steril 42:826.

Jones HW, Jr (1985). The selection of patients for in vitro fertilization. Proceedings of the twelth study groups of the Royal College of Obstetricians and Gynecologists, London.

Martin RH, Balkan W, Burns K, Rademaker AW, Lin CC, Rudd NL (1983). The chromosome constitution of 1000 human spermatozoa. Hum Genet 63:305.

Rodgers RJ, Oshea JD (1982). Purification, morphology, and progesterone production and content of three cell types isolated from the corpus luteum of the sheep. Aust J Biol Sci 35:441.

Ross GT (1974). Gonadotropins and prenatral follicular maturation in women. Fert Steril 25:522.

Veeck LL, Wrotham JW, Witmyer J, Jones HW, Jr (1983). Maturation and fertilization of morphologically immature human oocytes in a program of in vitro fertilization. Fertil Steril 39:594.

Wilkes, CA, Rosenwaks Z, Jones D, Jones HW, Jr. Pregnancy related to infertility diagnosis, number of attempts and age in a program of in vitro fertilization. Obstetrics and Gynecology (accepted for publication).

Zenzes, MT, Belkien L, Bordt J, Kan I, Schneider HPG, Nieschlag E (1985). Cytologic Investigation of human IVF Failure. Fertil Steril 43:883.

Progress in Developmental Biology, Part B, pages 289–298
© 1986 Alan R. Liss, Inc.

CLINICAL IMPLICATIONS OF THE USE OF FREEZE THAW AND DONOR
OOCYTE EMBRYOS

C. Wood, CBE, MBBS, FRCS, FRCOG, FRACOG; B.
Downing, MRCOG, FRACOG; J. Leeton, FRCOG, FRACS;
J.M. Talbot, FRCOG, FRACOG; A. Trounson, PhD.
Dept. of Obstetrics & Gynaecology, Monash
University, Queen Victoria Medical Centre, 172
Lonsdale Street, Melbourne, Victoria 3000.

Freeze thawing of human embryos was first developed in
Melbourne by Tuounson and Mohr as a result of a decision
made by the Queen Victoria Medical Centre Ethics
Committee.[1,2] In several patients undergoing the in vitro
fertilization (IVF) treatment embryos could not be transferred into the uterus owing to difficulties in passing the
catheter containing the embryos through the cervical canal.
The Ethics Committee was asked whether in cases of difficulty in human embryo transfer the freeze thaw technique
could be developed so that embryos could be stored until
the conditions for transfer were improved. Trounson had
previously been successful in freezing and thawing cattle
embryos and obtaining live healthy offspring. Difficulty
of embryo transfer (ET) occurs in about 1% of cases as a
result of a narrow or abnormal cervical canal. The rare
occurrence of uterine bleeding or acute illness are contra-
indications to ET, and freeze thawing of embryos would
again be useful.

As regimes for stimulating the production of more than
one oocyte improved it became commonplace for three of more
oocytes to be collected in a treatment cycle, so the
potential to develop a large number of embryos occurred.
Before the advent of embryo freezing it was common
practice, both in our own and many other IVF centres, to
transfer more than three embryos. This led to the production of twins in about 20% of pregnancies, triplets in
about 5% and quadruplets on one occasion.[3] Such multiple
pregnancies may not be acceptable to patients and also are
associated with a higher peri-natal mortality and
morbidity. Thus a second reason for freezing embryos
became apparent. If more than three embryos are developed

then the excess could be frozen and used to attempt to achieve conception at a subsequent date. This would occur within a month or two, should the first group of embryos not result in a pregnancy, or in a year or two should pregnancy occur. The risk of multiple pregnancies was reduced and the number of general anaesthetics and laparoscopies a woman might need to achieve pregnancy also were reduced.

Patients select themselves for freeze-thawing of embryos. More than three embryos are developed in about one in four of IVF treatment cycles, and these excess embryos are frozen. Very occasionally a patient does not wish to have embryos frozen and in this instance the number of oocytes fertilized is restricted to three. Only two of every three embryos (197/314) survive the freeze thaw process. Even among the embryos that survive some of the cells may be damaged.[2] Survival is defined as at least half the number of cells remaining intact after thawing. Pregnancy has resulted from embryos where up to half the cells have been damaged. Of 197 embryos transferred 14 pregnancies, 7%, have resulted, there being seven births including one set of twins. One of the patients had an IVF baby following immediate embryo transfer and is again pregnant following the transfer of the excess embryos stored at the time of the first IVF treatment.

The procedure of freeze thawing involves the use of a chemical preservant DMSO (dimethylsulphoxide) and a slow cooling and freezing process which takes several hours.[2] The embryos are stored in liquid nitrogen at -196°C and special precautions are taken against electrical failure of the unit and also to secure the embryos against interference or theft.

The facility for freeze thawing is explained to patients several months before IVF treatment. If patients have more than three embryos, the excess are frozen. If couples do not wish to have embryos frozen then they have to restrict the number of oocytes fertilized to three, as excess embryos cannot be discarded or used for research at the present time. Most couples prefer to have three embryos transferred immediately although occasionally couples choose two, freezing any excess.

Only about one in four patients have more than three embryos. Because two of every three embryos survive the freeze thaw process and because seven per cent of embryos transferred result in pregnancy,[4] freeze thawing only contributes a small amount to the overall efficiency of IVF. For those patients having embryos frozen the increase in pregnancy rate per laparoscopy is significant, about 5 - 6%. Freeze thawing has an important role in reducing some of the ethical problems associated with IVF and reducing the risk of twins and the number of treatment cycles that some patients might otherwise require.

If patients wish embryos to be frozen they sign a consent form prior to treatment in the IVF cycle. Subsequently, if more than three embryos are developed which require freezing the couples sign a second consent form. This deals with the problem of disposal of unwanted embryos should the couple die, divorce or change their minds about wishing to become pregnant. The majority of couples that sign this form have stated that they wish unwanted embryos to be given to another infertile couple.[5] Only a minority desire unwanted embryos to be used for research or to be disposed of by thawing. The need for predetermining the fate of unwanted embryos was emphasised by the uncertain fate of the Rios' frozen embryos after the parents tragically died in an aeroplane accident.[6] Legislation, in the form of an Infertility Bill, concerning freeze thawing of embryos was passed by the Victorian parliament at the end of 1984.[7] This is the first law controlling such procedures, although the law has not yet been enacted. In other Staes legislation concerning freeze-thawing is being prepared or under consideration. It is also possible that a report by the Asche Commitee on Reproductive Technology to the Family Court of Australia will result in Federal regulations or legislation.

The Infertility Bill also requests review of all frozen embryos after a storage period of five years. At this time the couple may decide whether they wish the embryos to be transferred or whether they can be donated or otherwise disposed of. Because most couples have frozen embryos transferred either within one or two months of the failed fresh embryo transfer, or within two years of completion of a pregnancy following the fresh embryo transfer, the IVF team will counsel all couples who still have unused frozen embryos after two years, well before the Government review date of 5 years. Regular review of couples with frozen embryos will determine what factors influence the attitudes of couples to prolonged storages of embryos. It is possible that in the situation of divorce, a couple who have an embryo stored may disagree concerning the disposal of a frozen embryo. In this case a custody suit, similar to that which may occur with children after divorce could ensue. The legal rights of the mother or father to the embryo would need to be determined, the previous agreement between the couple concerning the fate of an unwanted frozen embryo being taken into account. The cost of freezing embryos is on a sliding scale from $150 to $300 according to the number frozen and the cost of thawing an embryo is $50 if unsuccessful, and $200, if successful.

Unwanted stored embryos may be donated to other infertile couples. The infertile couples will be selected in a manner similar to that which exists for adoption and in accordance with the adoption regulations in Victoria. The presence of a normal uterus and normal menstrual cycle is required to ensure implantation of the thawed donated embryo. Matching of the recipient couple with the parents of the donor embryo may be feasible. Non-identifying information of the donors including social, educational and physical characteristics will be given to the recipients. They in turn will be able to give this information to the offspring if they so wish. The donors will not be paid but they will be informed to the outcome of the donation. The Infertility Bill states that the recipients of the donor embryo will become the legal parents and the donors of the embryo will have no claim on the offspring. In addition, the offspring will have no claim against the parents of the donor embryo. This avoids the possibility of claims by donor gamete children against the estate of the donors, such as may have arisen in the case of the Rios' embryos.

The risk of fetal malformation resulting from the process of freeze thawing is unknown. Study of other species where freeze thawing has been effective shows no increased risk of fetal malformation. Because only half the embryos survive the freeze thaw process it is probable that only the more robust embryos survive. Fetal malformation may be less common; certainly there is no evidence of an increased risk of fetal malformation in mamalian embryos after freeze thawing.[8] The incidence of complications during pregnancy and birth will be unknown until large numbers of babies have been born. Amongst non-frozen IVF pregnancies the risk of pre-term labour and peri-natal deaths mostly are associated with the occurrence of pre-term labour. However, many factors may be contributing to this, such as the older age of patients, multiple pregnancies, the presence of previous pelvic disease, or the IVF process itself.

Surveys of public attitudes to freeze thawing in Australia have shown that the majority of the community accept this. The Morgan Research Centre Pty. Limited in

1984 in a representative sample of 1,082 Australians found that 45% approved of freezing of embryos, 39% were opposed, whilst 16% of the population remained undecided. A survey carried out by the Australian College of Obstetricians and Gynaecologists showed that the majority of specialists were in favour of freeze thawing.[9] At the present time only one of the other eleven IVF Centres in Australia have commenced freeze thawing of embryos but several intend to do so in the near future.

The facility to freeze eggs may soon be available. This may have extensive use in gynaecology. Women who have diseases which endanger the life of the ovaries, such as, cancer, endometriosis, recurrent cysts and infection, would be able to store oocytes. Should the ovaries subsequently require removal to cure such diseases, the patients could become pregnant by fertilizing thawed oocytes in vitro using the husband's spermatazoa.

Oocyte freezing may be useful in family planning. Women deferring childrearing because of the pursuit of a career, the unavailability of a marriage partner, or the presence of ill health at a young age may be able to store oocytes for later use. Storage of oocytes at the time of sterilisation may also be an important method of conception for those women who later request sterilization reversal, particularly if sterilisation reversal is difficult or fails.

Oocyte donation to produce embryos has been developed for a variety of reasons; the absence of ovaries, either conginital or surgical, the presence of hypoplastic ovaries, such as strip ovaries in the Turner Syndrome, failure to procure ovulation using stimulation regimes, premature menopause, the occurence of oocytes which may transmit genetic disease, e.g. Huntington's chorea, Tay Sachs disease and fibrocystic disease of the pancreas, and ovaries which are inaccessable to both laparoscopic and ultrasonic oocyte collection. Indications may also include patients who repeatedly fail IVF because of abnormality of oocytes or embryos, or who repeatedly miscarry. Some of these patients may have associatd congenital malformations elsewhere in the body or may have suffered serious pelvic disease and therefore require careful assessment as to psychological and physical suitability to cope with pregnancy and child rearing. Patients are selected following referral by an infertility specialist to the IVF centre. Most of the patients have ovaries inaccessible to ultrasound or laparoscopic oocyte pickup, premature

menopause or genetic diseases. Very few patients with a
uterus and no ovaries have presented for treatment. The
possibility of pregnancy following oocyte donation may lead
gynaecologists to consider conservation of the uterus when
both ovaries are removed because of disease.

The donors of oocytes initially were patients who had an
excess of oocytes during IVF treatment. About one of eight
patients in 1983 and early 1984 were prepared to donate
oocytes. After pregnancies occurred in the freeze thaw
programme, oocyte donations occurred less often. For this
reason oocyte donors are being sought from patients being
sterilized. This is a better source of donors as infertile
patients donating oocytes may resent the recipient becoming
pregnant if they remain infertile. The waiting list
consists of over 100 patients and the waiting time for
treatment is uncertain because of the difficulty obtaining
donor oocytes.

The Infertility Bill in Victoria has determined
conditions and regulations for the donation of oocytes.[7]
The donors can be known or anonymous. Up to the present
time the donors have been anonymous. Although a number of
couples have inquired about friends and relatives acting as
donors most prespective known donors have changed their
mind after realising the demands of repeated IVF
treatments. Attempts are made to math the social and
physical characteristics of the donor with the recipient,
there is no financial reward for donation and the donors
are counselled by independent counsellors. The donors are
informed if pregnancy results from the donation and if
pregnancy does occur, non-identifying information
concerning the donor is given to the recipient. The donors
have no claim on the offspring and are free of obligation
to the offspring. Likewise the recipients of donor oocytes
are counselled by an independent counsellor, they are the
legal parents of the offspring and receive information
concerning the donors to give to the offspring. Special
problems are likely to occur between a known donor and
recipient, mainly involving the degree of social contact
between the donor, the recipient and the offspring,
particularly if they are close friends or relatives. Both
a psychologist and social worker will be involved in
counselling known donors and recipients should they wish to
proceed with such an arrangement. The advisory team may be
required to counsel couples concerning problems which may
arise during rearing of the child, and to provide

information to other couples wishing to undertake known donor arrangements in the future. The committees of enquiry in other States have all agreed to the use of donor embryos except for South Australia and Tasmania. The recommendastions are similar to the Victorian Bill except for the use of known donors, which remains uncertain in several States. At least three of other 11 IVF centres in Australia are using, or planning to use, donor oocytes.

The procedure of the donor oocyte embryo pregnancy may involve several techniques.[10] In women without functioning ovaries the production of an artificial menstrual cycle is required and involves the use of oestradiol and progesterone. These drugs are given in such a way to mimic plasma hormone levels during the natural menstrual cycle.[11] After three menstrual cycles to establish the stability of the system response, the recipient may have a donor oocyte embryo transfer. Should the recipient become pregnant, the pregnancy is maintained by continuing the use of oestradiol and progerserone for up to 19 weeks. Normally the placenta takes over the function of the corpus luteum in supporting pregnancy around the seventh to ninth week. In naturally conceived pregnancies there is usually a considerable decrease in plasma progersterone when the support of the pregnancy shifts from the corpus luteum to the placenta. Because of the possible risks of miscarriage during the time of the progesterone decrease, progesterone injections were continued for longer periods than was probably necessary, until the placenta had clearly established satisfactory progesterone levels. Because of the need to obtain blood samples frequently and regularly and the need to inject progesterone daily the stress on the patient is considerable. This is explained to the patient prior to treatment.

Patients who have normal ovarian function may require donor oocytes for other reasons, for example, genetic disease. The donor's and recipient's menstrual cycles have to be synchronised before donation can succeed. This can be done by manipulating the recipient's cycle, using steroid hormones and hCG.[12] This would be suitable should the prospective donor be known, for example, a patient having a sterilisation with a regulasr menstrual cycle, as there would be some chance of synchronising the LH surge in the recipient to within one or two days of the donor. The accuracy of synchronisation required in the human for successful transfer of donor embryos is as yet unknown. A simpler and more effective way to synchronise the unknown donor and recipients cycles has been evolved. A cohort of 30 potential recipients are kept on call. Each potential recipient notifies the IVF Centre of the date of the first day of the menstrual period. If a woman then donates an oocyte, the patient most closely matching the donor's menstrual cycle is contacted and the oocyte offered. Daily urinary LH levels ensures reasonable matching of the donor and recipient cycles. If the recipient refuses the donation, then the recipient next most closely matching the donor is contacted.

Freeze thawing also assists in the use of donor oocyte embryos. Synchronising of the donor's and recipient's menstrual cycles are unnecessary. The most suitable recipient can have the donor oocyte fertilised with her husband's semen and the embryo(s) is then frozen. The embryo can then be thawed and transferred on the day when embryo implantation is most likely to succeed. The disadvantage of using freeze thaw donor oocyte embryos is that only two of three embryos survive the freeze thaw process. When more donor oocyte embryos become available freeze thawing may be preferred as it simplifies the management of such a programme and would improve the matching between donor and recipient.

Four of 16 patients have become pregnant following the transfer[2,3] of donor oocyte embryos, three of the patients having a premature menopause which required the use of artificial menstrual cycles and artificial endocrine support during early pregnancy. These three pregnancies have important implications for reproductive biology. It establishes beyond any doubt that oestradiol and progesterone alone replace the function of the corpus luteum in supporting early pregnancy. It may also help to establish the role, if any, of other substances secreted by the ovary throughout pregnancy.

The costs of a donor oocyte pregnancy have not been established because of the experimental state of the programme and the changes which are likely to occur as new information becomes available with the establishment of each new pregnancy. The ordinary cost of an IVF treatment cycle, $3,500-4,000, will be reduced as the oocyte pickup will be part of a routine sterilization procedure, leaving the costs of the laboratory procedure of fertilization and ET, about $2,000. On the other hand extra costs will arise from use of the artificial menstrual cycles and artificial support of the pregnancy; this regime has not been finalized but the cost may be several thousand dollars.

There may be a need for doctors to counsel patients who either may be involved in the use of freeze-thaw or donor oocyte embryos or wish to avail themselves of the treatments. More important are the associated psycho--social, ethical and legal implications of the procedures. The ethical and legal aspects have been debated in Australia, especially in Victoria. Psycho-social studies of the patients, donors and children are being undertaken. Criticism of the procedures by the profession will be important in their development.

Acknowledgements

I wish to thank L. Freemann and P. Lutjen for supplying relevant information and to the whole IVF team who have contributed to the initial success of these procedures.

REFERENCES

1. Trounson A, Wood C, Leeton JF (1982). Freezing of Embryos. An ethical obligation. Med J Aust 2:332-333.
2. Trounson A, Mohr L (1983). Human pregnancy following cryopreservation, thawing and transfer of an eight-cell embryo. Nature 305:707-709.
3. Wood C, Downing B, Trounson A, Rogers P (1984). Clinical implications of developments associated with the technique of in vitro fertilization. Br Med J 289:978-980.
4. Downing B, Mohr L, Trounson A, Fueman LE, Wood C (1985). Birth after transfer of cryo preserved embryos. Med J Aust 142:409-411.
5. Burton B, Chan CLK, Pusyko Z, Wood C. Attitudes towards occyte and embryo donation and disposal (submitted for publication).
6. The "Sun"; June 18, 1984.
7. Infertility (Medical Procedures) Bill No. 2 Victoria (1984).
8. Ciba Foundation (1977). The freezing of mammalian embryos. Excerpta Medica (Amsterdam).
9. Keeping D, Hennessey J (1984). Ethics of IVF: The State of the Art in Australia. Fertility Society of Australia, Proceedings of the Third Scientific Meeting, p.1
10. Trounson A, Leeton J, Besanko M, Wood C. Pregnancy established in infertile patient after transfer of a donated embryuo fertilized in vitro. Conti A (1983). Br Med J 286:835-838.

11. Lutjen P, Trounson A, Leeton J, Findley J, Wood C, Renou P (1984). The establishment and maintenance of pregnancy using in vitro fertilization and embryo donation in a patient with primary ovarian failure. Nature 307:174-175.

12. Templeton AA, Van Look P, Lumsden MA, Angell R, Aitken RJ, Duncan AW, Baird DJ (1984). The recovery of pre-ovulatory oocytes using a fixed shcedule of ovulation and follicle aspiration. Br J Obstet Gynaecol 91:148-154.

Cell Differentiation During Development

Progress in Developmental Biology, Part B, pages 301–305

RETINAL DEVELOPMENT IN THE LIZARD <u>CALOTES VERSICOLOR</u> : CELL DIFFERENTIATION AND GLUTAMINE SYNTHETASE ACTIVITY

Suresh C. Goel and S. L. Shinde

Department of Zoology, University of Poona, Poona 411 007, India

INTRODUCTION

Studies on the cytodifferentiation of retinal cell types by the light and electron microscopy, as also on the cell death in the developing retina have been done in various vertebrate species (Uga and Smelser, 1973; Fischer, 1976; Bhattacharjee, 1977; Galvez et al, 1977; Kitahara, 1977; Blanks, 1982; Young, 1984). During the differentiation of the retina the glutamine synthetase (GS;L-glutamate:NH$_3$ ligase ADP; E.C.6.3.1.2) serves as a marker enzyme of the definitive Muller glia cells (Moscona and Linser, 1983). Consequently, it has been studied during the normal development and in vitro cultures of the retina (Linser et al, 1984; review, Reif-Lehrer, 1984). We undertook these studies on the lizard <u>Calotes versicolor</u>, since there is so far no report on the differentiation and GS activity of the developing retina in any reptilian species.

MATERIALS AND METHODS

Embryos were procured and paraffin sections for histology and cytochemistry were prepared by the methods described earlier (Shinde and Goel, 1983). The enzyme was assayed by its ɣ- glutamyltransferase (GT) activity according to the method of Kirk and Moscona (1963). Retinas from 6 to 14 specimens, depending on their size, were pooled for one experiment. Adequate controls were done to establish the optimum assay conditions and the substrate kinetics was studied (Fig. 1).

RESULTS AND DISCUSSION

The process of cell differentiation in the retina of Calotes, as in those of the other species (Young, 1984) progresses in general from the vitreal to the scleral and from the central to the optic lip area. This is apparent in the pattern of regionalization, appearance of the transient synaptic lines, differentiation and thickening of the photoreceptor layer, and organization of the nuclei in all the three layers. The Muller glial cells, however, are the last to undergo differentiation in Calotes, as in the rat, man and mouse (see Blanks, 1982). In some species (including rat and man) the glial cells have been reported to be the first cells to undergo differentiation (Kuwabara and Weidman, 1974) but it seems less plausible since it is not related with the time of rise of the GS activity (Reif-Lehrer, 1984). In Calotes the glial cells are distinguishable because of their giant nuclei, seen first at stage 40 in the inner two-third of the inner nuclear layer (INL). Their further cytological differentiation is indicated by the appearance of the outer limiting membrane at stage 42 and of the inner limiting membrane in the hatchling. The glial cell bodies are clearly seen as dark lines traversing the inner plexiform (IPL) layer.

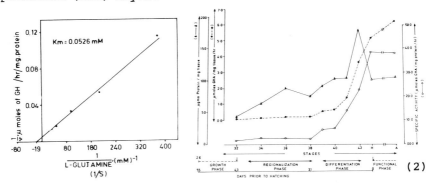

Figure 1. Lineweaver-Burk double reciprocal plot between different concentrations of glutamine (S) and GT activity of the enzyme (V) in retina of adult Calotes. V_{max} is 183.47 micro mole GH/hr/mg protein.
Figure 2. Pattern of GT activity in embryonic, hatchling (H) and adult (A) retina of Calotes. Also shown is µg protein/mg tissue in the retina.

The appearance and increase in the number of synaptic lines in both the plexiform layers, indicating synapse forma- tion and neuronal cell differentiation is being described here for the first time in any species. In the IPL these lines appear first at stage 35+ as two doublets in the cent- ral retina. Some neurites from both the INL and the ganglion cell layer can be seen reaching up to these synaptic lines. The number of lines gradually increases to 8 in the central retina, 5 in the pericentral retina, and 4 in the optic lip retina at stage 40. Later the lines become somewhat diffuse and appear as bands. The number of bands in the IPL of the adult decreases from 8 in the midcentral to 1 in the optic lip retina. In the outer plexiform layer there is al- ways 1 synaptic line in the entire retina throughout its development, beginning at stage 36.

The rise in the GS activity of the retina during embryo- nic development (Fig.2) quite clearly exhibits two major trends. One, the rise is multifold and sharp, and two, the time of rise (Fig.3) is related with the time when the animal begins to use the retina (Moscona, 1972; Moscona and Linser, 1983; Reif-Lehrer, 1984). The GS specific activity is clearly related to the functional phase and not with the growth and regionalization phase of the retina. Other obser- vations relating the rise to the function of retina are the increase in GS activity during final synaptogenesis (Sheffie- ld and Fischman, 1970), or at the time of development of ERG signals (Reif-Lehrer and Coghlin, 1973) or on the first appearance of rhodopsin (Witkovsky, 1963). Moreover, induc- tion, rise and inhibition in the GS specific activity is appropriately correlated with the differentiation and dediff- erentiation of the retina in vitro (Moscona and Linser,1983). Calotes versicolor happens to be the only species investiga-

Figure 3. Pattern of rise of GS activity in different animals.

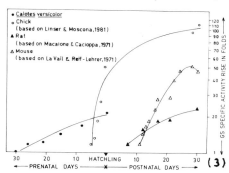

ted so far where adult levels of the GS specific activity are achieved immediately after hatching, and major rise occurs even before hatching, while the embryo is in its shell, buried deep under the soil.

It is tempting though hazardous, to comment on the final levels of the GS specific activity in the various species since the retina has the most active energy metabolism of all animal tissues (Reif-Lehrer, 1984). The highest levels seem to be present in the chick which has a high degree of visual acuity, while low levels are obtained in the rat which has low visual acuity. The relationship between the GS activity and the visual acuity may be for the following reason. It is probable that the retina of the species with high visual acuity tends to be metabolically more active and hence requires high levels of GS. It is already known that the GS activity is restricted to the glial cells of Muller (Linser and Moscona, 1979) and is especially high in the outer plexiform layer (Linser and Moscona, 1984), where synaptic transmission is most frequent. It is also known that glutamate, the product of GS activity, is a neurotransmitter (Reif-Lehrer, 1984), whereas ammonia/glutamine, the substrate for the GS activity is a nerve poison (Denman and Welder, 1984) and, if not immediately metabolized, may have toxic effect on retinal cells.

REFERENCES

Bhattacharjee J (1977). Sequential differentiation of retinal cells in the mouse studied by diaphorase staining, J Ant 123 : 272-282.

Blanks JC (1982). Cellular differentiation in the mammalian retina. In Hollyfield JG, Vidrio EA (eds) : "The Structure of the Eye," New York : Elsevier, pp 237-246.

Denman RB, Wedler FC (1984). Association-dissociation of mammalian brain glutamine synthetase (EC 6. 3.1.2) : effects of metal ions and other ligands. Arch Biochem Biophys 232 : 427-440

Fischer LJ (1976). Synaptic arrays of the inner plexiform layer in the developing retina of Xenopus. Devi Biol 50 : 402-412.

Galvez JM, Genis LP, Carmen P (1977). Inverted (displaced) retinal amacrine cells and their embryonic development in the chick. Exp Neurol 56 : 151-157.

Kirk DL, Moscona AA (1963). Synthesis of experimentally induced glutamine synthetase (glutamotransferase activity) in embryonic chick retina. Devl Biol 8 : 341-357.

Kitahara Y (1977). An electron microscopic study on the morphogenesis of the outer segment of the retinal rod. J Kansai Med Univ 28 : 919-944.

Kuwabara T, Weidman TA (1974). Development of the prenatal rat retina. Invest Ophthalmol 13 : 725-739.

Linser P, Moscona AA (1979). Induction of glutamine synthetase in embryonic neural retina : Localization in Muller fibers and dependence on cell interactions. Proc Natl Acad Sci USA 76 : 6476-6480.

Linser P, Moscona AA (1984). Variable CA-II comparatmentalization in vertebrate retina. Ann NY Acad Sci 429:430-446.

Linser PJ, Sorrentino M, Moscona AA (1984). Cellular compartmentalization of carbonic anhydrase-C and glutamine synthetase in developing and mature mouse neural retina. Dev Brain Res 13 : 65-71.

Moscona AA (1972). Induction of glutamine synthetase in embryonic neural retina : A model for the regulation of specific gene expression in embryonic cells. FEBS Proc 24 : 1-23.

Moscona AA, Linser P (1983). Developmental and experimental changes in retina glia cells : Cell interactions and control of phenotype expression and stability. Curr Topics Devl Biol 18 : 155-188.

Reif-Lehrer L (1984). Glutamate metabolism in the retina : A larger perspective. Curr Topics Eye Res 4 : 1-95.

Reif-Lehrer L, Coghlin J (1973). Conversion of glutamic acid to glutamine by retinal glutamine synthetase. Exp Eye Res 17 : 321-328.

Sheffield JB, Fischman DA (1970). Intercellular junctions in the developing neural retina of the chick embryo. Z Zellforsch Mikrosk Anat 104 : 405-418.

Shinde SL, Goel SC (1983). Corneal morphogenesis in the Indian garden lizard, Calotes versicolor (Agamidae) J Morph 175 : 293-306.

Uga S, Smelser GK (1973). Electron microscopic study of the development of retinal Mullerian cells. Invest Ophthalmol 12 : 295-307.

Witkovsky P (1963). An ontogenic study of retinal function in the chick. Vision Res 3 : 341-355.

Young RW (1984). Cell death during differentiation of the retina in the mouse. J Comp Neural 229 : 362-373.

Progress in Developmental Biology, Part B, pages 307–318

MOLECULAR AND CELLULAR DIFFERENTIATION OF MUSCLE, CARTILAGE, AND BONE IN THE DEVELOPING LIMB

Arnold I. Caplan

Biology Department
Case Western Reserve University
Cleveland, Ohio 44106 U.S.A.

INTRODUCTION

Embryonic development is characterized by the changing morphology of the embryo and the emergence of differentiated tissues. Three factors govern these observed changes: First and foremost, the genomic repertoire of the organism is the ultimate controlling element in that the organism will develop in a spatio-temporal pattern as dictated by the information encoded in its DNA. Second, the changes experienced by developing embryonic cells are predicated upon the previous decisions made by these cells or tissues; a fertilized egg is vested with full developmental potential while the mesenchymal cells in the developing limb bud cannot differentiate into heart muscle or sternal cartilage although at one point in development these mesenchymal cells had the potential to do so. And third, the decision made by individual cells are influenced by local cuing events (extrinsic factors); when uncommitted cells are placed into a foreign environment they modulate in response to those local cues as opposed to differentiating into a pattern as dictated by their location of origin. The interplay between these three factors governs the genesis of form and phenotype and leads to a complex organism composed of highly specialized tissues. This process of developmental change, however, does not stop at birth but rather continues through life to give rise to a maturing and, eventually, aging organism. It is my thesis that the changes which result in tissue dysfunction related to aging are a direct result of programmatic changes initiated during embryology which continue in adulthood and result in the dysfunction observed in the senescent organism.

These changes in development are dramatically observed as REPLACEMENT events wherein a progenitor molecule, cell, tissue, or complex structure is replaced by another variant. Usually this replacement involves the emergence of a more stringently controlled, more functionally specific activity or structure. These replacement variants of molecules, cells, or tissues are called ISOFORMS (Caplan et al., 1983).

An example of a molecular isoformic transition which occurs during development is the replacement of fetal hemoglobin by adult hemoglobin shortly after the birth of most mammals. The necessity for this replacement event is related to the oxygen-binding characteristics of fetal hemoglobin compared to the adult isoform. Fetal hemoglobin has a simple exponential oxygen saturation curve while adult hemoglobin evidences a sigmoidal saturation curve (Friedman, 1985). This sigmoidal curve is essential for delivering oxygen to the extremities of the organism under high oxygen demands. Fetal hemoglobin would surrender its oxygen too easily in an adult organism to be able to effectively deliver oxygen to these distal areas. Isoformic transitions involving not only molecules but cells and tissues occur during all of development; two examples will be emphasized below.

The Avian Limb

The avian limb develops from an outgrowth of the flank and is made up of two layers of tissue: an outer ectodermal covering and an inner mass of mesenchymal cells (Hinchliffe and Johnson, 1980). The embryonic mesenchyme changes from a loose organization of cells with large spaces between each cell into tissues which are more compactly arranged with minimal spaces between component cells. The spaces between the mesenchymal cells are filled with water which is highly structured. Extracellular matrix macromolecules are responsible for structuring this water and keeping the embryonic tissue in the non-compact cellular arrangements. The types of molecules found in the extracellular matrix are collagens, fibronectin, glycosaminoglycans such as hyaluronic acid (HA) and proteoglycans which are covalent combinations of glycosaminoglycans bound to a protein core; HA and proteoglycans are very highly negatively charged and structure very large amounts of water. During early phases of limb development, the mesenchymal cells are loosely arranged and

no regional differences can be discerned in the arrangement
or morphology of these cells. This stage is characterized
by high levels of HA (Toole, 1981) and of a large chondroitin sulfate proteoglycan (CSPG) in the extracellular
matrix (Royal et al., 1980). However, from fate map experiments, we know that a rod of cartilage will differentiate
first at the center or core of the limb which in turn will
be surrounded by more peripherally located muscle (Figure
1). Eventually this cartilage rod will be replaced by bone
which will be discussed in greater detail below. Concomi-
tant with the replacement of mesenchyme by differentiated
tissues, the progenitor matrices of HA and mesenchymal CSPG
are replaced by more complex tissue-specific matrices.

The first sign of regional morphological differences is
the distribution of the vasculature (Caplan, 1985; Drushel
et al., 1985); this occurs by stage 24 (4.5 days of
incubation) where the adult vascular pattern is finalized
prior to overt cytodifferentiation of cartilage, muscle, or
bone (Figure 1). The establishment of this vascular pattern

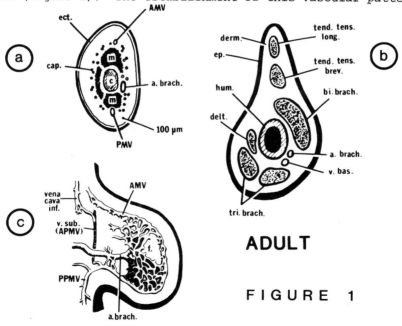

ADULT

FIGURE 1

Legend next page.

ST. 24

Figure 1. Anatomical relationship of the developing vascular network. At stage 24, the adult vascular pattern (c) is observed prior to any cytodifferentiation of muscle, "m", or cartilage, "c", indicated in (a) in the positions expected in subsequent stages. The single major artery (a. brach.) and major venous collecting vessels (PMV and AMV) as well as the distal capillary, "cap", network is apparent in cross-section. The adult tissue morphology is depicted in (b). See Caplan, 1985 for abbreviations.

is a function of both the intrinsic mitotic and self-assembly properties of the vascular cells and extrinsic cuing, most likely arising from the cell surface and the extracellular matrices of specific mesenchymal cells. Indeed, the developing vasculature may provide an extremely sensitive indicator of small preparatory changes which are taking place in the mesenchymal cells in different regions prior to mesenchymal cell differentiation. For example, by stage 24, all vasculature is excluded from the core region of the limb which will, in the next 8 to 12 hours, differentiate into cartilage (an avascular tissue). Detailed studies of the changing vasculature have stimulated our hypothesis that the vasculature reflects local changes as opposed to dictating or driving such changes, at least at these early stages of development (Caplan, 1985).

From this mass of highly vascularized, loose mesenchymal cells, three tissue types arise: cartilage, bone, and muscle. Rather than focus on the individual cellular lineages involved in the genesis of these complex morphologies, I focus on the extracellular matrices, since one class of molecules, the CSPG, can be used as a marker for individual phenotypes. More importantly, the CSPGs in early embryonic development establish progenitor matrices which are eventually replaced by other extracellular matrices, tissues, and complex structures.

Cellular Events

Mesenchymal cells in the developing limb cytodifferentiate first into a cartilage rod at the center of the limb. These chondrocytes make a specific extracellular matrix which gives cartilage its unique tissue properties. The two main constituents of this matrix are a special collagen called Type II collagen and a cartilage-CSPG. This cartilage-CSPG (Figure 2) has been characterized in detail and is made up of two classes of glycosaminoglycan chains covalently bound to a large core protein; this core protein is between 200,000 and 350,000 daltons. There are approximately 100 chondroitin sulfate chains (20,000 daltons) and approximately 50 keratan sulfate chains (9,000 daltons) covalently bound to this core protein in two adjacent regions. One end of the core protein, which is relatively void of carbohydrate, is capable of non-covalently binding to HA. This aggregate of about 50 proteoglycan monomers non-covalently associated with a single strand of HA is the predominant organizational form of proteoglycans in cartilage matrices. It has been shown that during cartilage development, maturation, and aging, the structure and molecular details of cartilage proteoglycan change (Caplan and Hascall, 1980; Caplan, 1981). In particular the ratio of the molecular weights of keratan sulfate to chondroitin sulfate change dramatically as a function of aging with the chondroitin sulfate chains about half the size (comparing young and old cartilage) and with keratan sulfate chains about 30 to 50% larger. The best evidence available indicates that the chondrocytes are not replaced by successive new generations of cells but rather that the changing biosynthetic program within these cells accounts for the observed variations as development proceeds (Roughley and White, 1980).

This sequence of biosynthetic changes is to be contrasted to the detailed cellular events which occur during myogenesis. These events involve the differentiation of mesenchymal cells into myoblasts, the proliferation and expansion of mononucleated myoblasts and eventually their fusion into multinucleated myotubes after which there is a massive up-regulation of the synthesis of muscle-specific proteins. These multinucleated myotubes are formed during a relatively restricted period of embryonic development and further changes of muscle mass following this period are primarily due to increases or decreases in the contractile apparatus within these myotubes. Isoformic transitions of contractile muscle proteins, for example myosins, are programmed into the further development of muscle and are most likely triggered by extrinsic signals (Caplan et al., 1983). For example, three myosin heavy chain isoforms can be separated from one another on two-dimensional electrophoretic gels: one from embryonic muscle, one found in neonatal muscle, and the last found in the adult. Most interesting is the fact that the replacement events in which the neonatal myosins are succeeded by the adult myosin take place within functional, load-bearing muscles. This transition takes place in a relatively short time period and occurs while other muscle proteins do not experience isoformic transitions. Thus, the transition from a neonatal to an adult muscle occurs by the replacement of specific isoformic molecular variants while the cells themselves are not replaced.

Recent studies indicate that two large CSPGs are found in developing muscle (Carrino and Caplan, 1984). One of these CSPGs is produced by muscle (M-CSPG) and has unique molecular characteristics. In particular, 40 to 60 extremely large chondroitin sulfate chains of an average of 70,000 daltons (3 to 4 times larger than the average cartilage chondroitin sulfate chains) and uniquely sulfated in the chondroitin-6-sulfate position to the 90th percentile are attached to a core protein which is approximately the same size as the core protein of cartilage-CSPG. This M-CSPG is associated with the cell surface and local extracellular matrix surrounding both individual myoblasts and myotubes. The M-CSPG is made only during embryonic muscle development and is not made by maturing or adult myogenic elements. Our hypothesis is that the M-CSPG constructs a progenitor extracellular matrix which reserves space for the next generation of muscle matrices, including the muscle basement membrane, which are more specific (Carrino and Caplan, 1985). In addition, we hypothesize that this enormous M-CSPG (4-5x10^6 daltons) structures extracellular water in an effort to reserve space for the future expansion of the developing myotube itself. Another CSPG, very much like an early mesenchymal-CSPG, is also found in in vivo muscle preparations. This CSPG is most likely produced by the mesenchymal cells involved with the connective tissue packaging of myotubes and represents the primitive, progenitor matrix of discrete muscle units.

In summary, as seen in Figure 2, progenitor mesenchymal cells, cartilage cells, hypertrophic cartilage cells, myogenic cells, and mesenchymal cells associated with myogenic elements all synthesize CSPGs whose structures and chemistries are indicative of the tissues of origin (Carrino et al., 1985). These proteoglycans are, themselves, isoformic variants which exhibit phenotypic specific structures.

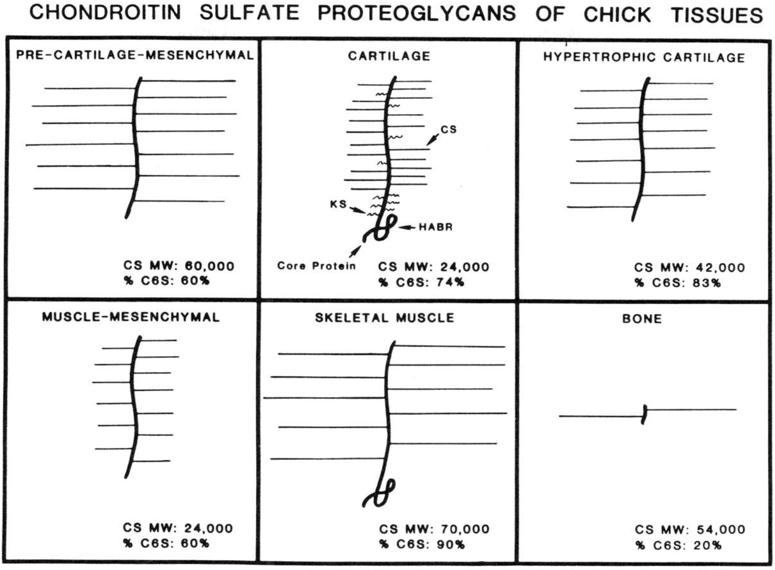

CHONDROITIN SULFATE PROTEOGLYCANS OF CHICK TISSUES

Figure 2. Chondroitin sulfate proteoglycans of chick tissues are depicted in caricature. The chondroitin sulfate (CS) chains, molecular weight (MW), and percent sulfation in the chondroitin-6 position (%C6S) are indicated for each proteoglycan (Carrino et al., 1985).

The Cartilage to Bone Transition

The concept of a progenitor extracellular matrix is an idea most commonly quoted for the cartilage to bone transition. In the growth plate of aves and mammals, the cartilage extracellular matrix serves as a scaffolding for mineral deposition and the formation of new bone. However, in embryonic long bone development this is not exactly the case. In the embryonic chick tibia where we have recently completed a detailed study (Pechak et al., 1985), the early appearing cartilage core is replaced by the marrow space, not by bone. The sequence in an overall and cellular sense is depicted in Figure 3.

DEVELOPMENT OF LONG BONE

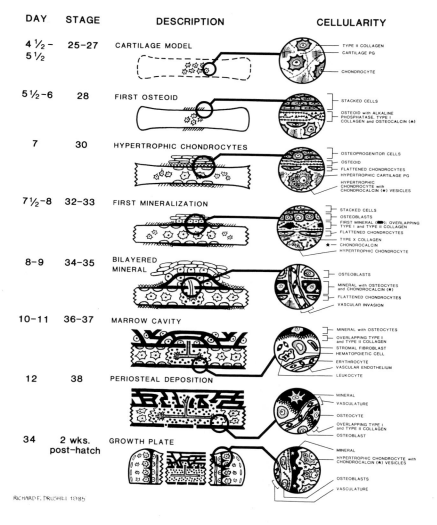

Figure 3. Morphological and cellular details involved in the development of the embryonic chick tibia. It is important to note: that first bone formation takes place outside of the cartilage core; that continued bone formation is periosteal; and that cartilage core defines the limits of and is replaced by the marrow cavity.

First, a rod of cartilage develops at the core of the limb (Figure 1, stage 25; Figure 3, top). Then <u>outside</u> this cartilage at the mid-diaphysis, a sleeve or collar of mesenchymal cells differentiates into osteoblasts and then forms osteoid which becomes mineralized into first bone. New bone continues to form in this manner both proximally and distally from this mid-diaphyseal region and, most importantly, radially to increase the diameter of the newly forming bone. This outward, circumferential increase in bone is in layers: the first layer is the first bone collar, then a vascularized, marrow space, then another layer of bone and so on. The new bone originates from a layer of "stacked cells" (6 to 8 cells thick) which are evident as early as stage 25-27 outside of the newly differentiating cartilage core. The number of layers of these stacked cells at stage 28 is approximately equal to the number of layers of bone that eventually form in the mid-diaphyseal region of the tibia although this could be completely fortuitous. Importantly, 80 to 90% of the <u>length</u> of the day 16-18 embryonic tibial bone is derived form this periosteal osteogenesis not from the replacement of cartilage by bone. The replacement of cartilage by bone does, indeed, take place at the proximal and distal ends of the bone but only after day 16; eventually, a growth plate configuration is established in these regions at the end of the bone.

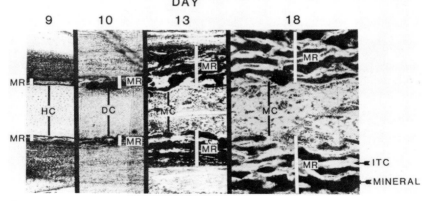

Figure 4. Collage of the mid-diaphyseal region of longitudinal sections aligned to show that the hypertrophic cartilage (HC) of day 9 is replaced by degenerating cartilage (DC) and eventually, day 13 and 18, by the marrow cavity (MC). Evident is the explansion of the mineralizing region (MR) and the formation of the intra-trabecular channels (ITC).

Figure 4 shows the mid-diaphyseal region of a tibia of a day 9, 10, 13, and 18 embryo to emphasize the point that the cartilage is replaced by marrow, not bone. This collage is constructed from longitudinal sections of the mid-diaphyseal region of the tibia on the days indicated. We have aligned these sections to show that the cartilage core or model is replaced by marrow as periosteal bone increases circumferentially with developmental age.

The replacement of cartilage by marrow is an important example of how morphologies are established: one tissue defines the limits for the tissue which replaces it. As emphasized in the Introduction, the extracellular matrix (cartilage in this case) defines and reserves the space for its replacement by a more functionally specific tissue, marrow. Because the cyto-differentiation of cartilage is observed first (stage 25) and first indications of bone are not observed until one or two days later (stage 28), many of us have assumed that the developing cartilage rod defines the limits of the surrounding bone. However, it may be that the commitment of the stacked cells to an osteogenic lineage, indeed, defines the limits of the cartilage model which is formed at the core of the limb. This reverse in our thinking is strengthened when we realize that the cartilage at the core is not replaced by bone but that cartilage defines the limits of the marrow cavity. These speculations provide a working hypothesis which structures some of our current experimentation.

Again, the emphasis of these examples is on the replacement of one tissue by another tissue in the orderly development of embryonic morphologies. By structuring a cartilage model which is replaced by marrow, the inner contour lines of the developing bone are defined. By realizing that the cartilage rod at the core of the limb is not replaced by bone, our thinking with regard to cause and effect relationships of the developing limb have, thus, been altered. The clear demonstration that the cartilage does not provide a scaffolding for embryonic long bone does not preclude the possibility that the cartilage may provide the scaffolding and organizational components for the mesenchymal cells of the marrow.

CONCLUSION

The ISOFORMIC REPLACEMENT THEORY is an important concept in developmental biology because it allows us to understand the organizational details at the molecular and cellular level involved with the genesis of discrete tissues (Caplan, 1981; Caplan et al., 1983). The use of extracellular matrix molecules of distinctive physical and chemical properties to structure progenitor matrices which are eventually replaced by phenotype-specific matrices is an important mechanism by which distinct morphologies are established. In the construction of a modern skyscraper, large wooden structures are built into which concrete is poured. These progenitor wooden structures provide the boundaries for the definitive concrete morphologies which give rise to floors and walls and other aspects of these buildings. In the same way, I envision that the extracellular matrices serve as the fabric which provide boundaries for the genesis of discrete morphologies. In embryology, the CSPGs may serve as the primary water-structuring components of such extracellular matrices. These molecules are programmatically synthesized with distinctive chemistries which contribute to individual and discrete extracellular matrices that serve to define the broad structural and molecular outlines of forming tissues and other complex embryonic structures. The elucidation of these chemistries and the details of the replacement events in which they function will allow a deeper understanding of the control of developmental events.

ACKNOWLEDGEMENTS

My colleagues, Drs. Carrino, Pechak, Weitzhandler, Kujawa, Syftestad, Drushel, and Lennon, are responsible for the data which support some of the generalizations put forth here. Supported by grants from NIH, MDA, and the Arthritis Foundation.

REFERENCES

Caplan AI (1981). The molecular control of muscle and cartilage development. In "39th Annual Symposium of the Society for Developmental Biology" Ed S Subtelney and U Abbott, Alan R Liss Inc NY pp 37-68.

Caplan AI (1985). The vasculature and limb development. Cell Diff 16:1-11.

Caplan AI, Hascall VC (1980). Structure and developmental changes in proteoglycans. In "Dilitation of the Uterine Cervix" Ed. F Naftolin and PG Stubblefield. Raven Press, NY pp 79-98.

Caplan AI, Fiszman MY, Eppenberger MY (1983). Molecular and cell isoforms during development. Science 221:921-927.

Carrino DA, Caplan AI (1984). Isolation and partial characterization of high-buoyant density proteoglycans synthesized in ovo by embryonic chick skeletal muscle and heart. J Biol Chem 259:12419-12430.

Carrino DA, Caplan AI (1985). Proteoglycan synthesis during skeletal muscle development. In "Molecular Biology of Muscle Development" UCLA Symp Bol 29. Ed. C Emerson, DA Fischman, B Nadal-Ginard, MAQ Siddiqui. Alan R. Liss Inc, NY in press.

Carrino DA, Weitzhandler M, Caplan AI, (1985). Proteoglycans synthesized during cartilage to bone transition. In "The Chemistry and Biology of Mineralized Tissue" Ed WT Butler. Ebsco Media Inc. Birmingham, AL pp 197-208.

Drushel RF, Pechak PG, Caplan AI (1985) The anatomy, ultrastructure, and fluid dynamics of the developing vasculature of the embryonic chick wing bud. Cell Diff 16:13-28.

Friedman JM (1985). Structure, dynamics, and reactivity in hemoglobin. Science 228:1273-1280.

Hinchliffe JR, Johnson DR (1980). The development of the vertebrate limb. Clarendon Press, Oxford, England.

Pechak DG, Kujawa, MK, Caplan, AI (1985). Morphological and histochemical events during first bone formation in embryonic chick limbs. in preparation.

Roughley PJ, White RJ (1980). Age-related changes in the structure of the proteoglycan subunits from human articular cartilage. J Biol Chem 255:217-224.

Royal PD, Sparks KJ, Goetinck PF (1980). Physical and immunochemical characterization of proteoglycans synthesized during chondrogenesis in the chick embryo. J Biol Chem 255:9870-9878.

Toole BP (1981). Glycosaminoglycans in morphogenesis. In "Cell Biology of Extracellular Matrix" Ed. ED Hay, Plenum Pub. NY pp 259-294.

Progress in Developmental Biology, Part B, pages 319–324
© 1986 Alan R. Liss, Inc.

CALCIUM STIMULATION OF EMBRYONIC PALATE MESENCHYMAL
PROSTAGLANDIN SYNTHESIS

Robert M. Greene and Martha R. Lloyd

Daniel Baugh Institute, Thomas Jefferson
University, Philadelphia, PA, 19107, U.S.A.

INTRODUCTION

Synthesis of prostaglandins and cyclic nucleotides has
been implicated as playing a role in normal ontogeny of the
secondary palate during late embryonic and early fetal
periods. Embryonic palate mesenchymal cells are capable of
synthesizing several different prostaglandins (Alam et al.,
1982; Chepenik and Greene, 1981), some of which may serve
as local modulators of palatal cAMP levels since these
cells respond to both prostaglandin E_2 (PGE$_2$) and prosta-
cyclin (PGI$_2$) with dose related increases in intracellular
levels of cAMP (Greene et al., 1981). Hormones, cyclic
nucleotides and Ca^{2+}, acting in an interrelated fashion,
are major regulators of a variety of eukaryotic cell
functions. Calcium exerts a marked influence on many
biological processes and plays a significant role in the
regulation of cellular activity. The remarkable diversity
of its effects is, however, mediated through a homologous
class of intracellular Ca^{2+}-binding receptor proteins
(Cheung, 1980). Of these, calmodulin appears to play the
critical role of mediating many of the functions of Ca^{2+} in
eukaryotes.

The present study quantified calmodulin levels during
development of the secondary palate and examined the effects
of Ca^{2+} plus ionophore A23187 on prostaglandin E_2 and cAMP
synthesis by embryonic palate mesenchymal cells in primary
culture. The influence of the calmodulin antagonist
trifluoperazine and EGTA on this action of Ca^{2+} was also
investigated.

RESULTS

Murine palatal cells in vitro were stimulated 72 h after seeding, during early exponential growth when these cells are maximally sensitive to agents which stimulate prostaglandin synthesis (fig. 1). In the presence of 1 mM Ca^{2+}, the cationophore A23187 induced a dose dependent stimulation of prostaglandin E_2 (PGE_2) synthesis (fig. 2).

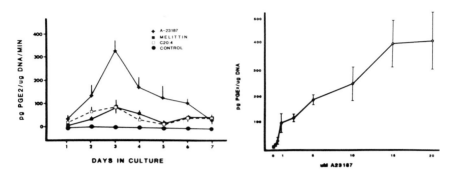

Figure 1. Effect of A23187, melittin and arachidonic acid (C20:4) on palate mesenchymal cell prostaglandin E_2 synthesis as a function of days in culture. Cells were grown to the time indicated, placed in serum-free medium and stimulated with 10 uM A23187 for 5 min or 10 ug/ml melittin or 5 uM C20:4 for 20 min. Vehicle controls received C_2H_5OH to a final concentration of 0.005% for 20 min. Values represent the mean ± S.D. of triplicate determinations.

Figure 2. The effect of different concentrations of A23187 on prostaglandin E_2 formation by primary cultures of palate mesenchymal cells in vitro. Cells were allowed to grow for 72 h. Serum containing medium was removed and replaced by medium free of any supplements. A23187 was added to culture dishes in the presence of 1.0 mM Ca^{2+} and incubation continued for an additional 5 min. Medium was assayed directly for prostaglandin E_2 and DNA in the cell layer was quantified spectrofluorometrically. Results are expressed as mean ± S.D. of no less than 3 determinations at each dose of A23187.

Levels of cAMP were not significantly altered from basal
levels (0.40 pM/ug DNA) in the presence of any dose of the
ionophore (data not presented).

Levels of calmodulin in embryonic palatal tissue were
analyzed by radioimmunoassay during formation of the
secondary palate from days 11 through 15 of gestation.
Levels of calmodulin did not significantly change during
this period of gestation, averaging 0.23 ng calmodulin/ug
protein (table I). Cellular calmodulin levels during either
logarithmic growth or confluency were not significantly
different from those found in vivo.

TABLE I. INTRACELLULAR LEVELS OF CALMODULIN IN EMBRYONIC
PALATAL TISSUE IN VIVO AND IN VITRO. Calmodulin levels
were determined by radioimmunoassay at the indicated gestational ages and after primary cultures of embryonic palate
mesenchymal cells entered a period of exponential growth
(96 h after seeding) or attained confluency (168 h after
seeding). Values represent the mean of three separate
determinations.

Stage		Calmodulin (ng/ug protein)
in vivo	— day 11	0.24 ± 0.04
	day 12	0.19 ± 0.06
	day 13	0.25 ± 0.02
	day 14	0.22 ± 0.03
	day 15	0.26 ± 0.11
in vitro	— 96 h	0.21 ± 0.01
	168 h	0.17 ± 0.10
adult mouse testes		0.83 ± 0.12

To examine the possible role of calmodulin in mediating the stimulatory effects of Ca^{2+} on palate mesenchymal
cell PGE_2 synthesis, we employed the calcium chelator EGTA
and the phenothiazine trifluoperazine (TFP). Table II
illustrates that pretreatment with EGTA blocked A23187
stimulation of PGE_2 synthesis by palate mesenchymal cells.
Pretreatment with 10 uM trifluoperazine also significantly
reduced the Ca^{2+}-induced increase in mesenchymal PGE_2
synthesis. The failure of trifluoperazine to inhibit the
stimulatory effects of exogenous arachidonate (1-100 uM) on

PGE_2 synthesis (only 100 uM dose shown) suggests that the inhibitory effects of TFP are expressed at the level of arachidonate mobilization. When exogenous calmodulin (0.1-20 uM) was used to stimulate palatal cell homogenates, no significant elevation of PGE_2 synthesis resulted from any dose used (data not presented).

TABLE II. EFFECT OF EGTA OR TRIFLUOPERAZINE ON THE ABILITY OF A23187 TO STIMULATE THE SYNTHESIS OF PROSTAGLANDIN E_2. Primary cultures of palate mesenchymal cells (72 h after seeding) were pretreated for 30 min with either 2.0 mM EGTA or 10 uM trifluoperazine and then stimulated with 5 uM A23187, or 100 uM arachidonic acid for an additional 5 min. Unstimulated values represent vehicle (.01% C_2H_5OH) controls.

Pretreatment	Treatment	Prostaglandin E_2 (pg/ug DNA)
--	--	3.0 + 1.3
--	A23187	250.1 + 26.2
EGTA	A23187	35.5 + 4.0*
TFP	A23187	78.4 + 29.4**
--	arachidonic acid	943 + 106.0
TFP	arachidonic acid	924 + 211.8

Statistical significance was determined by Student's t-test when compared with appropriate non-pretreated sample. Values represent the mean of no less than 3 separate determinations. * $p < 0.001$ ** $p < 0.01$

DISCUSSION AND SUMMARY

In the present study, the calcium ionophore A23187 was used as a stimulus for Ca^{2+}-dependent synthesis of prostaglandin E_2 by embryonic palate mesenchymal cells in vitro.

In the presence of Ca^{2+}, the phenothiazine trifluoperazine (TFP) binds to the Ca^{2+}-activated form of calmodulin (Levin and Weiss, 1978) and prevents its interaction with intracellular proteins (Brostrom et al., 1978; Levin and Weiss, 1980). Trifluoperazine can thus be used to investigate the participation of Ca^{2+}-calmodulin in the control of Ca^{2+}-dependent cellular events. The ability of trifluoperazine to prevent ionophore-induced stimulation of prostaglandin E_2 synthesis, in our study, must be interpreted with caution, however, since TFP has been shown to inhibit phospholipase A_2 (Withnall and Brown, 1982; Withnall et al., 1984). Observations that purified or membrane-associated phospholipase A_2 was refractory to calmodulin stimulation (Ballou and Cheung, 1983; DeWinter et al., 1984) imply that this enzyme is not directly controlled by calmodulin. The inability of exogenous calmodulin to stimulate palate mesenchymal PGE_2 synthesis in our studies is consistent with these reports. These results are consistent with a role for Ca^{2+} in mediating arachidonate mobilization and subsequent prostaglandin synthesis by embryonic palate mesenchymal cells. Although these cells contain significant amounts of intracellular calmodulin, the inability of exogenous calmodulin to stimulate PG synthesis implies that Ca^{2+} stimulation of palatal PG synthesis is not directly controlled by calmodulin.

REFERENCES

Alam I, Capitanio A, Smith JB, Chepenik KP, Greene RM (1982). Radioimmunologic identification of prostaglandins produced by serum-stimulated mouse embryo palate mesenchyme cells. Biochim et Biophys Acta 712:408–411.

Ballou LR, Cheung WY (1983). Marked increase in human platelet phospholipase A_2 activity in vitro and demonstration of an endogenous inhibitor. Proc Natl Acad Sci 80:5203–5207.

Brostrom MA, Brostrom CO, Breckenridge B, Wolff DJ (1978). Calcium-dependent regulation of brain adenylate cyclase. Adv Cyclic Nucl Res 9:85–99.

Chepenik KP, Greene RM (1981). Prostaglandin synthesis by primary cultures of mouse embryo palate mesenchyme cells. Biochem Biophys Res Comm 100:951–958.

Cheung WY (1980). Calmodulin plays a pivotal role in cellular regulation. Science 207:19–27.

DeWinter JM, Korpancova J, Van Den Bosch H (1984). Regulatory aspects of rat liver mitochondrial phospholipase A_2: Effects of calcium ions and calmodulin. Arch Biochem Biophys 234:243–252.

Greene RM, Lloyd MR, Nicolaou KC (1981). Agonist-specific desensitization of prostaglandin-stimulated cyclic AMP accumulation in palatal mesenchymal cells. J Craniofacial Genet Develop Biol 1:262–272.

Levin RM, Weiss, B (1978). Specificity of binding of trifluoperazine to the calcium-dependent activator of phosphodiesterase and to a series of other calcium-binding proteins. Biochem Biophys Acta 540:197-204.

Levin RM, Weiss, B (1980). Inhibition by trifluoperazine of calmodulin-induced activation of ATPase activity of rat erythrocytes. Neuropharm 19:169-174.

Withnall MT, Brown TJ (1982). Pancreatic phospholipase A_2 is not regulated by calmodulin. Biochem Biophys Res Comm 106:1049-1055.

Withnall MT, Brown TJ, Diocee BK (1984). Calcium regulation of phospholipase A_2 is independent of calmodulin. Biochem Biophys Res Comm 121:507-513.

Supported by NIH grant DE-05550.

Progress in Developmental Biology, Part B, pages 325–328
© 1986 Alan R. Liss, Inc.

CELL TYPE-SPECIFIC ANTIGENS IDENTIFIED WITH MONOCLONAL
ANTIBODIES IN THE ACCESSORY GLANDS OF MALE MEALWORM BEETLES

Karin A. Grimnes, Connie S. Bricker and G. M. Happ
Department of Zoology, University of Vermont
Burlington, Vermont 05405

INTRODUCTION

The accessory gland complex of Tenebrio molitor consists of two sets of paired glands: the bean-shaped (BAG)
and the tubular glands (TAG) (Fig. 1). These glands undergo
a change in competence correlated with the mid-pupal ecdy-
sterone peak. After eclosion, the BAG develops a complex
pattern of eight cell types (Dailey et al., 1980), and
produces at least 40 new proteins. Many of these proteins
are secreted and formed into the spermatophore, a multi-
layered structure used to transmit sperm to the female
during mating (Happ, 1984). We are interested in identifying cell type-specific antigens, and following their production, secretion and eventual role in spermatophore formation.

Monoclonal antibodies were generated against BAG
secretory masses (plugs) and screened against Towbin electro-
blots of accessory gland proteins. Immunoelectron microscopy was used to determine the sub-cellular localization of
antigen by the avidin-biotin peroxidase complex (ABC)
technique. Methods used for these studies are reported in
Black and Happ (1985) and Bricker et al., (1985).

RESULTS

Two clones were recovered which recognized proteins
specific to the BAGs. One antibody (PL 3.4) recognized a
single protein with two allelic forms (29Kd and 27.5Kd MW),
which was secreted into the plug with an apparent loss of
4Kd MW (Fig. 2a). A second antibody (PL 6.3) recognized a
9.5Kd protein and a 5Kd breakdown product (Fig. 2b). Both

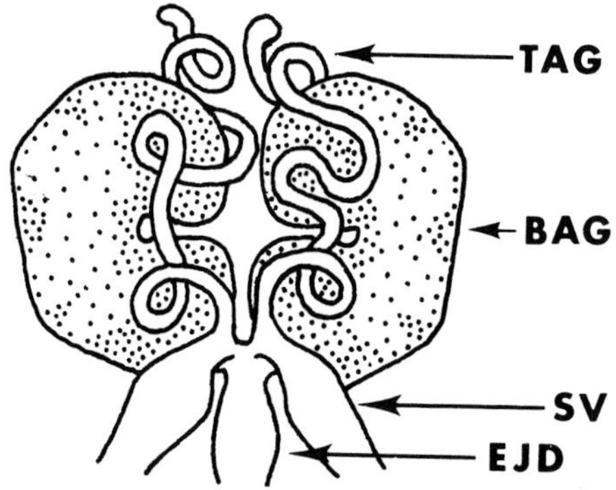

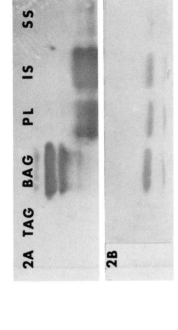

Figure 1. Accessory glands of Tenebrio molitor.
EJD = ejaculatory duct, SV = seminal vesicle

Figure 2. Immunoblot of accessory tissues.
A = PL 3.4, B = PL 6.3, PL = plug, IS = insoluble spermatophore, SS = soluble spermatopore.

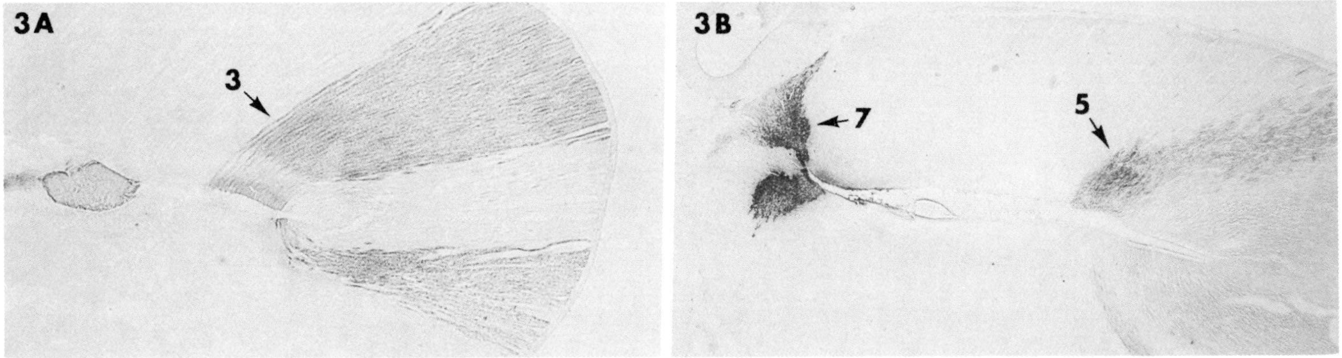

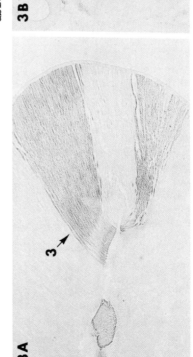

Figure 3. Immunohistochemical localization of (A) PL 3.4 antigen to cell
type 3 (400X) and (B) PL 6.3 antigen to cell types 5 and 7 of the BAG (300X).

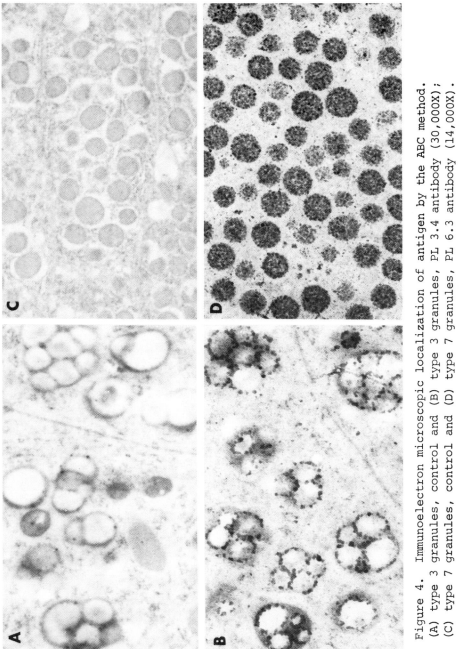

Figure 4. Immunoelectron microscopic localization of antigen by the ABC method. (A) type 3 granules, control and (B) type 3 granules, PL 3.4 antibody (30,000X); (C) type 7 granules, control and (D) type 7 granules, PL 6.3 antibody (14,000X).

antigens (PL 3.4 and PL 6.3) are incorporated into the water-insoluble spermatophore, and are differentiation-specific, reaching detectable levels by day 2 of adult life. Each antigen was cell type specific, with PL 3.4 restricted to type 3, and PL 6.3 found in cell types 5 and 7 (Fig. 3). Immunoelectron microscopic localization studies showed antigen was present within the characteristic granules of each cell type, with only trace amounts detected in the corresponding cytoplasm (Fig. 4). Antigen PL 6.3 was uniformly distributed through type 5 and 7 granules (type 5 not shown), however PL 3.4 antigen was concentrated in the cortex of type 3 granules.

These monoclonal probes will facilitate our studies of differentiation, pattern formation, and steroid-influenced development.

REFERENCES

Black PN, Happ GM (1985). Isolation, partial characterization, and localization of the A and B proteins from the tubular accessory gland of male Tenebrio molitor. Insect Biochem 15:639-650.

Bricker CS, Grimnes KA, Happ GM (1985). Preliminary localization of a cell type-specific antigen in the accessory glands of the male mealworm beetle by immunoelectron microscopy. In Bailey GW (ed): "Proceedings of the 43rd Annual Meeting of the Electron Microscopy Society of America", San Francisco: San Francisco Press, pp 584-585.

Dailey PJ, Gadzama NM, Happ GM (1980). Cytodifferentiation in the accessory glands of Tenebrio molitor. VI. A congruent map of cells and their secretions in the layered elastic product of the male bean-shaped gland. J Morph 166:289-322.

Happ GM (1984). Structure and development of male accessory glands in insects. In King RC, Akai H (eds): "Insect Ultrastructure, Vol 2", New York: Plenum Publishing Corporation, pp 365-396.

Progress in Developmental Biology, Part B, pages 329-331
© 1986 Alan R. Liss, Inc.

CYTOSKELETON IN ODONTOBLASTS OF RAT INCISORS

Sumio Nishikawa and Hironori Kitamura

Department of Oral Histology, Kanagawa Dental
College, Yokosuka, Kanagawa 238, Japan

INTRODUCTION

The odontoblast is responsible for secretion of procollagen and formation of dentin (Karim et al., 1980).
Moreover the odontoblasts may ingest some exogeneous material from predentin (Sasaki et al., 1982; Tanaka, 1980).
In spite of some evidence showing the involvement of cytoskeletal elements such as microtubules and actin filaments
in secretion of a variety of cells, little is known on the
cytoskeleton of odontoblasts.

This study revealed that actin filaments and intermediate filaments were major components in the odontoblast
process. For detecting of actin filaments, heavy meromyosin (HMM)(Ishikawa et al., 1969; Nishikawa et al., 1983)
and NBD-phallacidin (Barak et al., 1980) were used. For
preservation of microtubules, taxol (Natural products
Branch, NCI, NIH) was used.

RESULTS

Actin filaments decorated with HMM were distributed
mainly at the periphery of odontoblast process mostly as
bundles or networks in several places underneath the plasma
membrane (Fig. 1). Some coated vesicles related to actin
filaments. NBD-phallacidin labeled predentin in a thread-
like pattern, which showed the labeling of odontoblast
process. The terminal web of odontoblast was decorated
with HMM and labeled with NBD-phallacidin (Fig.2), which
showed that the terminal web contained the actin filament

as a major component. In the core of the odontoblast
process, intermediate filaments which were not decorated
with HMM were abundant. In the specimens treated with
0.5% Triton X-100 and taxol, intermediate filaments tended
to relate to the microtubules.

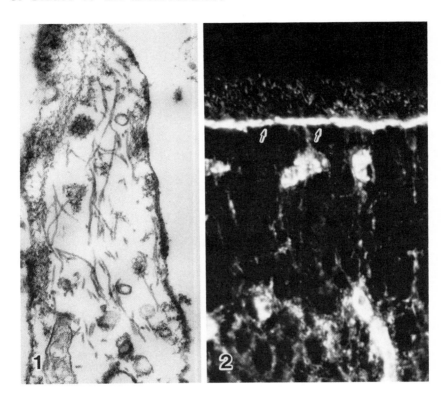

Figure 1. Odontoblast process in predentin, treated with
Triton X-100 and heavy meromyosin (HMM). Actin filaments
are decorated with HMM and give the appearance of arrowheads. Most of actin filaments located at the periphery
are present as bundles or networks with complex orientation. Coated vesicles or pits are sometimes attached to
actin filaments. Intermediate filaments are present in the
core of the process. Bar=0.2um.

Figure 2. A longitudinal section of odontoblasts treated
with NBD-phallacidin. Terminal webs contain actin filaments labeled with NBD-phallacidin (arrows). Bar=20um.

REFERENCES

Barak LS, Yocum RR, Nothnagel EA, Webb WW (1980). Fluorescence staining of the actin cytoskeleton in living cells with 7-nitrobenz-2-oxa-1,3-diazole-phallacidin. Proc Natl Acad Sci USA 77:980-984.
Ishikawa H, Bischoff R, Holtzer H (1969). Formation of arrowhead complexes with heavy meromyosin in a variety of cell types. J Cell Biol 43:312-328.
Nishikawa S, Kitamura H (1983). Actin filaments in the ameloblast of the rat incisor. Anat Rec 207:245-252.
Sasaki T, Ishida I, Higashi S (1982). Ultrastructure and cytochemistry on old odontoblasts in rat incisors. J Electron Microsc 31:378-388.
Tanaka T (1980). The origin and localization of dentinal fluid in developing rat molar teeth studied with lanthanum as a tracer. Arch Oral Biol 25:153-162.

Progress in Developmental Biology, Part B, pages 333–337

MOLECULAR BASIS FOR A PULMONARY MESENCHYMAL-EPITHELIAL INTERACTION

Joanna Floros, Martin Post, Robert M. Kay*, Barry T. Smith
Department of Pediatrics, Harvard Medical School, Boston, MA 02115, *Genetics Institute, Cambridge, MA 02140, U.S.A.

INTRODUCTION

Exogenous glucocorticoids precociously stimulate sur- factant production by lung epithelial type II cells and therefore reduce the incidence of respiratory distress syn- drome (RDS) when administered to mothers in premature labor. Our laboratory has shown that the glucocorticoid effect on the synthesis of surfactant is indirect (Smith 1978, Smith 1981). Glucocorticoids accelerate fetal lung maturation by acting on fetal lung fibroblasts to synthesize a polypeptide fibroblast pneumonocyte factor (FPF) which in turn stimu- lates type II cells to produce surfactant in vitro (Smith & Sabry 1983; Post et al 1984). In addition FPF has shown to accelerate lung maturation in vivo (Smith 1979, Post et al 1984). We have used a culture system, in which we can meas- ure the bioactivity of FPF, to address questions pertaining to the mode of action of glucocorticoids on FPF synthesis. The site at which glucocorticoids affect the synthesis of FPF was studied by a) the use of metabolic inhibitors and b) testing directly the bioactivity of the primary translation products from glucocorticoid induced and uninduced fetal lung fibroblasts.

RESULTS

The effect of metabolic inhibitors in the synthesis of FPF by lung fibroblasts. Fetal lung fibroblasts were incu- bated for 48 hrs in the presence or absence of 10^{-7}M cor- tisol in serum-free minimal essential medium. Inhibitors of protein synthesis (cycloheximide, 1ug/ml) or RNA synthesis (actinomycin D, 0.1ug/ml) were added for either the first or second 24 h portion of this incubation. After the incubation the media was collected and their effect on [Me^3-H] choline incorporation into saturated phosphatidylcholine (SPC) formation by alveolar type II cells was determined as described by Floros et al (1985). SPC is the major component of surfactant. Figure 1 shows that media from fibroblasts treated with either actinomycin D or cycloheximide has no effect on saturated phosphatidylcholine synthesis. The stimulatory effect seen in media from cortisol induced fibroblasts is abolished when actinomycin D is present during the first 24 h of the 48 h incubation. However no inhibition was observed when this drug was present only during the second 24 h period of incubation. Conversely cycloheximide blocks the stimulating effect of cortisol induced conditioned media on SPC synthesis by type II cells whether it is present during the first or second 24 h of the 48 h incubation period of cortisol with fibroblasts. These results suggest that both de novo RNA and protein synthesis is required for the cortisol induced FPF synthesis. These observations agree and extend those of Gross et al (1983).

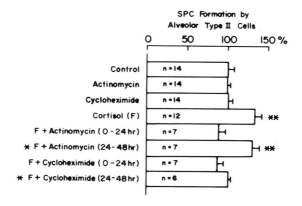

Fig. 1 Effect of actinomycin D and cycloheximide on fibroblast-pneumonocyte factor elaboration by fetal lung fibroblasts. Fetal lung fibroblasts were incubated with serum-free minimum essential medium containing the additions shown. The resulting conditioned media were then incubated for 6 h with fetal alveolar type II cells and their effects on [Me-^{3}H] choline incorporation into SPC were determined. The results presented are from two experiments and are expressed as percentage values of simultaneously determined

control (i.e. no medium additions) values (mean $\pm$ S.E.).

   Bioactivity of cell free translation products. Subsequently, we tested cell free translation products from dexamethasone treated and untreated fibroblasts for their ability to induce SPC synthesis by alveolar type II cells. Size fractionated RNA was prepared, translated in vitro and the primary translation products tested for bioactivity as described by Floros et al (1985). The results in Table 1A show that only cell free translation products of mRNA fractions 23-24 from dexamethasone treated fetal lung fibroblasts enhance the synthesis of SPC by type II cells. Translation products of mRNA fractions 23-24 from control cells had no effect on SPC synthesis. Similarly none of the other fractions of mRNA from either control or dexamethasone treated fibroblasts had any effect on SPC synthesis. The degree of stimulation by fractions 23-24 from steroid-treated fibroblasts was similar either after 7h or 22h of dexamethasone exposure.

   We also translated RNA fraction 24 from treated cells in the xenopus oocyte system and those results are shown in Table 1B. The oocyte translation products from the enriched RNA fraction 24 have an effect on SPC synthesis compared to the translation products from total RNA (Table 1B). The FPF activity confered by the oocyte translation products can be blocked by monoclonal antibodies raised against FPF (Post et al 1984). However this antibody didn't appear to have any significant inhibitory effect on the bioactivity from translation products performed in a cell free reticulocyte system (data not shown).

Table 1. Effect of Cell-free Translation Products or Oocyte Translation Products on SPC Formation by Fetal Alveolar Type II Cells

   mRNA was isolated from control & dexamethasone (dex)-treated fetal lung fibroblasts and size fractionated by methyl mercury-agarose gel electrophoresis. Translation products were tested for their effects on choline incorporation into SPC by fetal alveolar type II cells after 24 h of incubation. The results are expressed as percentage of control values, means $\pm$ S.E., three experiments.

A ADDITION	N	SPC FORMATION	B ADDITION	N	SPC FORMATION
Control	10	100.0 4.0	Control	4	11696 203
FPF[a]	6	158.3 3.4[b]	Total mRNA from dex-treated cells	4	12102 1185
Fractions 23-24 from dex-treated cells	11	130.0 6.9[c]	mRNA fraction 24 from dex-treated cells	3	15032 1498[d]
Other fractions from dex-treated cells	23	96.6 4.3 (range 54.7 -121.8)	mRNA fraction 24 h from dex-treated cells + FPFAb	4	12358 487[e]
Fractions 23-24 from control cells	11	104.6 7.2			
Other fractions from control cells	23	96.1 5.6 (range: 71.8-114.4)			

[a]As derived from conditioned medium from fibroblasts exposed to cortisol, as in Fig. 1
[b]$p < 0.001$ versus control
[c]$p < 0.005$ versus control
[d]$p < 0.1$ versus FPFAb inhibition (e)

In summary our results suggests that (a) glucocorticoids affect the synthesis of FPF at a pretranslational level, (b) posttranslational modifications are not necessary for FPF bioactivity (c) posttranslational modifications might be important for antigenicity.

REFERENCES

Floros J, Post M, Smith BT (1985). J Biol Chem 260:2265-2267.
Gross I, Ballard PL, Ballard RA, Jones CT, Wilson CM (1983). Endocrinology 112:829-839.
Post M, Floros J, Smith BT (1984). Nature (London) 308:284-286.

Post M, Smith BT (1984). Biochim Biophys Acta 793:297-299.
Smith BT (1978). In Stern L (ed): "Neonatal Intensive Care",
  New York:Masson, Vol 2, pp 25-32.
Smith BT (1979). Science (Wash. DC) 204:1094-1095.
Smith BT (1981). In Ritzen M, Aperia A, Hall K, Larsson A,
  Zetterberg A, Zetterstrom R (eds): "The Biology of Normal
  Human Growth", New York:Raven Press, pp 157-162.
Smith BT, Sabry K (1983). Proc Natl Acad Sci U.S.A., 80:1950-
  1954.

Ooplasmic Determinants

Progress in Developmental Biology, Part B, pages 341–344
© 1986 Alan R. Liss, Inc.

EXPRESSION OF ALKALINE PHOSPHATASE DETERMINANTS IN EGG
FRAGMENTS AND ANDROMEROGONS OF ASCIDIANS

William R. Bates and William R. Jeffery

Center for Developmental Biology and
Department of Zoology
University of Texas, Austin, Texas 78712 USA

INTRODUCTION

Determinants localized in the egg cytoplasm are thought
to regulate cell specialization during embryogenesis (Davidson, 1976). Two classes of determinants have been distinguished in ascidian embryos based on their differential
sensitivity to transcriptional inhibitors. The action of
determinants responsible for the expression of muscle acetyl-
cholinesterase (AchE) and a number of other tissue-specific
differentiations requires zygotic transcription (Crowther
and Whittaker, 1984). In contrast, the determinants which
control alkaline phosphatase (AP) synthesis in the endodermal cells appear to function independently of embryonic
gene expression (Whittaker, 1977). The AP determinants have
been suggested to be maternal mRNAs encoding AP, or substances modulating the translation of AP mRNAs, which are
localized in the egg and differentially segregated into the
endodermal cells. In the present investigation, the requirement of the zygotic genome for AP synthesis has been tested
in anucleate egg fragments and andromerogons.

METHODS AND RESULTS

Nuclear and anuclear fragments were microsurgically
prepared from unfertilized eggs and zygotes of the ascidian
Styela plicata. S. plicata eggs contain colored cytoplasmic
regions which enter specific embryonic cells. Two cytoplasmic regions were used to orient eggs for microsurgery.
The clear germinal vesicle plasm (ectoplasm) is located at
the animal pole in mature unfertilized eggs, while the

yellow crescent cytoplasm defines the vegetal hemisphere in
fertilized eggs. Nucleate and anucleate fragments of various volumes and cytoplasmic compositions were prepared
using the cytoplasmic regions for orientation. Egg fragments were surgically generated in the following manner.
While a steel needle was used to immobilize the egg, a
second sharp needle was used to tear a hole in the follicular envelope (FE). By applying pressure to the side of the
FE opposite to the hole with the needle used to puncture the
egg, the egg protoplasm was carefully squeezed out of the
puncture. The narrow cytoplasmic bridge linking the parts
of the cytoplasm inside and outside of the FE was severed
with the tip of the sharp needle. The egg fragments seal
quickly and, if they contain the zygotic nucleus, usually
gastrulate and develop into small larvae. To test the ability of anucleate fragments to express AP, pairs of zygotic
fragments were generated by puncturing the FE at random sites
with regard to the animal-vegetal axis. The fragments were
stained for AP when the control embryos reached the larval
stage. Two histochemical assays were used, that of Osawa
(1951) and a method developed in this laboratory in which
specimens were incubated in 1 mM 5-bromo-4-chloro-3 indolyl
phosphate (BCIP) for 2-3 hours at 37° C. The AP-dependent
dephosphorylation of BCIP results in the formation of in-
dole dimer coloring the specimen blue-green. In parallel
experiments, some fragments were stained for AchE activity
(Karnovsky and Roots, 1964).

Pairs of fragments were prepared 30 to 40 minutes
after insemination. Nucleate and anucleate fragments were
distinguished by phase microscopy and/or 4,6-diamine-2-phe-
nylin-dole (DAPI) fluorescence. The nucleate fragments
usually continued to develop, forming small larvae that
exhibited staining for AchE in their tail musculature and
AP in their gut region, whereas all of the anucleate fragments were negative for both AchE and AP (Table 1).

TABLE 1. AP and AchE expression in paired zygotic fragments

Enzyme	Fragmented pairs	Stained fragments	
		Nucleate	Anucleate
AP	39	35	0
AchE	15	14	0

The absence of AchE in the anucleate fragments was expected since it was previously shown that the synthesis of this enzyme depends on zygotic gene expression. The lack of AP in the anucleate fragments, however, was surprising considering that the AP determinants are thought to function independently of the zygotic genome. One explanation for these results may be that AP expression is independent of the zygotic nucleus, but sensitive to the volume and/or cytoplasmic composition of the anucleate fragments. This possibility was tested by preparing anucleate vegetal fragments consisting of up to 90% of the total zygote volume and containing virtually all of the endoplasm. Most of the nucleate animal fragments cleaved and developed AchE and AP (100% and 85% respectively) in some of their cells. None of the anucleate fragments developed AchE or AP, although the largest of them contained virtually all of the endoplasm. These results suggest that the lack of AP development in anucleate fragments is not due to a reduction in size or concentration of endoplasm.

The inability of zygotic anucleate fragments to express AP does not necessarily imply that the AP determinants require zygotic gene transcription. Determinants have previously been postulated to exist within the nucleus and to be partitioned into the appropriate cell lineages by a nuclear rather than a cytoplasmic segregation (Laufer and von Ehrenstein, 1981). A way to evaluate the possibility that determinants within or attached to the egg nucleus are responsible for AP synthesis is to introduce a non-maternal nucleus into an anucleate fragment. If the AP determinants are present in the anucleate fragments, but require nuclear activity to function, the nuclear transfer should promote AP development. The transfer of a paternal nucleus can be accomplished in ascidians by inseminating anucleate fragments produced surgically from unfertilized eggs. The fertilized fragments, known as andromerogons, frequently develop into haploid larvae. To obtain andromerogons, anucleate fragments from unfertilized eggs were prepared as described, except that the FE puncture was oriented above the animal pole region. In these experiments, a small fragment containing most of the ectoplasm and the female pronuclear chromatin was extruded leaving a larger anucleate fragment within the FE. Although none of the unfertilized anucleate fragments developed AP, AP was detected in 100% of the developing andromerogons. The synthesis of AP in andromerogons strongly suggests that AP determinants are present in the cytoplasm of the anucleate fragments and that they require nuclear activity for their function.

CONCLUSIONS

The expression of AP in endodermal cells of ascidian embryos has been cited as an example of a cell-lineage specific differentiation specified by the localization, segregation, and activation of cytoplasmic determinants in the absence of nuclear gene activity. The present results suggest that this idea, which is based entirely on experiments involving transcriptional inhibitors, must be re-evaluated. The nuclear requirement shown in the present study suggests that the AP determinants function by a cell-lineage specific activation of AP gene(s) and that maternal AP mRNAs are not used as cytoplasmic determinants.

REFERENCES

Crowther, RJ and Whittaker, JR (1984). Differentiation of histospecific ultrastructural features in cells of cleavage-arrested early ascidian embryos. Roux's Arch. 194:87-98.
Davidson, EH (1976). Gene Activity in Early Development. Second edition, Academic Press, New York.
Karnovsky, MJ and Roots, L (1964). A "direct-coloring" thiocholine method for cholinesterases. J. Histochem. Cytochem. 12:219-221.
Laufer, JS and von Ehrenstein, G (1981). Nematode development after removal of egg cytoplasm: Absence of localized unbound determinants. Science 211:402-424.
Osawa, S. (1951). Histochemical studies of alkaline phosphatase in the oogenesis and the early embryogenesis of the amphibia. Embryologia 2:1-20.
Whittaker, JR (1977). Segregation during cleavage of a factor determining endodermal alkaline phosphatase development in ascidian embryos. J. Exp. Zool. 202:139-154.

Progress in Developmental Biology, Part B, pages 345–348

DETERMINATION OF DORSOVENTRAL POLARITY IN THE XENOPUS EGG REQUIRES MICROTUBULES

Stanley R. Scharf, Marya B. Lieberman and W. Zacheus Cande

Departments of Zoology (S.R.S, M.B.L) and Botany (W.Z.C), University of California, Berkeley, CA 94720

It has been known for many years that the frog egg becomes polarized with respect to the point of sperm entry in the period between fertilization and first cleavage (see Gerhart, 1980 for a review). This process is classically referred to as grey crescent formation. On the basis of this superficial pigment asymmetry it is possible to predict the future dorsal-ventral axis of the embryo. In Xenopus, where lack of deep pigment makes a true grey crescent difficult to see, it has recently been shown that egg polarization occurs as a rotation of subcortical cytoplasm with respect to the egg surface, an event precisely analogous to the process of crescent formation. (Scharf et al., 1984; Vincent and Gerhart, 1985)

Recently, the critical developmental significance of this early egg polarization in establishing a primary region of unique dorsal potential has been more fully appreciated. Eggs which are perturbed during this process by a variety of physical treatments, including UV-irradiation, cold and hydrostatic pressure shock, continue to cleave normally, but develop into embryos lacking dorsal-anterior stuctures (Scharf and Gerhart, 1983). Here we report current experiments which define more clearly the cellular mechanisms of this crucial early localization process.

Our previous results with cold and pressure, which are known to reversibly depolymerize microtubules (MT), suggested that these cytoskeletal elements were involved in egg reorganization. MT are known to function in a variety of cellular transport phenomena and in the maintenance of cellular polarity (see Brinkley, 1982 for a review). We therefor treated eggs with the reversible MT drug nocodazole, which selectively disrupts MT organization. Eggs were immersed in a 0.5 micromolar nocodazole solution for 4 min at different times throughout the first cycle (details of this procedure will appear in Scharf, 1985). At this dose level cleavage is generally unaffected and eggs continue to develop. When eggs are treated before 75% of the time from fertilization to first cleavage, embryos showing the same axis deficient syndrome caused by UV, cold and pressure are produced (Table I). No other period prior to gastrulation shows this sensitivity (data not shown). Thus a unique MT requiring event occurs in the first cell cycle. The time course of egg sensitivity implies that this event is completed by the onset of mitosis, presumably a time when MTs function in the mitotic spindle and the egg's interphase-type MT organization is lost.

The immediate effect of nocodazole treatment is to inhibit translocation of subcortical cytoplasm with respect to the surface. In Xenopus this movement occurs in the 0.4-0.9 period and amounts to 300 to 400 micrometers (Scharf et al., 1984). In MT depolymerized eggs, it is limited to less than 40 micrometers (Scharf, 1985).

These results demonstrate a role for MT in the cytoplasmic shift that is responsible for dorsal-vental polarization and suggest that the subcortical region might be a zone of force generation in this process. We have thus begun to examine this region at the light and electron microscope levels. At the light level, we have discovered that a subcortical yolk-excluding zone located immediately below the plasma membrane changes in thickness during the first cell cycle in a manner coincident with the translocation event (Table 1). It attains maximal

TABLE 1. Stage Dependence of Nocodazole Sensitivity
and Subcortical Structural Organization

Normalized Time	Nocodazole Induced Axis Deficiency[1]	Thickness of Sub-cortical Yolk-Excluding Zone[2]
0.2	4.9	3
0.4	3.8	3
0.6	3.0	4
0.7	0.7	6
0.8	0.0	7
1.0	0.0	3

1 Measured on the Index of Axis Deficiency scale of
Scharf and Gerhart, 1983, in which 5.0 is maximal.
2 The thickness in micrometers of this region near
the equator (see Fig. 1), measured by light microscopy of glutaraldehyde fixed sections.

thickness at the end of translocation. This thickening does not occur in nocodazole-treated eggs
(data not shown) suggesting its formation is MT
dependent. Indeed, at the EM level we have visualized a population of subcortical MT in this region
that course parallel to the egg surface during the
translocation process (Fig. 1). Details of these
findings will be reported elsewhere.

In summary these data demonstrate a requirement
for intact MT during the early egg reorganizaton
that establishes the initial dorsoventral polarity
of the Xenopus egg. Future work will focus on the
details of egg interphase MT organization.

Support is gratefully acknowledged from the
Muscular Dystrophy Association (Post-doctoral fellowship to S.R.S.) and from the NIH (grant GM23238 to
W.Z.C.). Thanks also to Ray Keller for providing
facilities and to M.B.L. for technical support.

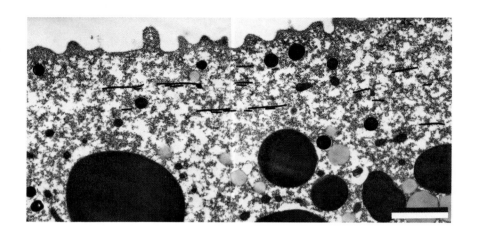

Figure 1. Visualization of egg mictotubules at the EM level. Shown is a subcortical region at time 0.75. Note that the large yolk platelets are excluded from the MT (drawn over with ink to enhance visibility) containing region. Scale marker is 2μM.

REFERENCES

Brinkley BR (1982). Organization of the cytoplasm. Cold Spring Harbor Symp Quant Biol 46:1029.

Gerhart JC (1980). Mechanisms regulating pattern formation in the amphibian embryo. In Goldberger RF (ed): "Biological regulation and development", New york: Plenum, pp 133–316.

Scharf SR (1985). Localization of dorsal potential in the Xenopus egg requires microtubules. Nature (in submission).

Scharf SR and Gerhart JC (1983). Axis determination in eggs of Xenopus laevis: A critical period before first cleavage identified by the commmon effects of cold, pressure and ultraviolet irradiation. Dev Biol 99:75–91.

Scharf SR, Vincent J-P and Gerhart JC (1984). Axis determination in the Xenopus egg. In Davidson EH and Firtel R (eds): "Molecular Biology of Development", New York: AR Liss, pp 51–73.

Vincent JP and Gerhart JC (1985). A subcortical rotation determines dorsoventral polarity in the Xenopus egg. Dev Biol (in submission).

Progress in Developmental Biology, Part B, pages 349–352
© 1986 Alan R. Liss, Inc.

A REINVESTIGATION OF THE PROCESS OF GREY CRESCENT FORMATION
IN XENOPUS EGGS.

Jean-Paul Vincent and John C. Gerhart

Department of Molecular Biology and Group in
Biophysics, University of California, Berkeley,
California 94720

INTRODUCTION

Specification of the amphibian dorso-ventral axis
takes place in the egg during the period between
fertilization and first cleavage when the grey crescent
forms. During this time the egg periphery reorganizes, for
which two different descriptions have been given.
According to the "rotation hypothesis", which applies to
Rana eggs, the egg cortex rotates by an arc of 30° relative
to the stationary subcortical cytoplasm (Ancel and
Vintemberger, 1948; Elinson, 1980). The "contraction
hypothesis" on the other hand, was proposed for Xenopus
eggs and asserts that there is a cortical contraction
focused at the sperm entry point that leads to stretching
of the opposite marginal zone (Lovtrup, 1958; Palecek et
al, 1978). We have reinvestigated the case of Xenopus eggs
with the following experiments. We imprinted one kind of
fluorescent dye pattern (nile blue) onto the subcortical
cytoplasm and another kind (fluorescein-lectin) onto the
egg surface. We then monitored the deformation and
movement of those two patterns.

METHODS

In the vegetal hemisphere, both dyes were applied in a
pattern as follows. Each egg was fit in an hemispherical
well made in a perforated sheet of stainless steel (hole
diameter=100 microns), and the dye (0.05% nile blue and 4%
ficoll in H_2O or 2 mg fluoresceinated potato lectin per ml
of H_2O) was introduced underneath for 5 min.

For the application of nile blue spots to the egg's animal hemisphere, a slightly different procedure was needed. One hemispherical well was made on a small piece of perforated sheet (area=10 mm^2). A drop of melted 2% agarose with 0.011% nile blue, pH 7 was then deposited on the concave side of the well and allowed to solidify. One fertilized albino egg was introduced into a shallow agarose well and covered by a prepared grid such as to fit the well onto the animal hemisphere. The grid was removed 5 min later and a pattern of fluorescent dye spots resulted. This method was not appropriate for the application of fluoresceinated potato lectin onto the animal hemisphere. We therefore resorted to the following procedure. The whole egg was stained for 5 min in a solution of fluoresceinated potato lectin and a laser beam was subsequently used to bleach a grid pattern on the uniformly stained animal surface. All the observations were made through a fluorescence microscope.

RESULTS

We first showed that when the egg is embedded in gelatin, the egg surface (marked by the fluorescent lectin) does not move nor deform extensively during the period between 0.3 and 0.9 (30% and 90% of the time between fertilization and first cleavage respectively). During the same period, the following movements of the subcortical cytoplasm of gelatin embedded eggs occur. Starting at time 0.3, the animal hemisphere subcortical cytoplasm converges toward a point, while the vegetal hemisphere is quiescent. At 0.45, an overall rotation of the animal and vegetal cytoplasm commences, superimposed on the animal hemisphere convergence, which has begun to attenuate. By 0.8-0.9 the rotation is complete, having accomplished a 30° displacement of the subcortical cytoplasm relative to the surface. The plane of rotation, which is most easily identified by observing the vegetal hemisphere, reliably locates the future dorsal midline of the embryo at the meridian on which the vegetal subcortical cytoplasm was most displaced toward the vegetal pole (fig. 1). We infer that the convergence focus in the animal hemisphere is at the point of sperm entry since artificially activated eggs do not undergo any convergence although a rotation still occurs in those eggs.

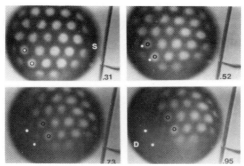

Figure 1. Successive frames showing the movement of
subcortical nile blue spots in the vegetal hemisphere of
gelatin embedded eggs. The egg is observed from below with
an inverted fluorescence microscope with the filter set
optimized for rhodamine. "S" denotes the meridian of the
egg which, in the animal hemisphere, bears the sperm entry
point. "D" refers to the "dorsal" meridian where the
neural groove was identified 24 hrs after fertilization.
Normalized time is indicated on each frame.

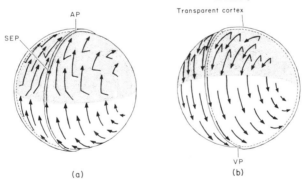

Figure 2. Schematic diagram of the movements of the
subcortical cytoplasm in a gelatin embedded egg. One half
of the cortex has been cut away so that the surface of the
subcortical cytoplasm is exposed. The thickness of the
remaining half of the cortex has been grossly exaggerated.
We studied a few free-floating egg as well. In that case,
the same relative movements occur, but it is the cortex
that undergoes the absolute rotation while the convergence

still occurs in the animal subcortical cytoplasm. In this figure, the egg at time 0.35 of the first cell cycle is shown. Each arrow indicates by its length and direction, the displacement of a point in the period until 0.8-0.9. a) Ventral view. The ventral meridian is 90° away from the lateral poles marking the axis of rotation. Note the cluster of pigment in the animal hemisphere, at the sperm entrance point. b) Dorsal view. The dorsal meridian is 90° away from the lateral poles.

The movement of vegetal subcortical cytoplasm relative to the egg surface can be instantaneously arrested by several experimental treatments. Those include UV irradiation of the vegetal hemisphere, cold treatment and injection of microtubule-depolymerizing drugs. UV and cold treatment have previously been shown to prevent the formation of a body axis in a dose dependent manner (Scharf and Gerhart, 1983). The application of either treatment at different times stops the rotation after different extent of completion. This allowed us to test a possible correlation between the decreased rotation and the truncation of the axis. This correlation holds. This gives strong support to the importance of the rotation in the vegetal hemisphere for the specification of dorsal axial development.

REFERENCES

Ancel P, Vintemberger P. (1948). Recherches sur le determinisme de la symetrie bilaterale dans l'oeuf des amphibiens. Bull Biol Fr Belg Suppl 31: 1-182.
Elinson RP (1980). The amphibian egg cortex in fertilization and early development. Symp Soc Dev Biol 38: 217-234.
Lovtrup S (1958). A physiological interpretation of the mechanism involved in the determination of bilateral symmetry in amphibian embryos. J Embryol Exp Morph 6(1): 15-27.
Palecek J, Ubbels GA, Rzehak K (1978). Changes of the external and internal pigment pattern upon fertilization in the egg of Xenopus laevis. J Embryol Exp Morph 45: 203-214.
Scharf SR, Gerhart JC (1983). Axis determination in eggs of Xenopus laevis: A critical period before first cleavage, identified the common effects of cold, pressure and ultraviolet irradiation. Dev Biol 99: 75-87.

Progress in Developmental Biology, Part B, pages 353–356

THE ULTRASTRUCTURAL ORGANIZATION OF THE ISOLATED CORTEX OF
A MOLLUSCAN EGG

Johanna E Speksnijder[*], Kees de Jong[*#], Wilbert AM Linnemans[#], and M Rene Dohmen[*]

[*]Zoological Laboratory and [#]Department of Molecular Cell Biology, University of Utrecht, Padualaan 8, 3584 CH Utrecht, The Netherlands

Introduction

The spatial organization of the cytoplasm has been the subject of intense investigations in recent years. This topic has special relevance for the study of early development since the spatial distribution of particular cytoplasmic components is of crucial importance in the determination of cell types in many organisms. A classic example of this localization phenomenon is constituted by the morphogenetic factors present in the polar lobes of molluscan and annelid eggs. Presumably, these factors are closely associated with the polar lobe egg cortex. In many species, the egg surface of the polar lobe is characterized by regional differences both of the surface architecture (Dohmen,1983; Speksnijder & Dohmen,1983) and of the plasma membrane (Speksnijder et al.,1985ab). It is obvious to assume that there is a relationship between these surface differentiations and the underlying morphogenetic factors. Cytoskeletal elements might function as an intermediate in this relationship, especially since it is now well documented that the cytoskeleton may serve as a framework for the positioning of specific components in an egg cell (Jeffery,1984). Therefore we studied the organization of the cortical cytoskeleton of the egg of Nassarius reticulatus by examining critical point-dried, rotatory shadowed whole mounts of cortices isolated on poly-L-lysine coated grids, in the transmission electron microscope.

Structural organization of the egg cortex

Examination of the isolated cortex by TEM reveals the presence of numerous membranous and filamentous structures. At the cytoplasmic side of the plasma membrane a dense network

of thin filaments (6–8 nm in diameter) with typical Y and X
shaped intersections can be observed (Fig. 1ab). In stereo
images, this filamentous lattice can be seen parallel and
closely apposed to the plasma membrane. Labeling experiments
with heavy meromyosin (HMM) demonstrate that the lattice
consists of actin-containing microfilaments.

An array of criss-crossing thick filaments (diameter 20–
25 nm) is present at some distance from the plasma membrane
(as inferred from stereo pairs). Labeling experiments with an
anti-tubulin antibody using the protein A-gold method for TEM
shows specific staining of these thick filaments, identifying
them as microtubules.

Apart from cytoskeletal structures, the isolated cortex
also contains other cellular organelles. Vesicles of various
sizes, and an interconnecting network of strings of small
vesicles and tubular cisternae can be found associated with
the cytoskeletal filaments (Fig. 1ab). This membranous network might represent part of a cortical endoplasmic reticulum, similar to the reticulum described in eggs of Xenopus
and sea urchin (Charbonneau & Grey,1984; Sardet,1984).

Associated with the plasma membrane, hexagonally-organized
clathrin-coated areas are present (Fig. 1b). These clathrin
coats are usually found in a flat, non-budding configuration.

Based on our observations on stereo pairs, we deduced a
schematic representation of the isolated cortex of Nassarius
eggs, which is shown in Fig. 1c.

Temporal differences in the organization of the egg cortex

Observations on cortices isolated at various stages during
the first cleavage cycle (i.e. from the extrusion of the 2nd
polar body to the 2-cell stage) reveal the dynamic organization of the cortical cytoskeleton. The density of the microfilamentous lattice increases at the time of polar lobe formation and decreases again at the end of first cleavage. In
contrast, the density of the array of cortical microtubules
decreases at polar lobe formation. At the end of first cleavage, however, microtubules reappear in the egg cortex. Since
the period of absence of cortical microtubules coincides with
the mitotic phase of the first cleavage cycle, this could indicate that cortical microtubules alternate with spindle microtubules. A similar phenomenon has been observed in starfish oocytes (Schroeder & Otto,1984).

In the uncleaved egg, clathrin-coated areas are present in
a flat configuration. At the time of polar lobe formation,
however, budding clathrin plaques can also be found. After
the polar lobe has been formed, the density of the clathrin-

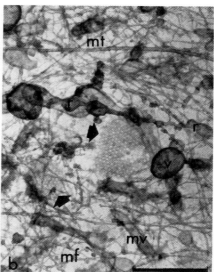

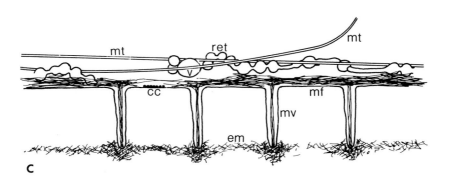

Fig. 1.(a) Edge of an isolated cortex showing the endoplas-
    mic reticulum associated with the microfilamentous lat-
    tice (bar = 2.0 um); (b) Hexagonally-organized clathrin
    coats (arrows) in the cortex of an uncleaved egg (bar =
    0.5 um); (c) Schematic representation of the organization
    of the isolated egg cortex; mt, microtubules; r, endo-
    plasmic reticulum; mf, microfilaments; v, vesicles; cc,
    clathrin coat; mv, microvilli; em, extracellular material.

coated areas is reduced considerably, which suggests a burst of endocytotic activity at the time of polar lobe formation.

Regional differences in the organization of the egg cortex

The spatial aspects of egg cortex organization were investigated by selectively preparing cortices from the animal and vegetal part of the egg. At the vegetal pole of the egg (i.e. the polar lobe area) the density of microvilli is much lower then on the rest of the egg surface, whereas the individual microvilli are much longer. This is in accordance with previous observations (Dohmen,1983; Speksnijder et al., 1985a). As a result, the length of the microfilament bundles in the microvilli and also the distance between two individual bundles is locally different. The organization of the microfilamentous lattice is not grossly different, although frequently more open spaces in the network, corresponding to microvilli-free areas, can be observed.

Conclusions

The isolated egg cortex of Nassarius contains a variety of cytoskeletal and membranous structures, which are organized in an interconnecting three-dimensional array. The density of cortical microfilaments and microtubules, and of the plasma membrane-associated clathrin coats changes in relation to the first cleavage cycle.

With respect to the density of microvilli and the organization of the underlying microfilament network, regional differences in cortex organization have been observed. At present it is not possible, however, to relate these differences to the localization of polar lobe determinants in the vegetal part of the egg. Still, these regional differences constitute another example of the polar organization of the egg surface in polar lobe-forming eggs.

References

Charbonneau M and Grey RD (1984) Dev Biol 102, 90-97
Dohmen MR (1983) In:"Time, Space, and Pattern in Embryonic
  Development" (WR Jeffery and RA Raff, eds) AR Liss, New
  York, pp 197-220
Jeffery WR (1984) Dev Biol 103, 482-492
Sardet C (1984) Dev Biol 105, 196-210
Schroeder TE and Otto JJ (1984) Dev Biol 103, 493-503
Speksnijder JE and Dohmen MR (1983) W Roux' Arch Dev Biol
  192, 148-155
Speksnijder JE et al. (1985a) Dev Biol 108, 38-48
Speksnijder JE et al. (1985b) Dev Biol 110, 207-216

Progress in Developmental Biology, Part B, pages 357–360
© 1986 Alan R. Liss, Inc.

OOPLASMIC DETERMINANTS IN AMPHIBIANS

Jutta Janeczek, Hildegard Tiedemann and
Heinz Tiedemann
Institut für Molekularbiologie und Biochemie,
Freie Universität Berlin, Arnimallee 22,
D-1000 Berlin 33, FR Germany

In 1923 Hans Spemann and Hilde Mangold discovered that
the blastoporal lip of a Triturus gastrula can induce an additional neural plate (Spemann, 1938). The neural inducing
activity is mediated by chemical substances which are protein in nature. The neural inducing activity of the blastoporal lip did not decrease after treatment with actinomycin
D, which inhibits mRNA synthesis (Tiedemann et al., 1967).
This suggested that either the factor or its mRNA are synthesized before gastrulation.

We have investigated whether neuralizing factors or its
mRNA's can already be found in Xenopus oocytes. The inducing
activity was tested by the implantation method on omnipotent
gastrula ectoderm of Triturus alpestris.

Mature oocytes contain neural inducing factors, which
are preferentially located in the ooplasm (52% forehead ind.)
whereas the germinal vesicles have a smaller neural inducing
activity (15% forehead ind.). The germinal vesicles were manually isolated and extensively washed in the culture solution so that the contamination with ooplasmic constituents
was very low (Bretzel et al., unpublished).

The ooplasmic neural inducing activity is present in
three defined subcellular fractions which were isolated by
repeated centrifugation on stepwise sucrose gradients (Janeczek et al., 1984). These are RNP-particles, small vesicles
from the microsomal fraction and the 100,000xg supernatant.
The subcellular fractions were tested as pellets after precipitation with ethanol. The inducing activity especially of

the RNP-particles and of the germinal vesicles, was however much lower when the fractions were tested in the native state. This suggests that the inducing factors are present in the oocyte and in early embryonic stages in a masked, inactive state and that they can be activated by treatment with ethanol.

The chemical properties of the neuralizing factors in the subcellular fractions are different. The RNP-particles have the highest inducing activity, which is largely abolished after treatment with trypsin or proteinase K. RNA isolated from RNP-particles by the phenol procedure has no inducing activity. After isoelectric focusing in 6 M urea the factor bands as a basic protein at pH 8-10.

The protein from the 100,000xg supernatant which elutes at an apparent M_r of about 130,000-150,000 (fr. IA) has the highest inducing activity of all chromatographic fractions (Fig. 1, 2). When the factor was isolated from gastrulae the percentage of smaller molecules with neural inducing activity was higher. This may suggest that the smaller molecules are generated from larger precursors. In addition proteolytic cleavage occurs during the preparation of the factor which can be prevented by the addition of protease inhibitors (α_2-macroglobulin, leupeptin).

The supernatant factor and the factor in the small vesicles are acidic molecules (I.P.~5.5). Acid hydrolysis of the supernatant factor at conditions whereby sialic acid is completely split from glycoproteins ($5x10^{-3}$ M H_2SO_4, 1 h at 95 °C) did not change its isoelectric point. Incubation at 37 °C with neuraminidase did on the other hand shift the isoelectric point of a part of the factor to pH 7-8. This is probably due to enzymes contaminating neuraminidase and enzymes in the supernatant. Reduction with mercaptoethanol under conditions where no proteolysis occurs did not change the molecular mass of the factor. That the factors in RNP-particles and in the small vesicles and the supernatant are biosynthetically related (i.e. by glycosylation or other modifications) seems to be possible, but has not yet been investigated.

RNP-particles and small vesicles induce in addition to forehead structures to a small extent hindheads with typical rhombencephalic structures and ear vesicles. The hindhead inductions show that a small amount of vegetalizing factor is also prelocated in the oocyte, because hindheads are induced

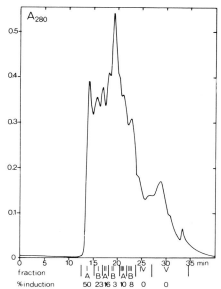

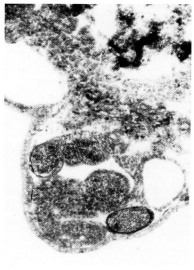

Figure 1. SE-HPLC of Xenopus oocyte sup. prepared without protease inhibitor (∿4 mg reduced
protein). Si 300 Diol 5 µm (Ser-
va, Heidelberg) 8x500 mm. 50%
formic acid, 0.6 ml/min. Abscissa: % forehead ind. with eye.

Figure 2. Histological section of a forehead induc-
tion on the belly of a Triturus alpestris larva. Eyes
with pigmented tapetum ni-
grum, noses and brain are
induced.

by a combined action of neuralizing and vegetalizing factors
(Saxén and Toivonen, 1962). The presence of a vegetalizing
factor was confirmed by experiments on the inducing activity
of intact presumptive endoderm from fertilized eggs and early embryonic stages (Asashima, 1975).

     The experiments have shown, that inducing factors which
are protein (or glycoprotein) in nature are at least in part
synthesized in the oocyte and stored. Are these factors actually involved in the physiological process of induction? Active neural inducing factor is at first found in the morula
stage in the dorsal marginal zone (Asashima, 1980) which induces, after its invagination in the gastrula stage, the neural plate in the overlying dorsal ectoderm. The induced neural plate in turn acquires neural inducing activity. Neural

inducing factor is also present in the presumptive neural ectoderm, but up to the gastrula stage in a masked, biological inactive state. Grunz and Hildegard Tiedemann (in press) have observed an induction dependent activation of the neuralizing factor in the 100,000xg sediment (which contains RNP-particles and small microsomal vesicles) and in the 100,000xg supernatant of neural plate homogenates. This induction dependent activation suggests that the neural inducing factors in the particulate fractions and in the supernatant are actually involved in the normal induction process. We are now preparing antibodies against the neural inducing factors. Injection of the antibodies into fertilized eggs should impair neural plate formation when these factors take part in the normal induction process.

Supported by Fonds der Chemischen Industrie and Deutsche Forschungsgemeinschaft.

REFERENCES

Asashima M (1975). Inducing effects of presumptive endoderm of successive stages in Triturus alpestris. Wilhelm Roux's Archives 177:301-308.

Asashima M (1980). Inducing effects of the grey crescent region of early developmental stages of Ambystoma mexicanum. Wilhelm Roux's Archives 188:123-126.

Janeczek J, Born J, John M, Scharschmidt M, Tiedemann H, Tiedemann H (1984). Ribonucleoprotein particles from Xenopus eggs and embryos. Eur J Biochem 140:257-264.

Saxén L, Toivonen S (1962). "Primary Embryonic Induction." New York: Academic Press.

Spemann H (1938). "Embryonic Development and Induction." New Haven: Yale Univ. Press.

Tiedemann H, Born J, Tiedemann H (1967). Embryonale Induktion und Hemmung der Ribonucleinsäuresynthese durch Actinomycin D. Z Naturforsch 22b:649-659.

Progress in Developmental Biology, Part B, pages 361–364
© 1986 Alan R. Liss, Inc.

MICROTUBULE ORGANIZATION DURING POLAR CAP MITOSIS AND POLE
CELL FORMATION IN THE DROSOPHILA EMBRYO

Richard Warn

School of Biology, University of East Anglia,
Norwich NR4 7TJ, U.K.

INTRODUCTION

How is cell shape and form determined during
development? One system to investigate such problems is
the Drosophila embryo where only two kinds of cells, but
with very different morphologies, are initially produced.
Most of the egg is cleaved into columnar blastoderm cells
but the small group of pole cells, from which the germ
cells come, form as much smaller spherical cells. The
manner and timing of pole cell formation is quite different
from that by which blastoderm cells are cleaved (Warn et
al., 1985) and these differences are regulated by maternal
factors.

In order to study possible differences in spindle
organization that may have a role in the determination of
cell shape, the microtubule distribution of the polar
surface caps during cycle 10 is described, and compared
with previous observations of microtubule organization for
the somatic blastoderm caps (Warn and Warn, 1985).

MATERIALS AND METHODS

These were as described previously (Warn and Warn,
1985). To observe the posterior pole from the top, the
embryo tips were cut off and stuck to siliconized slides
directly.

RESULTS

At prophase the centrosomes migrate to opposite sides of the nucleus forming the future spindle poles (Figures 1a & b). During this process microtubules are still attached to the migrating centrosomes. Prometaphase is marked by microtubule growth between the centrosomes giving rise to the spindle (2a & b). The metaphase spindle is fusiform with reduced staining in the interzonal region (3a & b) and is very similar in shape to that of the somatic caps. Both polar and kinetochore fibres can be discerned within the spindle. Anaphase (4a & b) is characterized by a lengthening of the spindle and an elongation of the aster fibres. From the end of anaphase onwards spindle microtubules adjacent to the asters stain less strongly and it appears that they are progressively reduced in number (5a & b). The remnant of the spindle, a brightly staining stembody, disappears more slowly. This pair of photographs, of a late telophase stage, also demonstrates the early separation of the centrosomes at the end of the cell cycle. Again all these features are shared with the somatic cap spindle. Cleavage to form the pole cells occurs as soon as the cells move into interphase. By this time, the stembody has disappeared (6a & b). Microtubules radiate from the centrosomes around the nuclei whilst cell membranes are extended between the pair of daughter nuclei.

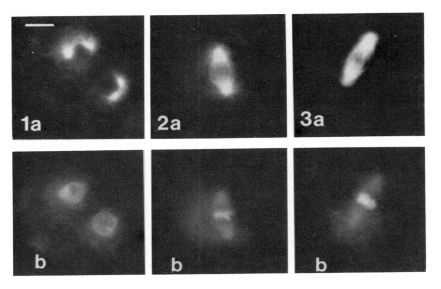

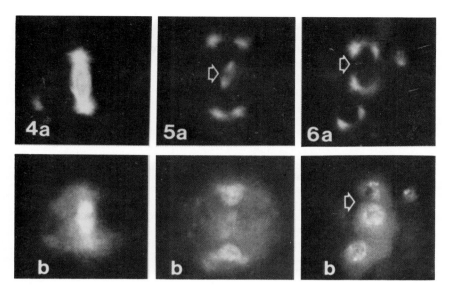

Figs 1-6 (All photo pairs a-anti-tubulin b-DAP1 nuclear
staining bar=8 μ) 1. prophase 2. prometaphase 3. metaphase 4. early anaphase 5. late telophase
(arrow-stembody) 6. interphase (arrows-region of cleavage)

DISCUSSION

During mitosis the organization of the polar cap
spindle closely resembles that of the somatic caps in all
the respects studied. The major features in common include
the shape and mode of formation of the spindle, the
distinctive stembody, and the very early splitting of the
centrosome. (Compare the results presented here with those
of Warn and Warn, 1985). These findings parallel previous
observations of the similar F-actin distributions prior to
cell formation (Warn et al, 1985).

No equivalent was found of the basket-like microtubule
organization which occurs in the somatic caps during the
formation of the cellular blastoderm (Fullilove and
Jacobson, 1971; Warn and Warn, 1985). This structure may
be important in nuclear elongation, a process which occurs
during blastoderm cell formation but not in pole cells.

In conclusion, the data suggest the gross structural features of mitosis are rather similar and that the essential features of cytoskeletal activity required to produce the two kinds of cell operate during cleavage. Thus the organization and time of action of the F-actin contractible ring structures, rather than the spindle, are likely to be major factors determining pole cell or blastoderm cell shape.

REFERENCES

Fullilove SL, Jacobson AG, (1971). Nuclear elongation and cytokinesis in Drosophila montana. Dev. Biol 26:560–577.
Warn RM, Smith L, Warn A, (1985). Three distinct distributions of F-actin occur during the divisions of polar surface caps to produce pole cells in Drosophila embryos. J Cell Biol 100:1010–1015.
Warn RM, and Warn A (1985). Microtubule arrays present during the syncytial and cellular blastoderm stages of the early Drosophila embryo. Exp Cell Res In Press.

Progress in Developmental Biology, Part B, pages 365–368
© 1986 Alan R. Liss, Inc.

AN IMMUNOLOGICAL TECHNIQUE FOR ISOLATION OF RNA INVOLVED IN
UV-INDUCED AND PHOTOREPAIRABLE EFFECTS ON DEVELOPMENT

Roger G. Phillips and Klaus Kalthoff

Center for Developmental Biology, Department of
Zoology, University of Texas at Austin,
Austin, Texas 78712.

INTRODUCTION

    Three UV-inducible effects on early development of the
midge, Smittia, can be reversed by subsequent irradiation
with light of longer wavelengths (photorepair). 1) UV
irradiation of the anterior end of the egg results in
replacement of cephalic and thoracic segments by a mirror
image duplication of abdominal segments (double abodomen).
2) UV irradiation of the posterior end of the egg inhibits
pole cell formation and results in adult sterility. 3)
Lateral UV irradiation of the egg results in decreased
protein synthesis and developmental arrest. Evidence
reviewed below indicates that the photorepairable portion
of these effects results from the generation of pyrimidine
dimers in RNA. A monoclonal antibody has been prepared
which binds uridine dimers in RNA. We propose to use this
antibody for the isolation of RNA which has been "tagged"
with dimers by the UV irradiation procedures producing
these three effects. The "tagged" RNA will then be used to
probe a cDNA library for clones containing inserts
homologous to RNA sequences which are selectively "tagged".

RNA DETERMINANTS

    Anterior UV irradiation of Smittia eggs inactivates
factors necessary for the specification of cephalic
segments (anterior determinants). The analysis of anterior
determinants reviewed below has been presented and
referenced in detail by Kalthoff (1979). The anterior

determinants are RNase-sensitive, UV-sensitive and photorepairable, indicating that they include an RNA component. Centrifugation of the eggs redistributes the determinants and results in double cephalons (replacement of the posterior end of the embryo with a mirror image duplication of the cephalic segments) and inverted embryos, as well as double abdomens. Combined irradiation and centrifugation experiments (Kalthoff et al, 1982) show that both operations affect the same determinants which are not associated with nuclei, mitochondria or yolk particles.

Inhibition of pole cell formation by posterior irradiation of Smittia eggs also involves a localized cytoplasmic nucleic acid component. This is indicated by the UV action spectrum and potential for photorepair, and the localization of the target posterior to the cleavage stage nuclei (Brown and Kalthoff, 1983). Okada reports evidence for an RNA component in pole cell formation in Drosophila (this volume).

PHOTOREPAIR OF PYRIMIDINE DIMERS

UV-induced early embryonic arrest and reduction of protein synthesis in Smittia are correlated with pyrimidine dimer formation in RNA (Jackle and Kalthoff, 1980). Irradiation that induces arrest also reduces in vivo protein synthesis . RNA extracted from irradiated embryos stimulates in vitro protein synthesis to a lesser extent than RNA from unirradiated embryos. These effects are substantially mitigated by photorepair. The frequency of pyrimidine dimers in RNA extracted from embryos increases with irradiation and decreases with photorepair. The extent of photorepair is correlated to the frequency of dimers, but not protein crosslinks, in the RNA.

APPLICATION OF THE ANTI-DIMER ANTIBODY

Irradiation conditions which inactivate anterior or pole cell determinants with large photorepairable sectors "tag" some RNA components of these determinants (and other RNA) with pyrimidine dimers. The "tagged" RNA may be isolated by immunoprecipitation with an anti-pyrimidine dimer antibody. By comparing "tagged" RNA from embryos irradiated under conditions producing different developmental effects, RNA associated with the determinants may be identified. Localization, stage and spectral sensitivity provide selective irradiation conditions for anterior and pole cell determinants.

Sequences in "tagged" RNA populations may be compared by differential hybridization on duplicate filters of an egg cDNA library. Clones containing inserts complementary to RNA sequences which are "tagged" selectivley during inactivation of determinants will be used to assay the localization of the sequence by in situ hybridization and to prepare RNA for bioassays.

CHARACTERIZATION OF THE ANTI-DIMER ANTIBODY

Mice were immunized with "dimer-enriched" oligouridylic acid covalently conjugated to bovine serum albumin. Pyrimidine dimers can be characterized as follows (Varghese, 1972). 1) They are generated both by irradiation at wavelengths below 300 nm and by irradiation above 300 nm with a sensitizing agent such as acetone. 2) Their generation requires adjacent pryrimidines in nucleic acid polymers. 3) They are photochemmically reversible and at lower wavelengths (240 nm) the monomer is favored. Pyrimidine dimer formation disrupts the conjugated ring of the two pyrimidines resulting in a substantial decrease of absorbance at 260 nm. The "dimer-enriched" oligo uridlylic acid was prepared by acetone-sensitized irradiation at wavelengths greater then 300 nm. Reirradiation at 240 nm caused a substantial increase in absorbance at 260 nm confirming the presence of pyrimidine dimers in the immunogen.

Hybridomas were prepared using spleen cells from the immunized mice in the UT Hybridoma Facility under the direction of Dr. Paul Gottlieb. The hybridoma clones were assayed for antibody showing differential binding to RNA irradiated at 254 nm without sensitization insuring that positive clones would meet the first criterion listed above. A clone was identified which produces an antibody binding a photoproduct which exhibits all the characteristics of a pyrimidine dimer. The antibody binds polyuridylic acid (poly U) irradiated at 260 nm or at 313 nm with acetone photosensitization but not unirradiatied poly U. The antibody fails to bind the alternating co-polymer of uridylic acid and adenylic acid regardless of irradiation. Binding increases with increasing fluence at either 280 nm or 313 nm with acetone sensitization, but decreases with subsequent reirradiation at 240 nm. The antibody precipitates dimer-rich poly U in a modified Farr assay (Strickland and Boyle, 1981). Irradiated poly U shows competition in this assay in proportion to its dimer content from 1% to 90% dimers.

The antibody binds irradiated RNA but not irradiated DNA. Both irradiated poly U and irradiated poly dU are bound. Irradiated poly C and poly dC are bound to a lesser extent and irradiated poly dT is not bound. We conclude that the specificity for irradiated RNA results from the specificity for uridine dimers and that binding of irradiated poly C may result from deamination of the cytidine dimers to uridine dimers.

REFERENCES

Brown PM, Kalthoff K (1983). Inhibition by Ultraviolet Light of Pole Cell Formation in Smittia sp (Chironomidae, Diptera): Action Spectrum and Photoreversibility. Dev Biol 97:113-122.
Jackle H, Kalthoff K (1980). Photoreversible UV-inactivation of Messenger RNA in an Insect Embryo (Smittia spec., Chironomidae, Diptera). Photochem Photobiol 42:749-761.
Kalthoff K (1979). Analysis of a Morphogenetic Determinant in an Insect Embryo (Smittia sp., Chironomidae, Diptera). in Subtelny S, Konigsberg IR (eds): "Determinants of Spatial Organization" New York: Academic Press, pp 97-126.
Kalthoff K, Rau K-G, Edmond JC (1982). Modifying Effects of Ultraviolet Irradiation on the Development of Abnormal Body Patterns in Centrifuged Insect Embryos (Smittia sp., Chironomidae, Diptera). Dev Biol 91:413-422.
Strickland PT, Boyle JM (1981). Application of the Farr Assay to the Analysis of Antibodies Specific for UV Irradiated DNA. J Imm Meth 41:115-124.
Varghese AJ (1972). Photochemistry of Nucleic Acids and Their Constituents. In Giese AL (ed): "Photophysiology, Volume VII" pp 207-274.

Molecular Biology of Extracellular Matrix

Progress in Developmental Biology, Part B, pages 371–376

MOLECULAR BIOLOGY OF EXTRACELLULAR MATRIX: STRATEGY AND REDUNDANCY

Robert L. Trelstad, M.D.

Department of Pathology
Rutgers Medical School
University of Medicine and Dentistry of New
Jersey, Piscataway, New Jersey 08854

Seemingly unrelated events in the summer of 1985 have caused me to read and reread the title of the Minisymposium, Molecular Biology and Extracellular Matrix, which I chaired at the ISDB meeting in August. Hal Slavkin and I agreed upon the title and it was cast into print well over a year before the meeting.

Where is the article 'the' in the title? Where is article 'the' in title? Was this the convenience of space or was this deliberate? Are these thes essential or extraneous?

I spent a good deal of informal time at the 'Structural Macromolecules - Collagen' Gordon Conference in July discussing strategies of research. In the enthusiasm of the moment, there are many scientists who have embraced the techniques of modern biology without reflecting on broader biological perspectives and biological hierarchies. I ask my children where chickens come from and they are apt to answer: 'From plastic packages in the supermarket.' I asked my colleagues at lunch in New Hampshire if they had ever chased, beheaded, plucked, dressed and eaten a chicken. Most had not.

On Thursday evening at the Gordon Conference an effort was made to bring a variety of thoughts together on the genesis of form. Formal discussions ranged from the homeo box, to phage assembly, to the Fibonacci series and sunflowers. Are there mathematical and physical factors which apply in form generation? Certainly. Are there

factors of form generation embedded in the genes?
Certainly. Are there factors for morphogenesis which
operate epigenetically? Certainly. Do these factors operate
simultaneously and separately, independently and together?
Certainly. How do we dissect their individual effects? How
do we logically sum their aggregate effects?

The guidance cues or systems available to birds in
their navigation include at least solar position,
perception of polarized light, stellar position, olfaction,
local land mass recognition, an internal clock and
geomagnetism. These factors operate simultaneously and
perhaps even independently in some kind of hierarchy. Birds
home on cloudy days without difficulty. Redundancy as well
as expendability are inherent in the navigational system.
One effect, homing, has multiple causes and mechanisms.

The proceedings of a meeting on Fibrosis at the Ciba
Foundation in the fall of 1984 was published in the summer
of 1985. During the meeting there were a number of
discussions, which are included in the proceedings, about
the problem of collagen fibril assembly (Trelstad and Birk,
1984). I believe that a central question in morphogenesis
and/or in the stabilization of derived form is the way in
which the collagens are woven into an extracellular fabric.
I do not believe this is simply a physicochemical process
even though collagen fibril assembly has served as a
paradigm for 'self assembly' for several decades. The cells
determine where, when and with what orientation matrix is
deposited. Architects and bricklayers determine where, when
and with what orientation walls are established; the
intrinsic properties of the bricks are related to
constraints on local wall order. The same is certainly
going to be true for matrix assembly, but invoking 'cell
assembly' in the process prompts arguments of neovitalism
and anti-reductionism.

The meeting of the British Society for Cell Biology at
Trent Park outside of London in September presented a broad
landscape of matrix phenomena. I was struck upon listening
to juxtaposed discussions of fibronectin and plasminogen
activator that each protein or, as Peter Albersheim pointed
out at the August ISDB meeting, each polysaccharide carries
important information in short sequences. The information
content of a protein is potentially limitless. If the
L-arginyl-glycyl-L-aspartyl-L-serine sequence in

fibronectin is sufficient for cell attachment, is it reasonable to assume that the rest of the protein is just a carrier? For fibronectin we know the answer is no (Pierschbacher and Ruoslahti, 1984). Moreover, we also know that for the fibronectins there is one gene, multiple proteins (Schwarzbauer et al., 1983); one protein, many functions. Thus, one gene, multiple phenotypes and one phenotype, multiple genes, recalling the navigating birds.

Can we be more explicit about matrix phenotype and the multiplicity of matrix genes? I think so. The heteropolymeric character of the matrix is probably the rule. We have been thinking for years that 'a collagen fibril' was chemically composed of one gene product. Recent evidence would suggest that we adopt the opposite extreme and cautiously work backward. All collagen fibrils are heteropolymeric and those comprised of a single collagen type, or of collagen alone, are the exception. There are now at least ten types of collagen comprised of at least fifteen different gene products. That these collagens are interwoven in the body fabric rather than segregated into unique domains seems likely. The message to me of the Mov13 mouse is not that morphogenesis does not need type I collagen; it is that the absence of type I collagen in heteropolymeric structures does not preclude their formation (Breindl et al., 1984). Architectural redundancy in which one effect has many causes.

I was browsing in Blackwell's in Oxford before the British meeting and came upon several sections which had an unexpected thematic continuity. First was a large collection on English language structure. Grammar is an architecture of verbal understanding. We think and store information in words and diagrams; selections and sequences of words form our intelligence, our ability to guess right and see new order (Barlow, 1983). Close by was a section on artificial intelligence. There are algorithms which can now deal with words and grammar, algorithms which can help us store, examine and predict multiple causes from multiple effects; single causes from multiple effects; multiple effects from single causes; single effects from single causes (Bonnet, 1984). The computer is going to be to thinking what the tractor is to eating.

And then came the shelf with Levins and Lewontin and 'The Dialectical Biologist.' These authors address the

philosophy of biological problem solving and suggest that
Cartesian reductionism is insufficient to allow
understanding of larger, complex systems. Their arguments
for a Marxist dialectic should be read and discussed.

I know the entire amino acid sequence of type I
collagen; I know its entire gene structure. I know that it
is formed with additional peptide extensions which are
enzymatically processed outside the cell. I know that the
sites of fibril assembly in the tendon and corneal
fibroblasts in the chick embryo are within extracytoplasmic
compartments (Birk and Trelstad, 1984). The assemblage of
the stress bearing tendon and the optically transparent
cornea are events which require a synchronized network of
forces extending from the intermolecular to the
intercellular. They cannot be easily divided and discerned.

Yet it is the only way at present that we know how to
proceed.

But as we continue with our molecular dissections of
the extracellular matrix, we need to question whether the
analysis of the whole will come from a simple summation of
the parts we find as we disassemble. I think not. I see
heterogeneity and redundancy in matrix structure and in
cellular mechanisms. I see ambiguity as well as polyphony
in the language of the proteins and polysaccharides that
are both structural elements and signals, both causes and
effects, both a matrix and a mentor (Trelstad, 1985). I see
interlocking networks of algorithms which the cells employ
and which we cannot decipher easily without recognition of
a 'cellular intelligence', of single cell mechanisms for
the integration of multiple signals, of multiple strengths,
of multiple characters, of multiple significances both from
within and without. I see position, time and space as
components of the whole which are not entirely available to
molecular explanation or exploration.

I wandered through the poster sessions at the ISDB and
was awash in complex systems. Each has many parts; each has
unexplained behaviors.

I wander back through this essay and ask again, what
happened to the article 'the' in the title of the
Minisymposium. Without taking any credit for forethought,
let me suggest that 'thes' absences indicate that 'the

molecular biology' of 'the extracellular matrix' would have
implied a narrow viewpoint to which none of us subscribe. A
minor point, perhaps, but I'd rather view molecular biology
and extracellular matrix as 'field phenomena' within which
we must explore relationships without prejudice or
narrowness.

> With relaxed abandon these thoughts
>   build to the fowling:
> is matrix morphogenesis
>   a dialectical dilemma
>   or
>   a Cartesian catastrophe?
>   I don't know,
>   but at least think about it
>   when you're at the supermarket.

REFERENCES

Barlow HB (1983). Intelligence, guesswork, language. Nature
    (London) 304:207-209.
Birk DE and Trelstad, RL (1984). Extracellular compartments
    in matrix morphogenesis: collagen fibril, bundle and
    lamellar formation by corneal fibroblasts. J Cell Biol
    99:2024-2033.
Bonnet A (1984). Strategies for Understanding Structured
    English. In Buchanan BG, Shortliffe EH (eds): "Rule-Based
    Expert Systems," Reading, Massachusetts: Addison-Wesley,
    pp 613-634.
Breindl M, Harbers K, Jaenisch R (1984). Retrovirus-induced
    lethal mutation in collagen I gene of mice is associated
    with an altered chromatin structure. Cell 38:9-16.
Levins R and Lewontin R (1985). "The Dialectical
    Biologist." Cambridge: Harvard University Press.
Pierschbacher MD and Ruoslahti E (1984). Cell attachment
    activity of fibronectin can be duplicated by small
    synthetic fragments of the molecule. Nature (London)
    309: 30-33.
Schwarzbauer JE, Tamkun JW, Lemischka IR, Hynes RO (1983).
    Three different fibronectin mRNAs arise by alternative
    splicing within the coding region. Cell 35:421-431.

Trelstad RL and Birk DE (1984). The fibroblast in
  morphogenesis and fibrosis: cell topography and
  surface-related functions. In Evered D, Whelan J (eds):
  "Fibrosis, Ciba Foundation Symposium 114," London,
  Pitman, pp 4-19.
Trelstad RL (1985). Glycosaminoglycans: Mortar, Matrix,
  Mentor. Lab Invest 53:1-4.

Progress in Developmental Biology, Part B, pages 377–380
© 1986 Alan R. Liss, Inc.

AUTORADIOGRAPHIC STUDY OF THE ORIGIN OF BASEMENT MEMBRANE
COMPONENTS IN THE AVIAN EMBRYO

Fernand Harrisson

Department of Anatomy and Embryology,
State University Center of Antwerp,
171, Groenenborgerlaan, B-2020 Antwerpen, Belgium

INTRODUCTION

In spite of a large variability in the chemical
composition of the basement membrane, it is believed that
the cells that are underlaid by a basement membrane are
responsible for the biosynthesis and the assembly of its
components (for review, Kefalides et al., 1979) . In recent
years, evidence for the contribution of underlying tissue
to the synthesis of the lamina densa and/or lamina lucida
of an epithelium has, however, been found (Brownell et al.,
1981 ; Sariola et al., 1984 a, b ; Warburton et al., 1984 ;
Harrisson et al., 1985) . To test the hypothesis that the
basement membrane could be of dual origin, we used avian
blastoderms which, at the time of gastrulation, are composed
of three cell layers known as (1) the upper layer or epiblast, facing to the vitelline membrane and resting upon a
basement membrane devoid of reticular fibers, (2) the middle
layer or mesoblast, which develops by ingression of upper
layer cells at the level of the primitive streak, and by
lateral migration along the basement membrane of the upper
layer, and (3) the deep layer, consisting of endophyll,
hypoblast, and definitive endoblast, and thus heterogenous
in structure and origin . To visualize a possible participation of the deep layer into the synthesis of the basement
membrane of the upper layer, we transplanted metabolically
labelled quail deep layers into chicken blastoderms . The
ability to distinguish chicken from quail cells after nuclear staining, combined with autoradiographic labelling of
the extracellular matrix, made it possible to determine the
origin of cells and labelled compounds in the chimeres .

MATERIALS AND METHODS

Fertilized chicken and quail eggs were incubated to obtain stage 3 blastoderms (Hamburger and Hamilton, 1951) In a first step, the quail embryos were cultured for 2 h on a medium containing 0.5 ml egg white, 0.5 ml Ringer solution mixed with 3 mg agar, and 24 μCi D-[6-^{3}H] glucosamine hydrochloride (34.6 Ci/mmol) or 42 μCi L-[6-^{3}H] fucose (20 Ci/mmol) . In a second step, we obtained chimeres by transplantation of labelled quail deep layers into unlabelled chicken blastoderms deprived of their own deep layer, according to a method described previously (Harrisson et al, 1985) . The chimeres were further cultured for 5 h on the above medium without tritiated precursor . Chase experiments were performed by adding an excess of unlabelled D-glucosamine or L-fucose to the culture medium of some chimeres . The embryos were fixed in a mixture of 96 % ethanol, 35 % formaldehyde, and 1 % acetic acid (75:20:5 by vol.) . A Feulgen staining was performed on hydrated, 6 μm thick paraffin sections before dipping in Ilford L4 nuclear emulsion and further processing for autoradiography (for details, Harrisson et al., 1985) .

RESULTS

After transplantation of a glucosamine-labelled quail deep layer into an unlabelled chicken blastoderm, the autoradiographs did not only demonstrate silver grains over the quail tissue as expected, but also at the basal side of the chicken epiblast where a basement membrane is present (Fig. 1) . This label was restricted to the region situated immediately above the quail tissue . The labelling of the basement membrane was most obvious at the level of the endophyllic crescent, suggesting that mesoblast cells do not intervene in this process . Chase experiments showed that the distribution and the density of the silver grains were essentially the same as without the addition of unlabelled glucosamine to the culture medium . It is concluded that low molecular weight compounds, macromolecular material, and/or catabolic products are transferred from quail tissue to the basement membrane region of the chicken epiblast .

The autoradiographic experiments (with or without chase) involving the use of tritiated fucose to label glycoproteins in the quail embryos, resulted in labelling

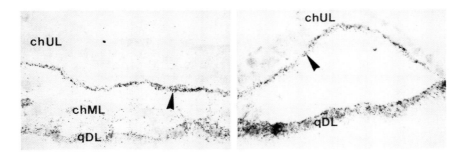

Figures 1-2. Autoradiographs of chimeric embryos obtained
by transplantation of a D-glucosamine-labelled (Fig. 1,
with chase) or of a L-fucose-labelled (Fig. 2, without
chase) quail deep layer (qDL) into an unlabelled chicken
blastoderm . The arrowheads indicate the basement membrane
region at the level of the primitive streak (Fig. 1) and
at the level of the endophyllic crescent (Fig. 2) . x300 .
chML, chicken middle layer ; chUL, chicken upper layer .

of the basement membrane region in the chimeres according
to a gradient increasing from the primitive streak to the
edge of the area pellucida (Fig. 2) . The presence of unlabelled chicken mesoblast cells or of labelled quail mesoblast cells between chicken upper layer and quail deep
layer did not influence the final labelling pattern in the
basement membrane . It is concluded that, at least, glycoproteins are synthesized by the deep layer and deposited
into the basement membrane of the upper layer . Glycoproteins are thus transferred from one epithelium to another, without participation of a mesenchyme .

DISCUSSION

     The results indicate the participation of underlying
tissue in the synthesis of, at least, basement membrane
glycoproteins . Although the nature of these glycoproteins
has to be investigated further, it is worth to note that
carbohydrate analyses of the collagen component of various
basement membranes did not reveal the presence of fucose
(see Kefalides et al., 1979) . This would implicate that a
class of non-collagenous glycoproteins originates from the
deep layer in chimeric avian embryos . This hypothesis is
supported by the observation that Chicken deep and upper
layers but not middle layer in culture have the capability

to synthesize, at least, fibronectin and laminin (Sanders, 1980 ; Mitrani and Eyal-Giladi, 1982), both glycoproteins being present in the basement membrane of the epiblast (for references, Harrisson et al, 1985b) . In parallel to the observations of others (Brownell et al, 1981 ; Sariola et al, 1984a ; Warburton et al., 1984), it may be postulated that the deep layer is responsible for the production of fibronectin and its deposition in the basement membrane of the epiblast, since the chicken mesenchyme is not able to produce this molecule in culture (Sanders, 1980) . This basement membrane fibronectin is obviously not plasma-derived, as suggested for basement membranes having a filtration function, nor is it derived from mesenchyme .

REFERENCES

Brownell AG, Bessem CC, Slavkin HC (1981). Possible functions of mesenchyme cell-derived fibronectin during formation of basal lamina. Proc Natl Acad Sci USA 78:3711-3715.
Hamburger V, Hamilton H (1951). A series of normal stages in the development of the chick embryo. J Morphol 88:49-92.
Harrisson F, Van Hoof J, Vanroelen Ch, Vakaet L (1985a). Transfer of extracellular matrix components between germ layers in chimaeric chicken-quail blastoderms. Cell Tissue Res 239:643-649.
Harrisson F, Vanroelen Ch, Vakaet L (1985b). Fibronectin and its relation to the basal lamina and to the cell surface in the chicken blastoderm. Cell Tissue Res, in press.
Kefalides NA, Alper R, Clark CC (1979). Biochemistry and metabolism of basement membranes. Int Rev Cytol 61:167-228.
Mitrani E, Eyal-Giladi H (1982). Cells from early chick embryos in culture. Differentiation 2:56-61.
Sanders EJ (1980). The effect of fibronectin and substratum-attached material on the spreading of chick embryo meso-derm cells in vitro. J Cell Sci 44:225-242.
Sariola H, Kuusela P, Ekblom P (1984a). Cellular origin of fibronectin in interspecies hybrid kidneys. J Cell Biol 99:2099-2107.
Sariola H, Timple R, von der Mark K, Mayne R, Fitch JM, Linsenmayer TF, Ekblom P (1984b). Dual origin of glomer-ular basement membrane. Dev Biol 101:86-96.
Warburton MJ, Monaghan P, Ferns SA, Rudland PS, Perusinghe N, Chung AE (1984). Distribution of entactin in the basement membrane of the rat mammary gland. Evidence for a non-epithelial origin. Exp Cell Res 152:240-254.

Progress in Developmental Biology, Part B, pages 381–384
© 1986 Alan R. Liss, Inc.

REGULATION OF EXTRACELLULAR MATRIX METABOLISM BY GROWTH
FACTORS IN HUMAN SKIN FIBROBLASTS

Ryu-ichiro Hata, Hironobu Sunada, Katsuhiko Arai
and Yutaka Nagai

Department of Tissue Physiology, Medical
    Research Institute, Tokyo Medical and Dental
    University, Tokyo 101, Japan

INTRODUCTION

        In order to investigate the regulation mechanisms of
extracellular matrix metabolism, human skin fibroblasts
were cultured in Dulbecco's modified Eagle's medium
containing 10% fetal bovine serum (DMEM) in the presence or
absence of epidermal growth factor (EGF) or of sodium
ascorbate (Ascorbate).

MATERIALS AND METHODS

Cell Culture and Metabolic Labeling: The cells were plated
in 35mm or 60mm dishes and grown in DMEM until confluent.
Then the cells were further cultured in the presence or
absence of EGF (2-50ng/ml) or of ascorbate (0.05-1mM) for 1
to 5 days.
        The cells were labeled with [^{3}H]proline (Hata et al.,
1983, 1984b) or with [^{3}H]glucosamine (Ninomiya et al.,
1982) for the last 24 h.
Determination of DNA: Quantity of DNA was determined by a
fluorometric method as described previously (Hata et al.,
1984a).
Analysis of Collagen and Non-collagenous Proteins: After
the incubation the medium and the cell layer were combined
and processed for the determination of collagen and non-
collagenous proteins with purified Cl. histolyticum
collagenase as described previously (Hata et al., 1980).
        Type analysis of the collagen was performed by sodium
dodecylsulfate- 5% polyacrylamide slab gel electrophoresis
as described (Hata et al., 1985).

Analysis of Total Hydroxyproline: Cells were incubated
with chromatographically purified [³H]proline for 24 h and
processed as described previously (Hata et al., 1985).
Cell Membrane Transport: Cells were cultured in DMEM with
or without addition of growth factors and then incubated
with 10μCi of [³H]proline for the last 10 min and cell
membrane transport of [³H]proline was determined as
reported previously (Hata et al., 1984b).
Isolation and Analysis of Glycosaminoglycans: Glycosaminoglycans were isolated and identified by two-dimensional
electrophoresis (Hata and Nagai, 1972, 1973) on cellulose
acetate membranes as described (Ninomiya et al., 1982).

RESULTS AND DISCUSSION

     The presence of EGF (2-50ng/ml) or ascorbate
(0.05-1mM) in the culture medium for 4-5 days stimulated
growth and production of non-collagenous proteins of the
cells (Fig. 1). And these factors acted synergistically
when both were present in the medium. Collagen production
by the cells was also activated by the presence of
ascorbate, while it was reduced in the presence of EGF
(Fig. 1) as reported on cultured osteoblasts (Hata et al.,
1984a). Total hydroxyproline which is a marker of total
synthesis of collagen was also increased in the presence of
ascorbate or decreased in the presence of EGF, suggesting
that the main effect of these growth factors on the
collagen metabolism is on the synthesis rather than on the
degradation of collagen by the cells.
     Cell membrane transport of [³H]proline was also
activated by the presence of ascorbate but not by EGF (Fig.
1).
     On the other hand, production of acidic glycosamino-
glycan, especially hyaluronic acid, was greatly activated
by the presence of EGF, but it was not so prominent in the
presence of ascorbate.
     These results show that both growth factors regulate
the metabolism of extracellular matrix components in human
skin fibroblasts in quite a different manner.

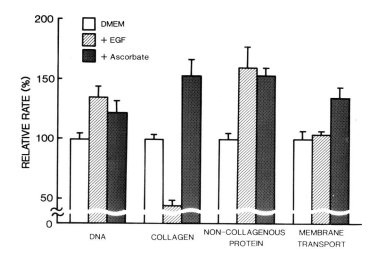

Figure 1.   Effects of EGF and ascorbate on the metabolism
            of human skin fibroblasts in culture.
       Cells at confluent stage were cultured at $37^{\circ}C$ in the
absence or presence of EGF (10ng/ml) or sodium ascorbate
(Ascorbate, 0.1mM) for 4 days. Sodium ascorbate (0.1mM)
was supplemented in every dish for the last 24 h.
       Relative rates of DNA synthesis, collagen synthesis,
non-collagenous protein synthesis, and of cell membrane
transport of [^{3}H]proline were determined as described under
Materials and Methods. Data are the percentages of the
control (DMEM) values.

REFERENCES

Hata R, Hori H, Nagai Y, Tanaka S, Kondo M, Hiramatsu M, Utsumi N, Kumegawa M (1984a) Selective inhibition of type I collagen synthesis in osteoblastic cells by epidermal growth factor. Endocrinology 115: 867–876.

Hata R, Nagai Y (1972) A rapid and micro method for separation of acidic glycosaminoglycans by two-dimensional electrophoresis. Anal Biochem 45: 462–468.

Hata R, Nagai Y (1973) A micro colorimetric determination of acidic glycosaminoglycans by two dimensional electro-phoresis on a cellulose acetate strip. Anal Biochem 52: 652–656.

Hata R, Ninomiya Y, Nagai Y, Tsukada Y (1980) Biosynthesis of interstitial types of collagen by albumin-producing rat liver parenchymal cell (hepatocyte) clones in culture. Biochemistry 19:169–176.

Hata R, Ninomiya Y, Sano J, Konomi H, Hori H, Sunada H, Tanaka S, Kabuki K, Nagai Y, Tsukada Y (1985) Activation of collagen synthesis in primary culture of rat liver parenchymal cells (hepatocytes). J Cell Physiol 122: 333–342.

Hata R, Sunada H, Arai K (1984b) Reciprocal effects of excess potassium salts in the culture medium on type I and type III collagen synthesis by human skin fibroblasts. Cell Biol Int Rep 8: 433–440.

Hata R, Sunada H, Nagai Y (1983) Sodium ion modulates collagen types in human fibroblastic cells in culture. Biochem Biophys Res Commun 117: 313–318.

Ninomiya Y, Hata R, Nagai Y, Tajima S, Nishikawa T, Hatano H (1982) Glycosaminoglycan metabolism by scleroderma fibroblasts in culture. Biomedical Res 3: 70–82.

Progress in Developmental Biology, Part B, pages 385–395
© 1986 Alan R. Liss, Inc.

EVIDENCE FOR GLYCOSAMINOGLYCANS (GAG) ROLE IN AVIAN
LUNG MORPHOGENESIS

Paolo Carinci, Ennio Becchetti, Giordano
Stabellini, Rita Evangelisti and Amedeo
Pagliarini.
Institute of Histology and general Embryo
logy, University of Ferrara, Via Fossato
di Mortara, 64, 44100 Ferrara, Italy.

INTRODUCTION

It is a well established fact that mesenchyme plays a regulatory role in bronchial branching
and epithelial cytodifferentiation during lung de
velopment (see Goldin, 1980, for a review). However the mechanisms involved in this activity are
still unknown. Several biochemical and histochemi
cal data show that mesenchymal glycosaminoglycan
(GAG) pattern exhibits relevant qualitative and
quantitative changes which are related to lung mor
phogenesis (Radhakrisnamurthy et al., 1980; Carinci,
1981; Schmid et al., 1982). The suggestion may the
refore be advanced that GAG are involved in mesen
chymal regulatory processes.

To test this possibility, we have examined the
effect on lung morphogenesis of modifying GAG pat
tern in chick embryo lung explants by means of en
zymatic treatments and exogenous GAG administration.

Our results conclusively show a causal relation between mesenchymal GAG and bronchial branching
and thus indicate GAG involvement in mesenchymal
regulation on associated epithelium.

MATERIAL AND METHODS

Hubbard fertilized eggs, provided by Selice Incubator Company (Bubano, Imola, Italy), were in cubated at 38° C and 60% of relative humidity. Lungs were removed under sterile conditions from embryos of 6 days, staged according to the Hambur ger-Hamilton table (Hamilton, 1952), cut into dx. and sn. lung halves. Each half was then placed in culture dishes on testacea membrane in the presen ce of suitable culture medium and incubated for 2, 3 or 6 days at 37° C. According to the method of Wolff and Haffen (1952) semisolid natural media we re used. Standard nutrient was composed of 6 parts of 1% in Gey's saline balanced, 6 parts of 199 syn thetic medium (GIBCO) and 400 i.u./ml of penicillin and streptomycin. Test cultures were administered with standard nutrient incorporated with: a) chon droitinase ABC (Seikagaku Kogyo) at the final con centration 0.32 U/ml; b) testicular hyaluronidase (Miles) 285 µg/ml; c) chondroitin 4,6 sulphate (CS) + Dermatan sulphate (DS) + Hyaluronic acid (HA) (1:1:1) at the final concentration 142 µg/ml; d) CS + DS (1:1) 142 µg/ml; e) HA, 142 µg/ml. The GAG were purchased from the Sigma Company. In one set of experiments nutrient was changed after 2 days with standard medium and cultures were maintained for another 4 days. Cultures were daily observed and photographed under a Leitz stereomicroscope at 30 magnification.

Explants were fixed in Bouin fluid and routi- ne histological procedures were followed. Serial sections (5 µm) were cut at intervals of 100 µm and stained for morphological examination with hemato- xylin-eosin.

For histochemical analysis we used procedures in order to detect glycoproteins (GP) and glycosaminoglycans (GAG) and to distinguish between different GAG (Scott and Dorling, 1965; Zaniboni and Carinci, 1968; Becchetti et al., 1984): sequential staining with 1% Alcian blue 8GX (Fluka), 0.3 M $MgCl_2$ in acetate buffer (0.1 M, pH 5.8) and PAS, before and after dimedone treatment(5% in absolute ethanol, 5 hrs, 60° C); sequential staining with 1% Alcian blue, 0.3 M $MgCl_2$ and 1% Alcian yellow GXS (Chroma), 0.025 M $MgCl_2$ in the same buffer; staining with 1% Alcian blue 0.65 M $MgCl_2$ in acetate buffer. Sections were also incubated with testicular hyaluronidase (Merck, 1 mg/ml in 0.1 M phosphate buffer pH 7, 6 hrs at 37° C). Control sections were incubated in buffer alone.

Bronchial branching was evaluated by counting epithelial ramifications under a stereomicroscope. Random controls were also performed on histological slides. Statistical analysis was carried out through a T-test for paired data and the difference was significant at 0.05 level.

RESULTS

Each half of 6-day lung rudiment is formed of epithelial tubules and surrounding mesenchyme. Mesobronchus (Ms) is covered by a pluriseriate epithelium from which secondary bronchi spring out (4 ento-bronchi, En; 1 ecto-bronchus, Ec ; all lined by a simple cylindrical epithelium). Both lie on an evident basal membrane (bm), scarcely PAS positive, dimedone sensitive (glycoproteins), strongly alcianophilic at 0.65, 0.3 and 0.025 M $MgCl_2$, more at En and Ec level, partially removable by testicular hyaluronidase (HS, CS, DS, HA). Mesenchyme is loose; the ground substance exhibits different reactivity in the various regions: slightly PAS reactive and clearly alcianophilic at 0.025 M

$MgCl_2$, abolished by hyaluronidase (HA) around the Ms, weakly reactive in 0.3 M $MgCl_2$ Alcian, total- ly removed by hyaluronidase treatment (CS) around the En; poorly reactive at the same molarity around the Ec.

Control Cultures

     After 48 hrs in vitro, lung explants grow well, epithelial tubules extend outwardly. 4 En, para- bronchi, P, derived from En, covered with a simple isoprismatic epithelium, 3-4 Ec, 2-4 laterobronchi, L, and 3-5 air sacs, a.s., lined by a simple squa mous epithelium are present (Fig. 1; Table 1).Bm of $2^{nd}/3^{rd}$ subdivisions are slightly PAS positive, clearly alcianophilic in 0.065, 0.3 and 0.025 M $MgCl_2$, partially removed by testicular hyaluroni- dase (HS, CS, DS, HA); bm of a.s. is less alciano philic, particularly in 0.65 and 0.3 M $MgCl_2$. Me- senchymal ground substance is alcian reactive at 0.3 M $MgCl_2$, largely abolished by hyaluronidase (CS), with a different intensity in relation to the various sites: maximum in the outer region of the growth, clearly around the En and Ec, poorly at L and P levels and scarcely around the a.s..

     3 day cultures show more growth and more epi thelial tubules are detectable (new P have emerged from En; 5 Ec; 4-5 L; 2-3 dorsobronchi (D); 4-5 a. s.; Fig. 2). Basement membranes of Ms and P are PAS positive and alcianophilic at 0.65, 0.3 and 0.025 M $MgCl_2$; bm of 2nd order bronchi are stron- ghly alcianophilic at the same molarities, bm of a.s., PAS positive. Mesenchymal ground substance exhibits the same heterogeneous histochemical pat- tern as at 48 hrs, with a more PAS reactivity aro- und the P.

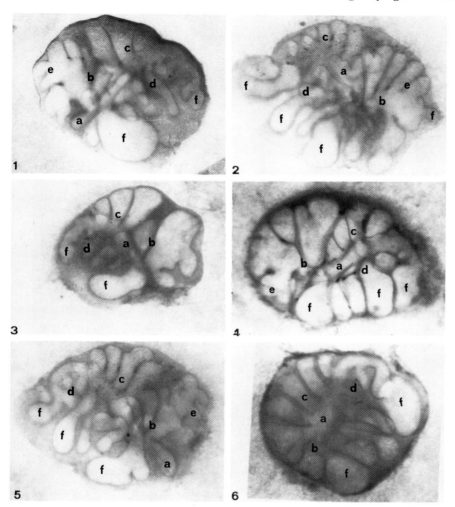

Figures 1-6. Lung explants maintained in different nutrients as follows, photographed under stereomicroscope (x30). 1) 48 hrs, 199; 2) 72 hrs, 199; 3) 48 hrs,chondroitinase ABC; 4) 48 hrs, chondroitinase ABC + 4 days, 199; 5) 48 hrs, CS + DS + HA; 6) 48 hrs, HA.
a, Ms; b, En; c, Ec; d, L; e, P; f, a.s. (for abbreviations see Results).

After 6 days in vitro lung explants show features of morphogical involution and a strong bronchial ramification decrease. Also in 6 day cultures,
where the nutrient was changed after the first 48
hours, a noticeable reduction of ramifications is
present (Table 1) Histochemical picture is consistent with the 48 hour one.

Enzymatic Treatment

48 hour lung explants maintained in presence
of chondroitinase ABC grow much less than controls
and epithelial tubules are significantly reduced
(3 En, 3-4 Ec, 2-4 L, poorly developed, 2-3 a.s.)
(Fig.3; Table 1). Bm are poorly reactive in 0.3 M
$MgCl_2$ Alcian, partially abolished by hyaluronidase.
Mesenchymal ground substance shows a sharp decrease
in alcianophilia at the same molarity (less CS con
tent); and a PAS positivity dimedone sensitive.

After 3 days, cultures do not grow further
and a.s. are enormously dilated. Histochemical
pattern is unchanged.

2 day cultures transferred in standard nutrient
exhibit, after another 4 days in vitro, a complete
recovery of growth and bronchial branching (4 En,
3-5 Ec, 3-5 L, 2-3 a.s., sometimes P emerging from
En) (Fig. 4; Table 1). Alcian reactivity at 0.3 M
$MgCl_2$ is strongly increased with a pattern compara
ble to that of 48 hr in vitro control cultures.

Also in 48 hr lung cultures added with testicu
lar hyaluronidase a growth decrease and bronchial bran
ching reduction are detectable (3 En poorly developed; 2-3 Ec; 2-4 L; 1-3 a.s.). Strongly reduced alcianophilia at 0.025 M of $MgCl_2$ hyaluronidase sen-

TABLE 1. BRONCHIAL BRANCHING AT DIFFERENT TIME INTERVALS OF IN VITRO MAINTENANCE

TREATMENTS	48HRS		72HRS		6 DAYS*	
	CULTURES NUMBER	2ND+3RD SUBDIVISION / CULTURE	CULTURES NUMBER	2ND+3RD SUBDIVISION / CULTURE	CULTURES NUMBER	2ND+3RD SUBDIVISION / CULTURE
		X ± DS P		X ± DS P		X ± DS P
CONTROLS	27	16.52 ± 1.99	6	20.33 ± 2.34	13	16.72 ± 3.20
CHONDROITINASE ABC	16	12.50 ± 2.19 >0.001	6	13.00 ± 2.00 >0.001	12	18.66 ± 2.52 >0.2
TESTICULAR HYALURONIDASE	8	12.69 ± 1.51 >0.001	6	14.66 ± 3.05 >0.01	4	16.00 ± 3.50 N.S.
CS + DS + HA	12	18.10 ± 1.83 >0.05				
CS + DS	12	18.27 ± 1.85 >0.02				
HA	12	14.20 ± 1.00 >0.01				

* TRANSFERRED IN STANDARD MEDIUM AFTER 48 HRS AND MAINTAINED FOR ANOTHER 4 DAYS

sitive (HA) both at bm and at mesenchymal ground
substance level. At 0.3 and 0.65 M MgCl$_2$ alcian
reactivity is still present (HS).

After 3 days epithelial tubules are poorly
increased, well dilated. Histochemical pattern is
similar to that above described. A recovery of bron
chial ramifications is observable if transferring
48 hr cultures in standard medium (Table 1).

Exogenous GAG Addition

2 day lung cultures added with CS + DS + HA
grow well and exhibit an increase in bronchial ra
mifications (4 En well developed, 4-5 Ec, 4-5 L,
3-5 a.s.; P have buds both from En and Ec) (Fig.5).
Bm are clearly alcianophilic in 0.025, 0.3 and 0.65
M of MgCl$_2$ partially removed by hyaluronidase and
slightly PAS reactive. 0.3 M MgCl$_2$ alcianophilia,
hyaluronidase sensitive, of ground substance, much
stronger than controls, shows an heterogeneous pic
ture: clear in the outer region of the explants
around the En, Ec, and P; weak around the L;poor
around the a.s.. A similar pattern is shown by explants added with CS + DS. HA added explants grow
more than controls and less than sulphates GAG added (Fig. 6, Table 1); however epithelial ramifica
tions are fewer (4 En, 3-4 Ec, 3-4 L, 2-4 a.s.) and
dilated. Bm and ground substance show the same histochemical reactivity as control cultures.

DISCUSSION

6 day lung rudiment explanted in vitro and sup
ported with synthetic nutrient continues its growth
and development for 2-3 days. Epithelial branching
shows similar features and mesenchymal ground sub-

stance exhibits analogous GAG pattern heterogeneity as observed <u>in vivo</u> (Becchetti et al., manuscript
in preparation). It is worthy of note to stress
that lung explants develop slowly in natural media
(serum or extract) so indicating the importance
of environmental conditions (Carinci and Simonelli,
1971; Dameron, 1972).

Enzymatic treatments or exogenous GAG additions
are able to quantitatively and qualitatively affect
mesenchymal GAG distribution of lung cultures. Under these condition, growth and epithelial branching
are significantly altered. In particular we notice
that sulphate GAG accumulation is spatially and chro
nologically correlated with epithelial budding.

When sulphate GAG are removed, epithelial bran
ching stops, when their accumulation takes place
again epithelial branching starts. A correlation
between GAG distribution and epithelial differentiation has also been observed in avian skin development (Becchetti et al., 1984). In addition, a
regulatory system must be present to determine the
different accumulation of individual GAG in the va
rious regions of lung rudiment. We have previously
shown, in embryonic skin, the existence of heterogeneity of fibroblasts for lectins surface receptors (Caruso et al., 1985) and demonstrated the in
volvement of these receptors in the control of GAG
secretion (Evangelisti et al., 1984).A similar mechanism could be operative in lung rudiment.

We conclude that GAG distribution is relevant
for the pattern of epithelial branching; that infor
mation for GAG distribution is also present on 6th
day of incubation, and we suggest that this information may be dependent on the presence of heterogeneous fibroblast populations.

Aknowledgments

    This work is in part supported by a grant from
the Ministero della Pubblica Istruzione (Italy).

REFERENCES

Becchetti E, Stabellini G, Caruso A, Carinci P
    (1984). Exogenous glycosaminoglycans (GAG) are
    able to modulate avian skin differentiation (epi
    thelial keratinization and feather formation). J
    Embryol exp Morph 82: 25-40.
Carinci P (1981). The mesenchymal during develop-
    ment: composition of the ground substance, regu-
    latory factors, embryological significance. Bas
    Appl Histochem 25: 267-277.
Carinci P, Simonelli L, (1971).Effects of puromycin
    on chick embryo lung development in vitro. Z Anat
    Entwickl -Gesch 135: 108-116.
Caruso A, Stabellini G, Evangelisti R, Becchetti E,
    Carinci P (1985). Avian skin embryonal fibrobla-
    sts heterogeneity for lectins surface receptors.
    Cell Biol Int Rep, in press.
Dameron F (1972). Rôle du mésenchyme dans la dif-
    férenciation anatomique et cytologique du pummon
    d'oiseau. Bull Soc Zool de France 97: 497-503.
Evangelisti R, Bodo M, Caruso A, Becchetti E, Ca-
    rinci P (1984). Extracellular glycosaminoglycans
    (GAG) released by chick embryonic fibroblasts. A
    possible involvement of surface receptors. Cell
    Tissue Res 238: 241-245.
Goldin G V (1980). Toward mechanism for morphogene
    sis in epithelio-mesenchymal organs. Q Rev Biol
    55: 251-265.
Hamilton H L (1952). Lillie's development on the
    chick. An Introduction. New York: H/Holt.
Radhakrisnamurthy B, Williams J, Berenson G S (1980).
    The composition of glycosaminoglycans in develo-

ping rabbit lungs. Proc Soc Exp Biol Med 164: 287-291.

Schmid K, Grundbock-Jusco J, Kimura A, Tschopp A F, Zollinger R, Binette J P, Lewis W, Hagashi S (1982). The distribution of the glycosaminogly-cans in the anatomic components of the lung and the changes in concentration of these macromole cules during development and aging. Biochim Bio phys Acta 716: 178-187.

Scott J E, Dorling J (1965). Differential staining of glycosaminoglycans (mucopolysaccharide) by alcian blue in salt solution. Histochemic 5: 221-233.

Wolff E, Haffen K C (1952). Sur une méthode de cul ture d'organes embryonaires in vitro. Tex Rep Biol Med 10: 463-472.

Zaniboni G, Carinci P (1968). Caratterizzazione istochimica dei polisaccaridi acidi. IV colora-zione in presenza di diverse concentrazioni sa-line. Boll Soc It Biol Sper 44: 670-673.

Progress in Developmental Biology, Part B, pages 397–400
© 1986 Alan R. Liss, Inc.

THE STRUCTURE OF SHORT-CHAIN COLLAGEN GENES

Guillermina Lozano, Yoshifumi Ninomiya and
Bjorn R. Olsen
Department of Biochemistry, UMDNJ-Rutgers
Medical School, Piscataway, New Jersey 08854

INTRODUCTION

Collagens are extracellular proteins that form supramolecular aggregates such as fibers alone or in concert with
other extracellular matrix proteins. Although all collagen
molecules contain characteristic triple helical domains, it
is now clear that there are several distinct classes of
structurally related collagens in different tissues.

Peptide analysis, partial amino acid sequencing and the
isolation of two cDNAs has allowed us to determine the
structure of a novel collagen, Type IX collagen (van der
Rest et al., 1985). This protein is a disulfide bonded protein found in hyaline cartilage and it consists of three
unique polypeptide chains named α1, α2 and α3. These polypeptides form molecules with three triple helical domains
separated by globular domains. The cDNAs pYN1738 and
pYN1731 encode the α1(IX) and the α2(IX) polypeptides,
respectively (Ninomiya and Olsen, 1984; Ninomiya et al.,
1985).

ISOLATION AND CHARACTERIZATION OF THE α2(IX) GENE

The cDNA pYN1731 was used to screen a Charon 4A Eco RI
library (Lozano and Vasios, unpublished). A positive clone
GL858 was isolated and further characterized (Lozano, et
al., 1985). The restriction map showed a single Eco RI
insert of 16 kb and several Bam HI sites. When a Bam HI
digest was run on a 1% agarose gel, blotted and hybridized
to the cDNA, three Bam HI fragments of sizes 2.0, 1.5, and

0.9 kb hybridized. The 2.0 kb fragment contains most of the coding information for the 3' half of the gene. The 1.5 kb Bam HI fragment contains sequences that correspond to the 5' end of the cDNA and the 0.9 kb fragment has been determined to contain the 3' end of the gene.

The three Bam HI fragments were sequenced and their exon/intron structure determined. The 3' half of the α2(IX) gene contains 9 exons. The exons encoding triple helical sequences range in size from 33 bp (exon 6) to 147 bp (exon 5, figure 1). While fibrillar types I, II and III collagen genes contain exons which are 54 bp or multiples of 54 bp encoding collagenous domains (Yamada et al., 1980),

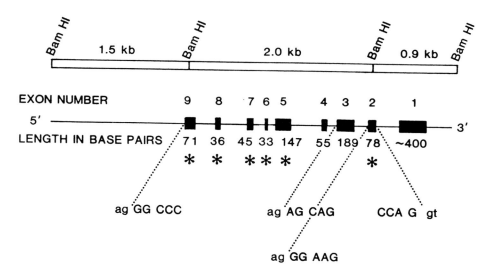

Figure 1. Diagram showing the exon/intron structure of the 3'end of the α2(IX) collagen gene. The three Bam HI fragments of clone GL858 hybridizing to the cDNA are indicated. The exon number (numbering from the 3' end) and exon sizes in base pairs are also given. Asterisks denote exons containing triple helical sequences only. Exon 4 and part of exon 5 encode a globular domain separating two collagenous domains and exon 1 encodes the carboxyl end of the α2(IX) chain. Several exon/intron junctions are shown to illustrate the interrupted codons.

this is not the case for exons of the α2(IX) gene. Furthermore, the α2(IX) gene contains several interrupted codons at exon/intron junctions (figure 1). The entire nucleotide sequence of the 9 exons has been published (Lozano et al., 1985). Although the exon sizes show considerable variation, a basic repeat of 36 bp can be distinguished. This has led us to hypothesize that the α2(IX) gene has evolved by multiple duplications from a gene containing a 36 bp coding unit. In contrast, the fibrillar collagen genes probably arose from a gene that contained a 54 bp coding unit. We, therefore, conclude that at least two classes of collagen genes exist. Class A includes the fibrillar collagen genes, whereas the type IX collagen genes belong to Class B.

GENE EXPRESSION DURING DEVELOPMENT

The α2(IX) cDNA pYN1731 was used to determine the presence of type IX mRNA at different stages of development of the chick embryo. RNA was isolated from 4, 6, and 10 day whole embryos and from 17 day dissected chick sterna (Adams et al., 1975). Slot blot analysis was first used to detect the presence of the mRNA for α2(IX) by assessing increasing amounts of RNA ranging from 1 ug to 20 ug per slot for embryonic RNA and approximately 1 ug to 10 ug for sternal RNA. The filters were hybridized with pYN1731 and to a chick actin probe as control (Cleveland et al., 1980). While the latter mRNA was detected at all stages in amounts proportional to the amount of total RNA loaded, the α2(IX) mRNA was only detected in 17 day sternal RNA. To determine the intactness of the RNA and the specificity of the hybridization, 10 ug of each of the RNAs were run in duplicate on a 1% methyl mercury hydroxide gel, blotted onto Gene Screen (New England Nuclear) and probed with either the α2(IX) or the actin cDNA. The cDNA pYN1731 hybridized specifically to two mRNAs of about 2500 and 3000 bases in length and actin cDNA hybridized to the expected mRNA, thus implying that our RNA was not degraded. The α2(IX) mRNA is therefore not detectable by slot blot hybridization prior to day 10 of chick embryo development.

In conclusion, these studies have begun to define the temporal expression of the α2(IX) gene during development as well as providing evidence for a novel class of collagen

genes. Further characterization of genes for other collagens should allow a genetic classification of the collagen
multigene family.

REFERENCES

Adams SL, Sobel ME, Howard BH, Olden K, Yamada KM,
de Crombrugghe B, Pastan I (1977). Levels of translatable
mRNAs for cell surface protein, collagen precursors, and
two membrane proteins are altered in Rous sarcoma virus-
transformed chick embryo fibroblasts. Proc Natl Acad Sci
USA 74: 3399-3403.

Cleveland DW, Lopata MA, MacDonald RJ, Cowan NJ, Rutter WJ,
Kirschner MW (1980). Number and evolutionary conservation
of α- and β-tubulin and cytoplasmic α- and γ-actin
genes using specific cloned cDNA probes. Cell 20: 95-105.

Lozano G, Ninomiya Y, Thompson H, Olsen BR (1985). A distinct class of vertebrate collagen genes encodes chicken
type IX collagen polypeptides. Proc Natl Acad Sci USA 82:
4050-4054.

Ninomiya Y, Olsen BR (1984). Synthesis and characterization
of cDNA encoding a cartilage specific short collagen.
Proc Natl Acad Sci USA 81: 3014-3018.

Ninomiya Y, van der Rest M, Mayne R, Lozano G, Olsen BR
(1985). Construction and characterization of cDNA
encoding the α2 chain of chicken type IX collagen.
Biochem 24: 4223-4229.

van der Rest M, Mayne R, Ninomiya Y, Seidah NG, Chretien M,
Olsen BR (1985). The structure of type IX collagen. J
Biol Chem 206: 220-225.

Yamada Y, Avvedimento VE, Mudryj M, Ohkubo H, Vogeli G,
Irani M, Pastan I, de Crombrugghe B (1980). The collagen
gene: Evidence for its evolutionary assembly by amplifica-
tion of a DNA segment containing an exon of 54 bp. Cell
22: 887-892.

Progress in Developmental Biology, Part B, pages 401–404
© 1986 Alan R. Liss, Inc.

CHANGES IN EXTRACELLULAR MATRIX OF CHICK EMBRYONIC BONE DURING INDUCED CALCIUM DEFICIENCY

Olena Jacenko and Rocky S. Tuan

Department of Biology
University of Pennsylvania
Philadelphia, PA 19104

INTRODUCTION

The effects of calcium (Ca) deficiency on cell differ- entiation during chick embryonic bone development were examined. Chick embryos removed from their calcareous egg- shell at incubation day 3 and placed into long-term, in vitro culture, developed severe calcium deficiency. The embryos showed reduced total body Ca, lowered Ca and phoshate content in serum and bones (long bones and calvaria), and poor mineralization and gross malformations of the skeleton. In addition, Ca deficiency also sig- nificantly altered the temporal pattern of collagen expres- sion in the skeletal tissues. Previous findings in this laboratory showed that the cartilage-specific collagen type II, typically absent in intramembranous bones, is synthesized by the calvaria of Ca-deprived, shell-less (SL) embryos (Tuan and Lynch, 1983). These observations suggest- ed that Ca, in addition to forming the structured inorganic phase of the extracellular matrix (ECM), may actively regulate cellular differentiation and gene expression steps leading to the biosynthesis of specific, organic ECM components. The presence of these ECM components may in turn affect skeletal mineralization. Understanding how Ca regulates calvarial cell differentiation should provide significant information on skeletogenesis in general. The SL culture system offers an unique means for such a study, since total embryonic Ca levels can be modulated during bone formation, thus providing a genuine experimental model of bone cell differentiation in situ than is possible with in vitro bone organ cultures.

We report here a detailed cytohistological study of the
chemical composition of the ECM of normal (N) and SL
calvaria using standard histological staining and fluorescence immunohistochemistry of collagen types. Lateral
paraffin sections of day-14 and -17 calvaria were stained
with hematoxylin and eosin, alizarin red, and alcian blue at
pH 1 for histological analysis. Affinity purified antibodies to collagen types I and II were used to localize the
temporal and spatial distribution of type II collagen in
calvarial cryosections. Antibody specificity was
established by immuno-precipitation, -blotting, and -
histochemistry. In addition, the biosynthesis of type X
collagen, an apparent marker of hypertrophied chondrocytes
on the verge of osseous transformation (Schmid and Conrad,
1982; Grant et al., 1985), was studied in endochondral long
bones and intra membranous calvaria in both sets of embryos.
For this study, tissues were radiolabelled with [^{3}H]Pro in
organ culture, extracted (Gibson et al., 1983), and analysed
for newly synthesized proteins by SDS-PAGE and fluorography.
Embryonic Ca status was also varied by supplementation of
eggshell pieces or $CaCO_3$ to SL embryos. Results from these
cytoh istological and biochemical studies revealed
significant, Ca deficiency-induced differences in the
cellular development of the SL calvaria.

RESULTS

Alizarin staining confirmed poor Ca deposition in SL
calvaria. The most striking differences was seen in day-14
bones, where only initial foci of mineralization were
detected in SL calvaria. The basophilic nature of SL trabe-
culae was also depicted by patchy staining with both eosin
and hematoxylin, whereas the acidophilic, bone-like matrix
of N bones stained strongly and exclusively with eosin.
Alcian blue staining at pH 1 for sulfated proteoglycans,
characteristically found in cartilage, revealed intense
staining in day-14 SL calvaria (Fig. 1A&B), substantial but
patchy staining in day-14 N (Fig. 1C&D) and day-17 SL
calvaria, and absence of coloration in day-17 N bones. The
staining was localized primarily to the ECM and lacunar
linings in SL calvaria, and was completely removed by preincubation with testicular hyaluronidase.

Indirect fluorescence immunohistochemistry indicated
low levels of type II collagen-positive staining in day-14 N
calvaria, usually localized in the outer regions (Fig. 2A &

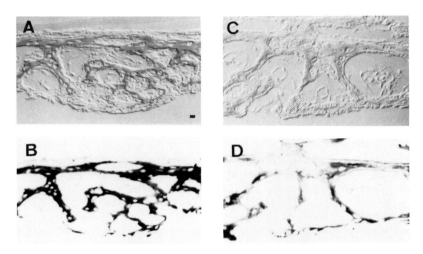

Fig. 1.   Alcian blue - stained calvaria of day - 14 SL
          (A & B) and N (C & D) embryos.   A & C, nomarski;
          B & D, bright field.   Bar = 10 um.

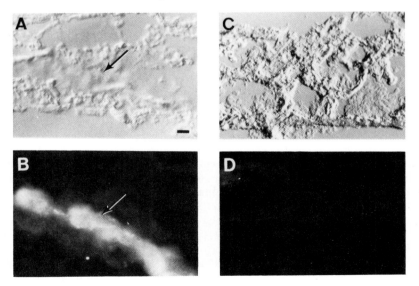

Fig. 2. Collagen type II immunofluorescence in day - 14
         SL (A & B) and N (C & D) calvaria.   A & C,
         nomarski; B & D, fluorescence.   Bar - 10 um.

B). Intense type II collagen staining was evident in all regions of day-14 SL calvaria, and was localized primarily to undermineralized areas as indicated by the pitted calvarial surface observed with Nomarski optics (Fig. 2C & D). Specific staining was also present in isolated cells which may correspond to chondrocyte-like cells that appeared in response to systemic Ca deprivation. No staining was observed in day-17 N bones, whereas cells and lacunar linings of day-17 SL calvaria remained fluorescent.

Biochemical analysis revealed the presence of bacterial and animal collagenase-sensitive, low M_r bands (59K, 50K and 42.5K) in the supernatant of tissue-associated fractions (Schmid and Conrad, 1982) of all day-14 and -17 long bones, the latter at a higher concentration. In the calvaria, a significant amount of the 59K band was present in the day-14 SL sample, implying the presence of hypertrophying chondrocytes. Faint 59K bands were also detected in day-14 N and day-17 SL calvaria, but not in day-17 N samples. The 59K band shared the reported properties of type X collagen, such as absence of disulfide bonds, and pepsin conversion to a 45K band, and susceptibility to collagenase (Schmid and Conrad, 1982). Preliminary results showed that shell and $CaCO_3$ supplementations to the cultured embryos resulted in a switch from the SL phenotype to one more similar to that of N embryos with respect to both type II as well as type X collagen.

REFERENCES

Gibson G, Kielty C, Garner C, Schor S and Grant M (1983). Identification and partial characterization of three low-molecular-weight collagenous polypeptides synthesized by chondrocytes cultured within collagen gels in the absence and in the presence of fibronectin. Biochem J 211:417-426.

Grant W, Sussman M and Balian G (1985). A disulfide-bonded short chain collagen synthesized by degenerative and calcifying zones of bovine growth plate cartilage. J Biol Chem 260: 3798-3803.

Schmid T and Conrad H (1982). A unique low molecular weight collagen secreted by cultures chick embryo chondrocytes. J Biol Chem 257: 12444-12450.

Tuan R and Lynch M (1983). Effect of experimentally induced calcium deficiency on the developmental expression of collagen types in chick embryonic skeleton. Dev Biol 100: 374-386.

Progress in Developmental Biology, Part B, pages 405–408
© 1986 Alan R. Liss, Inc.

ENAMEL PROTEIN AND OSTEONECTIN IN DEVELOPING TEETH

Hardy Limeback, Pierre S. Tung, Mary MacKinnon
and Jaro Sodek
Faculty of Dentistry, University of Toronto,
Toronto, Canada   M5G 1G6

INTRODUCTION

The developing tooth rudiment has become a useful
system for the investigation of heterotypic cell and tissue
interactions during mammalian organogenesis (Slavkin, 1974;
Kollar, 1983). The exact molecular events that are
required for the induction of ameloblast and odontoblast
differentiation preceding the organized deposition of
enamel and dentin are still unknown. Differentiation-
specific proteins produced in both tissues have been
identified and their appearance in developing teeth signify
the terminally differentiated state of the tissue. For
example, the onset of amelogenesis has been characterized
by the appearance of amelogenins in the extracellular
matrix (Slavkin et al., 1982) or by the detection of
messenger RNA coding for enamelins (Zeichner-David et al.,
1983). The signals of induction of differentiation of the
enamel epithelium may originate from direct cell-cell interactions with differentiated odontoblasts following basement
membrane dissolution or from cell contact to components in
the newly-secreted predentin (Ruch, 1984).

Osteonectin, a major bone matrix glycoprotein that
binds both collagen and hydroxyapatite (Termine et al.,
1981a), has also been detected in dentin (Termine et al.,
1981b; Tung et al., 1985). Although its function in dentinogenesis is unknown, osteonectin may be involved in, or
be an indication of, differentiation of dental tissues. To
investigate these possibilities and to attempt to elucidate
the function of osteonectin in dentin we have examined

developing tooth organs using immunohistochemical localization techniques to detect the first appearance of both enamel protein and osteonectin.

METHODS

Sheep antiserum directed against an extract of porcine amelogenin proteins was partially purified by sodium sulfate precipitation and DEAE-cellulose exchange chromatography. These polyclonal antibodies were affinity purified using CNBr-activated Sepharose 4B coupled to a low MW fraction of porcine amelogenin purified on a Biogel P30 gel-sieving column. Polyclonal anti-osteonectin antibodies were affinity purified as described by Tung et al. (1985).

First molar tooth organs were dissected from 100-200 gm porcine fetuses obtained in utero and fixed for 24 h at 4°C in periodate-lysine-paraformaldehyde (McLean and Nakane, 1974) also containing 0.1% glutaraldehyde. Demineralization was achieved in one week with daily changes of 12% EDTA in PBS at 4°C. Some tissues were processed without demineralization. After thorough washing in PBS and dehydration in graded ethanol, all tissues were imbedded in Paraplast. Sections of 5 µm thickness were deparaffinized, hydrated and pretreated with 1% H_2O_2 in ethanol for 30 min to remove endogenous peroxidase activity. The sections were washed and preincubated with 0.1 mg/ml goat IgG in TBS. This was followed by incubation with the affinity purified antibodies in appropriate dilutions. Goat anti-rabbit (osteonectin) or rabbit anti-sheep (amelogenin) affinity purified F(ab')$_2$ fragments were used in the second antibody incubation. This was followed by incubation with peroxidase-antiperoxidase, and then with the substrate, (3,3')-diaminobenzidine tetrahydrochloride (0.5 µg/ml) in 0.01% H_2O_2 for colour development. Non-immune antibodies were used at each antibody incubation step for the controls.

RESULTS AND DISCUSSION

Enamel protein and osteonectin were detected in regions of the cusp tips of the developing tooth organs where differentiation of both ameloblasts and odontoblasts had occurred (Figure 1). Enamel protein staining was detected in the cytoplasm of differentiated ameloblasts and in

newly-secreted enamel matrix, the latter being intensely
stained. Osteonectin staining was confined to the mineralized dentin adjacent to the newly-secreted enamel matrix.
Enamel protein staining extended further apically along
the developing cusp than the osteonectin staining. These
results suggest a temporal relationship between the synthesis of enamel protein by ameloblasts and osteonectin by

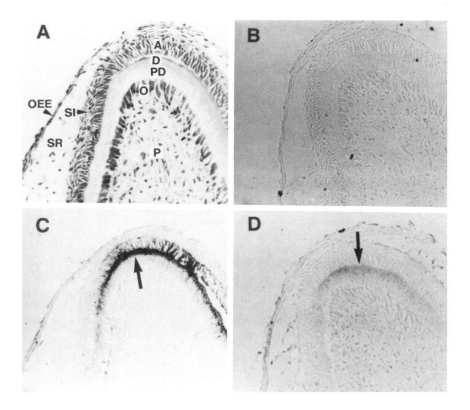

Figure 1. Immunohistochemical localization of enamel protein and osteonectin in the cusp tip region of a developing
porcine tooth. A. Hematoxylin-eosin stain. OEE: outer
enamel epithelium, SR: stellate reticulum, SI: stratum
intermedium, P: pulp, O: odontoblasts, PD: predentin,
D: dentin, A: ameloblasts. B. Control. C. Enamel protein.
D. Osteonectin. The arrows show the position of the
dentoenamel junction. X 110.

odontoblasts. However, since enamel proteins appear to be deposited prior to the occurrence of osteonectin in the mineralized dentin, it is assumed that osteonectin is not likely to be one of the dentin components involved in the induction of ameloblast differentiation. Rather, it is possible that the initial synthesis of enamel protein signals the odontoblasts to synthesize and deposit proteins such as osteonectin in the mineralizing dentin. However, confirmation of this requires further investigation using the developing tooth system.

REFERENCES

Kollar EJ (1983). Epithelial-mesenchymal interactions in the mammalian integument: tooth development as a model for instructive induction. In Sawyer RH, Fallon JF (eds): "Epithelial-Mesenchymal Interactions in Development", New York, Praeger, pp 27-49.

McLean IW, Nakane PK (1974). Periodate-lysine-paraformalde-hyde fixative. A new fixative for immunoelectronmicro-scopy. J Histochem Cytochem 22:1077-1087.

Ruch JV (1984). Tooth morphogenesis and differentiation. In Linde A (ed): "Dentin and Dentinogenesis", vol. I, Boca Raton, CRC Press, pp 47-79.

Slavkin HC (1974). Embryonic tooth formation: a tool for developmental biology. In Melcher AH, Zarb GA (eds): "Oral Sciences Reviews", vol. 4, Copenhagen, Munksgaard, pp 1-136.

Slavkin HC, Zeichner-David M, MacDougall M, Bringas P, Bessem C, Honig LS (1982). Antibodies to murine amelo-genins: localization of enamel proteins during tooth organ development in vitro. Differentiation 23:73-82.

Termine JD, Kleinman HK, Whitson SW, Conn KM, McGarvey ML, Martin GR (1981a). Osteonectin, a bone-specific protein linking mineral to collagen. Cell 26:99-105.

Termine JD, Belcourt AB, Conn KM, Kleinman HK (1981b). Mineral and collagen-binding proteins of fetal calf bone. J Biol Chem 256:10403-10408.

Tung PS, Domenicucci C, Wasi S, Sodek J (1985). Specific immunohistochemical localization of osteonectin and collagen types I and III in fetal and adult porcine dental tissues. J Histochem Cytochem 33:531-540.

Zeichner-David M, MacDougall M, Slavkin HC (1983). Enamelin gene expression during fetal and neonatal rabbit tooth organogenesis. Differentiation 25:148-155.

Progress in Developmental Biology, Part B, pages 409–414
© 1986 Alan R. Liss, Inc.

THE OSTEOBLAST AND OSTEOCLAST CYTODIFFERENTIATION

Philip Osdoby, Merry Jo Oursler, and Fred
Anderson
School of Dental Medicine, Washington University,
St. Louis, Missouri 63110

INTRODUCTION

The kinetics of osteoblast and osteoclast cytodifferentiation and regulated fluctuations in bone cell
activity effect skeletal form and calcium homeostasis.
Despite recent advances in the identification of local and
humoral effects of bone growth and remodeling (Canalis,
1983), much remains unknown. In this context focal
alterations in bone remodeling suggest that regional-local
influences may supercede systemic regulatory homeostatic
control processes.

Bone forming osteoblasts are derived from the
mesenchyme while bone resorbing multinucleated osteoclasts
originate from blood-borne precursor cells. Osteoblast
expression precedes cartilage vascularization which in turn
precedes osteoclast formation in developing limbs (Osdoby
and Caplan, 1981). Additional evidence supporting an
osteoblast mesenchymal origin includes observations in
which phenotypically uncommitted limb mesenchyme differentiate into osteoblasts in vitro (Osdoby and Caplan, 1979).
Evidence for a monocyte-macrophage blood-borne origin for
osteoclasts include studies in which the osteoclast defect
in osteopetrotic animals has been cured by marrow transplantation, parabiosis, and spleen cell injection (Marks,
1983).

The role for cell interactions has been investigated
in developing bone systems. Morphological studies suggest
that osteoblast expression is a pre-requisite for osteoclast

formation. Kahn et al. (1981) reported that osteoclast
precursors are found in day 3 embryos but osteoclasts do not
appear until 4 days after osteoblast expression begins.
Thesingh and Burger (1983) reported that mesenchymal cells
are required for giant cell formation when marrow cells
were co-cultured with metatarsal bones. Recently Burger
et al. (1984) using a similar approach concluded that live
bone was necessary for osteoclast formation and marrow
contained more osteoclast precursors than peritoneal exudate
macrophage populations. Morphological studies from this
laboratory (Osdoby et al. 1983) showed that monocytes
co-cultured with mesenchymally derived osteoblasts formed
cells similar in appearance to osteoclasts. Giant cells
formed alone differed morphologically. Until recently
little information has been available to determine if
osteoclasts represented a unique giant cell of bone or
were equivalent to other giant cells formed throughout body
tissues (Haythorn, 1929). Therefore the lack of definitive
osteoclast markers has left the interpretation of the
morphological studies open.

Recently, this laboratory has developed a monoclonal
antibody library raised with osteoclasts as immunogen
(Oursler et al. 1985). Monoclonal antibodies that exclusively recognize osteoclasts have been identified. These
osteoclast-specific antibodies do not recognize monocytes,
giant cells derived from either monocytes or marrow nor
foreign body giant cells. The development of these reagents
provides an immunological approach to identify osteoclasts,
discriminate them from other giant cells, and determine if
bone factors may be required for osteoclast formation.

METHODS

Cell Isolation and Culture: Osteoclasts, monocytes,
stage 24 limb mesenchyme, and skin fibroblasts were isolated
by methods described by Osdoby et al. (1982).

Mixed Phenotype Experiment: In mixed phenotype
experiments monocytes were inoculated into culture dishes
at 100×10^6. On either day 2 or day 4 of culture monocytes
were overplated with either stage 24 mesenchyme (osteoblasts)
or skin fibroblasts.

Immunohistochemical Analysis: At various times after
co-culture mixed phenotype cultures were fixed and reacted

with an osteoclast-specific antibody (121F). Antibody binding was visualized with fluoroscein-conjugated anti-mouse IgG (Sternberger, 1974).

Radioimmunoassay: To quantitate the appearance of the 121F antigen in mixed cultures a competitive radioimmuno-assay was developed (Oursler et al. in preparation).

RESULTS

Chick hatchling circulating monocytes were isolated and cultured. In culture, monocytes fuse and form large multinucleated giant cells (Figure 1B). Under specific culture conditions these multinucleated giant cells display plasma membrane processes similar to, but not identical to, those observed on cultured osteoclasts (Figure 1A). When monocytes are co-cultured with stage 24 mesenchymal cells (osteoblasts) giant cells develop surface morphologies and ultrastructures indistinguishable from osteoclasts. These cells appear to resorb the mineralized matrix produced by the cultured osteoblasts (Figures 1C and 1D). Monocyte-derived giant cells formed alone or in the presence of skin fibroblasts do not exhibit fluorescent localization of the 121F osteoclast-specific antibody at any time. However, some giant cells formed in the presence of osteoblasts bind the osteoclast-specific antibody (Figures 1E and 1F).

Table 1 summarizes the results of the radioimmunoassay (RIA) for monocytes grown in culture for 4 days and then overplated with various phenotypes including osteoblasts. Briefly, 121F antibody (osteoclast-specific) was bound to RIA plates, extracts of samples to be tested was added along with iodinated osteoclast extract (4300 counts) and the presence of antigen in the sample was determined by the competition of binding to the antibody. In the categories of individual and mixed cells the only competitive binding was observed when monocytes were co-cultured with osteoblasts. Furthermore, with increase time more 121F antigen was present.

FIGURE 1

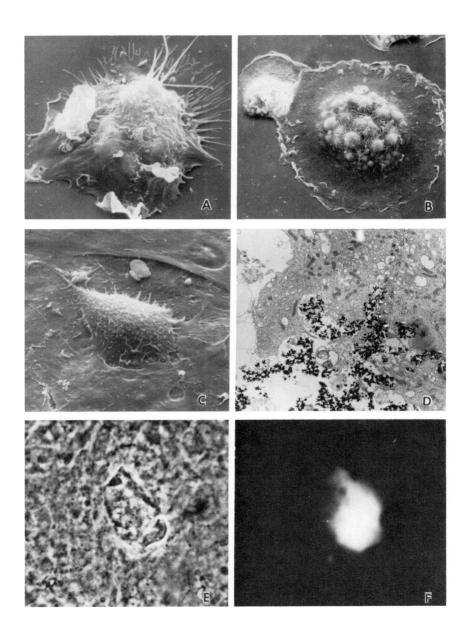

TABLE 1   121F RADIOIMMUNOASSAY

Cell Type	Time (Days of Co-culture)		
	1	6	8
Monocytes	4196	–	4369
Monocytes + Osteoblasts	4220	3719	2670
Monocytes + Fibroblasts	4189	4071	4142
Osteoblasts	4202	4290	4258
Fibroblasts	4219	4255	4142
Osteoblasts + Fibroblasts	4185	4359	4271

CONCLUSIONS

The results of these experiments provides direct immunological support for the hypothesis that osteoblasts are necessary for the development of unique osteoclast-specific antigens in monocyte derived giant cell cultures. Similar results have been obtained with marrow-derived giant cell cultures. Like other cells of the macrophage family it appears that the resident tissue plays an important role in the cell specialization of these cells. It is therefore possible that osteoblast dysfunction could alter osteoclast expression and bone remodeling. The nature of these osteoblast signals and the determination of the functional role for the osteoclast-specific molecules are areas of active investigation.

REFERENCES

Burger E, Van Der Meer J, and Nijweide P (1984). Osteoclast formation from mononuclear phagocytes: role of bone forming cells. J. Cell Bio. 99:1901.
Canalis E (1983). The hormonal and local regulation of bone formation. Endocrine Reviews 42:62.
Haythorn S (1929). Multinucleated giant cells. Arch Pathol 7:651.

Kahn A, Simmons D, and Krukowski M (1981). Osteoclast precursor cells are present in the blood of preossification chick embryos. Develop Biol 84:230.

Marks S (1983). The origin of osteoclasts. J. Oral Pathol 12:226.

Osdoby P and Caplan A (1979). Osteogenesis in cultures of limb mesenchymal cells. Develop Biol 73:84.

Osdoby P and Caplan A (1981). First bone formation in the developing chick limb. Develop Biol 86:147.

Osdoby P, Martini M, and Caplan A (1982). Isolated osteoclasts and their presumptive precursor, the monocyte, in culture. J. Exp Zool 224:331.

Osdoby P, Martini M, and Caplan A (1983). The development of long bones of the limb: Cell and Matrix interactions of osteoclasts and monocytes. Limb Development and Reg. Pt. B Pg. 229. Kelley R, Goetinck P, MacCabe J (eds): Alan R. Liss, Inc. N.Y.

Oursler M, Bell L, Clevinger B, and Osdoby P (1985). Identification of osteoclast-specific monoclonal antibodies. J. Cell Biol 100:1592.

Sternberger L (1974). Immunohistochemistry, Prentice Hall, N.J.

Thesingh C and Burger E (1983). The role of mesenchyme in embryonic long bones as early deposition sites for osteoclast progenitor cells. Develop Biol 95:429.

This work was supported by grants from the Arthritis Foundation and N.I.H.

Epithelial—Mesenchymal Interactions

Progress in Developmental Biology, Part B, pages 417–424

CELL-CELL INTERACTIONS IN THE MEDIATION OF HORMONE DEPENDENT DIFFERENTIATION OF MAMMARY EPITHELIUM

Frank E. Stockdale, Darrell J. Wiens, and Jedd F. Levine

Department of Medicine, Stanford University School of Medicine, Stanford, California 94305

INTRODUCTION

Mammary epithelium forms a branching ductal system within a pre-existing fat pad in the developing mammal. While it has often been suggested there may be an interaction between the adipocytes and epithelium of the gland which fosters the differentiation of the epithelium and the formation of ducts and alveoli within the mammary gland, such a relationship has been difficult to demonstrate. Recently we developed an in vitro cell culture model system to study the nature of the interaction of adipose tissue with mammary epithelium from mice (Levine and Stockdale, 1984, 1985). In the model system 3T3-L1 cells (Green and Kehinde, 1974) were used as an adipocyte substrate on which to culture mammary epithelial cells. 3T3-L1 cells (here after designated L1 cells) are a line of cells which when incubated in insulin and dexamethasone differentiate into adipocytes which accumulate a fat vacuole and express many enzymes associated with adipocytes in vivo (Green and Kehinde, 1975). This co-culture system permits measurements of mammary epithelial function while in intimate contact with adipocytes in a setting where one can control the exposure of the epithelium to various hormones without perturbing the relationship with the adipocytes. The questions we wished to pursue were the importance of the interaction of the epithelium with adipocytes in the regulation of proliferation of the epithelium; its importance in establishing hormone sensitivity of the epithelium, in fostering the expression of milk protein sysnthesis, and in ultrastructural changes within and around the epithelium that result from this interaction.

Effects of Cell-Cell Interactions on Growth of Mammary Epithelium

Cell-cell interactions foster cell proliferation of mammary epithelium in co-cultures of adipocytes and other cell types. To study the effects of adipocytes on the regulation of mammary epithelial proliferation, mammary epithelium from midpregnant mice was plated on L1 cells and several control substrates. DNA synthesis in the mammary epithelium was monitored by colony size, tritiated thymidine incroporation, labeling index, and cell count. Cell proliferation was analyzed after two days of attachment to irradiated L1 cells, to tissue culture dishes alone, or to irradiated 3T3-C2 cells (3T3 line that does not form adipocytes). There was a 4.8 fold increase in tritiated thymidine incorporation into the epithelium when plated on the adipocytes compared to tissue culture dishes alone. The 3T3 C2 cell (C2 cell) substrate also increased tritiated thymidine incorporation but to a lessor degree than did the L1 cell substrate (2.5 fold). The effects were reflected in the number of epithelial cells initiating DNA synthesis in that labelling index of the epithelium on the adipocytes was 4.1 fold greater than on plastic and 2.6 greater on the C2 cellular substrates. Colony area was 3.4 times greater when the epithelium was plated on the L1 cellular substrate. The effects were seen most evidently in dishes that had been fixed and stained with antibodies to keratin where it was clear that the stained areas of epithelial cells were much larger than those on other substrates (Levine and Stockdale, 1985).

The nature of the effect of the adipoctyes on the growth of mammary epithelium was via both extracellular matrix material and soluble factors. To determine if living cells were required as substrates for these effects on growth, mammary epithelium was plated under two additional conditions. The substrate attached material (SAM) (Rheinwald, 1980; Levine and Stockdale, 1984) remaining on a tissue culture dish after the L1 or C2 were removed from the dishes with EDTA, was used to determine the role of extracellular components in mediating the growth effects of these two cell types on mammary epithelium. Dishes with L1 or C2 SAM substrates were equally effective in increasing cell number (13.3 fold for C2 SAM vs 12.3 fold for the L1 SAM) over the cell number produced on tissue culture plastic alone.

Not only was the extracellular material important for the growth of the epithelium but soluble factors in the medium were as well. This was shown by plating the same number of epithelial cells on normal tissue culture dishes after which medium was changed to that conditioned by either C2 or L1 cells for 24 hours. Compared to fresh medium L1 cell-conditioned medium alone produced a 6 fold increase in cell number while C2 cell-conditioned medium produced a 3 fold increase in epithelial cell number. The addition of conditioned medium to epithelium growing on SAM from L1 cells produced additive effects on cell number.

These results on growth indicate that the interaction of adipocytes with epithelial cells involves several components. There is a component that does not require that the adipocytes be metabolically active. Thus the interaction underlying initiation of growth was mediated in part through materials deposited outside the cell (SAM). It is not clear if the material(s) in the conditioned medium are distinct from those in SAM, but the additive effect on cell proliferation suggests the materials in the medium responsible for growth initiation are distinct from those in SAM. Importantly, these results show that there is not just initiation of DNA synthesis, but a net increase in cell number when mammary epithelium is grown on the extracellular materials derived from L1 and other cells.

Differentiation of Mammary Epithelium on Cellular Substrates

The nature of the cell-cell interaction between adipocytes and mammary epithelium that promotes growth may be different than that which fosters differentiation of the mammary epithelium. The production of the casein family of phosphoproteins and α-lactalbumin serve as excellent indices of hormone dependent differentiation in this sytem. When the mammary epithelium was placed on irradiated L1 cells for three days and the lactogenic hormones, insulin, hydrocortisone, and prolactin were added there was the production of casein within hours of hormone addition (Levine and Stockdale, 1985). Immunohistochemical staining of the co-cultures with monoclonal antibodies specific to α -, β-and γ -casein or α -lactalbumin revealed that all four proteins were synthesized in these cultures of mammary epithelium and L1 cells. When the same epithelial cells were plated in control dishes of tissue culture plastic alone, no casein or α -lactalbumin was synthesized. This response was hormone dependent in that the addition of insulin alone to the L1 epithelial co-cultures did not initiate casein or α -lactalbumin synthesis. Hormone-dependent casein synthesis was also effected by the nature of the cellular substrate, since if the epithelium was plated on cell layers of irradiated human foreskin fibroblasts (HFSF), or Swiss 3T3 cell there was also no synthesis of casein.

However, both C2 cells and L1 cells (both converted and unconverted to adipocytes) interact with the epithelium to produce hormone dependent differentiation events.

Unlike the effects of cell-cell interactions on initiating and sustaining epithelial cell proliferation, extracellular components alone are not sufficient to initiate hormone-dependent differentiation. When mammary epithelium was plated on SAM from the L1 or other cell types and the lactogenic hormones were added to the medium, casein production was not detected. Conditioned medium alone placed on epithelium growing on plastic also failed to illicit casein production.

Thus the cell-cell interaction between adipocytes and mammary epithelium results in the acquisition of hormone sensitivity by the epithelium. This hormone sensitivity results in the production of at least four mammary gland specific proteins, all caseins components (α, β, γ) and α-lactalbumin in response to insulin, hydrocortisone, and prolactin. Milk proteins are not only detected in homogenates of the cells themselves, but are secreted in large amounts into the culture medium (more than 20 μg/24 hour period from one 60-mm dish). The response was not seen if the extracellular matrix remaining after EDTA extraction of the adipocytes was the substrate upon which the epithelium rests. In this respect there was a distinction between the interactions with adipocytes that lead to proliferation and those that lead to hormone dependent differentiation.

Ultrastructural Changes in Mammary Epithelium Interacting with Adipocytes

The hormone-dependent differentiation of mammary epithelium interacting with adipocytes appears to require contact with cells. This suggests that there may be dynamic processes involved that faciliate hormone dependent differentiation. The most obvious effects that the interaction might have would be those associated with the polarization of the cell, an aspect of cytodifferentiation in a system associated with secretion of proteins and lipids. Polarization of mammary epithelium in vivo is evidenced by the appearance of a basal lamina at the basal surface of the epithelial cells, the positioning of the cell nucleus and the Golgi apparatus within the basal portion of the cell, and the appearance of microvilli at the apical or luminal cell surface.

Sections through the epithelium in the model cell culture system revealed distinct ultrastructural differences depending upon the presence or absence of the cellular substrate and the type of cellullar substrate. Epithelium on the plastic substrate lacks evidence of polarization; there was no intracellular evidence of polarization; there were few microvilli; no basal lamina or secretory vacuoles were seen, though there was rough endoplasmic reticulum and some Golgi apparatus. Analysis of the same epithelium on NFSF cell substrates revealed more evidence of cytodifferentiation, but a general lack of polarization. In these co-cultures with NFSF cells there were more microvilli and extracellular fibrillar material, but there was no evidence of a basal lamina. Epithelium in co-culture with L1 cells demonstrated marked epithelial polarization. The epithelial cells had a striking basal lamina by 14 days in culture consisting of an inner lamina rara and an outer lamina dense which was contacted by fibrils from the extracellular matrix (Fig. 1). There were distended cisternae of rough endoplasmic reticulum and the Golgi vesicles were increasingly abundant in epithelial cells associated with the L1 cells. Duct-like structures formed in cultures grown with L1 cells whether or not lactogenic hormones were present, but only in the presence of lactogenic hormones were milk proteins synthesized by these structures.

DISCUSSION

A number of investigators have demonstrated that the matrix on which the mammary epithelial cells attach in vitro alters their response to hormones (Emerman et al., 1977; Kratochwill, 1969; Lee et al., 1984; Yang et al., 1980; Ormerod and Rudland, 1982; Salomon et al., 1981; Wicha et al., 1982). In the model system described here the interactions that the epithelium normally experiences are as closely mimicked as one can in a two-dimensional in vitro system. These studies demonstrate that cell-cell interactions alter growth and hormone-dependent differentiation of mammary epithelium. The L1 adipocytes have the greatest effect on both of these parameters. Though the hormonal conversion of L1 cells to true adipocytes was not a requirement for hormone mediated production, there was greater evidence of differentiation in cultures where such conversion was present. The results of these experiments show that growth was mediated by both soluble and attached cellular materials and suggest that cytodifferentiation must be mediated by additional factors since conditioned medium and SAM are not sufficient for hormone-dependent differentiation to occur.

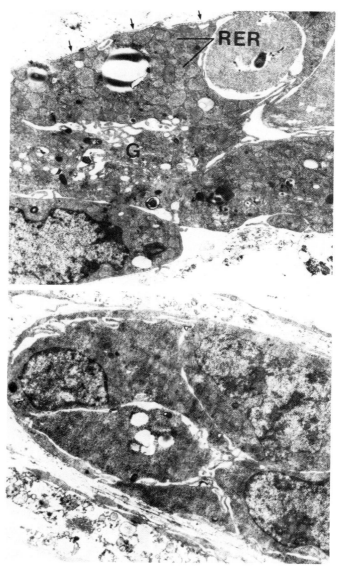

Figure 1. **Top.** Adipocyte-mammary epithelial co-culture treated with insulin, prolactin and hydrocortisone for 14 days. A continuous basal lamina (arrows), round and distended rough endoplasmic reticulum (ER) and Golgi area (G) indicate polarity and secretory function. **Bottom.** Co-culture treated with insulin only. Basal lamina is discontinuous and ER profiles are flat (10,000x).

Differentiation in this system is separable into two components: cytodifferentiation, that is the synthesis of milk proteins, and morphogenesis of ducts which can occur independently of one another. In short term cultures in the presence of lactogenic hormones (Levine and Stockdale, 1985), milk proteins are synthesized without apparent formation of any duct-like structures. Continued culture of mammary epithelium on L1 substrates results in the formation of ductal structures even if lactogenic hormones are not present (Wiens and Stockdale, 1985). Thus, it is possible to see histodifferentiation of the epithelium without evidence of the production of the secretory products characteristic of this gland. However, these ductal structures formed in the absence of lactogenic hormones will undergo cytodifferentiation and produce milk proteins if subsequently exposed to lactogenic hormones. The distinction between histotypic and cytotypic differentiation (formation of cellular products) is an important one since one does not see both aspects of differentiation in all culture systems used to study mammary epithelial function. This co-culture system distinguishes between these two components of mammary gland formation and function--thus, mimicking what happens during mammary gland formation and function in the animal.

ACKNOWLEDGEMENTS

The authors wish to thank Gloria Garcia for her assistance in the preparation of this manuscript. This research was supported by NIH Grants #HD19419 and HD07244. Jedd F. Levine is a recipient of a Damon Runyon-Walther Winchell Cancer Fund Fellowship, DRG-020.

REFERENCES

Emmerman JT, Enami J, Pitelka DR, Nandi S (1977). Hormonal effects on intracellular and secreted casein in cultures of mouse mammary epithelial cells on floating collagen membranes. Proc Natl Acad Sci USA 74:4466-4470.

Green H, Kehinde O (1974). Sublines of mouse 3T3 cells that accumulate lipid. Cell 1:113-116.

Green H, Kehinde O (1975). An established preadipose cell line and its differentiation in culture. II. Factors affecting the adipose conversion. Cell 5:19-27.

Kratochwill K (1969). Organ specificity in mesenchymal induction demonstrated in embryonic development of the mammary gland in the mouse. Dev Biol 20:46-71.

Lee E Y-H, Parry G, Bissell MJ (1984). Modulation of secreted proteins of mouse mammary epithelial cells by the collagenous substrata. J Cell Biol 98:146-155.

Levine JF, Stockdale FE (1984). 3T3-L1 adipocytes promote the growth of mammary epithelium. Exp Cell Res 151:112-122.

Levine JF, Stockdale FE (1985). Cell-cell interactions promote mammary epithelial cell differentiation. J Cell Biol 100:1415-1422.

Ormerod JE, Rudland PS (1982). Mammary gland morphogenesis in vitro: formation of branched tubules in collagen gels by a cloned rat mammary cell line. Dev Biol 91:360-375.

Rheinwald JG (1980). Serial cultivation of normal human epidermal keratinocytes. In: Methods in Cell Biology (ed CC Harris, BF Trump and GD Stoner) Vol 21A, p 229, Academic Press, New York.

Salomon DS, Liotta LA, Kidwell WR (1981). Differential response to growth factor by rat mammary epithelium plated on different collagen substrata in serum-free medium. Proc Natl Acad Sci USA 78:382-386.

Wicha MS, Lawrie G, Kahn E, Bagavandoss P, Mahn T (1982). Extracellular matrix promotes mammary epithelial growth and differentiation in vitro. Proc Natl Acad Sci USA 79:3213-3217.

Yang J, Richards J, Guzman R, Imagawa W, Nandi S (1980). Sustained growth in primary culture of normal mammary epithelial cells embedded in collagen gels. Proc Natl Acad Sci USA 77:2088-2092.

Progress in Developmental Biology, Part B, pages 425–428
© 1986 Alan R. Liss, Inc.

DIHYDROTESTOSTERONE (DHT) UNCOUPLES CELL INTERACTIONS IN
DEVELOPING LUNG

John Torday

Department of Pediatrics, Harvard Medical School,
Boston, MA   02115.

INTRODUCTION

Fetal lung maturation culminates in the production of
pulmonary surfactant, a lipid-protein complex which lines
the alveoli, preventing atelectasis. The production of
surfactant is exquisitely regulated by an expanding list of
hormones, some of which accelerate surfactant production
(cortisol, thyroxin, catecholamines), and others which
delay surfactant production (insulin, dihydrotestosterone).[1]

Animal studies have indicated that the well-recognized
sex difference in the rate of fetal lung maturation is associated with androgens in fetal circulation[2]. To determine whether androgens affect lung surfactant production
directly, and if so by what mechanism, the effects of the
androgen dihydrotestosterone (DHT) on this process were
studied in cell culture.

RESULTS

When organotype cultures of day 19 fetal rat lung are
treated with cortisol (Table 1) there is an 80-100% increase in synthesis of saturated phosphatidylcholine (SPC),
the major component of surfactant. This stimulation is due
to the production of fibroblast-pneumonocyte factor (FPF)
by the fibroblasts, which stimulates SPC synthesis by the
epithelial cells, as indicated by the inhibition of the
cortisol response. When the DHT response by the fibroblast
and epithelial cell were looked at independently, it was

found that both the FPF production by the fibroblast (Table 2) and the FPF response by the epithelial cells (Table 3) were blocked, but basal activity was unaffected. When epithelial cells were washed free of DHT, they became FPF responsive asgain within 1 hour.[3]

TABLE 1	^{3}H-SPC (dpm/10^6 cells/24h)
control	3820+180
cortisol (1 x 10^{-7}m)	7960+190*
cortisol + Ab	3980+196
DHT	3680+210
DHT + cortisol	3790+170

TABLE 2	^{3}H-SPC (dpm/10^6 cells/6h)
control	13600+2400
cortisol	29867+1280*
DHT	11800+2480
DHT + cortisol	13550+3200

TABLE 3	^{3}H-SPC (dpm/10^6 cells/6h)
control	13200+1860
cortisol	26850+3180*
DHT	12120+1680
DHT + cortisol	14880+4860

$*p < 0.01$

In other studies I observed that using sex-specific cultures male cultures synthesized less SPC than females. Moreover, mole fibroblasts produce less FPF than female fibroblasts; however, there was no difference in the basal or FPF-stimulated response by sex-specific epithelial cells[4]. This may be due to the rapid reversibility of the androgen effect on the epithelial cells observed in the DHT experiments.

Therefore DHT blocks cortisol-dependant surfactant synthesis both at the fibroblast and at the epithelium, thus uncoupling the cell-cell interactions which mediate this process.

Androgens also affect fetal lung growth, both in vivo[5] and in vitro[6]. Therefore, the effects of DHT on growing fibroblasts and epithelial cells were also investigated. Fibroblast growth was unaffected by DHT, however, epithelial cell growth was stimulated. (Fig. 1) Furthermore, when SPC synthesis and response to FPF were examined in cells grown in DHT it was found that 1) the synthesis of SPC was decreased (Fig.1) and 2) the response to FPF was blocked and irreversible ;by washing out the DHT, i.e. the

FPF effect was no longer DHT-dependent. Interestingly, if the cells were allowed to grow in DHT-free conditions, the SPC production and FPF response returned to normal, suggesting constitutive phenotypic changes in the epithelial cells due to DHT treatment (not shown).

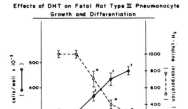

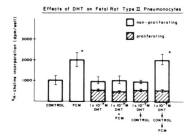

Fig.1.Effects of DHT on fetal rat lung epithelial cell growth and differentiation.The number of cells per culture is displayed as a solid line and is quantified on the left-hand ordinate the rate of ^{3}H-choline incorporation into ^{3}H-SPC is displayed as a broken line and is quantified on the right-hand ordinate. Each data point represents the mean +SD of 6 replicate cultures from at least 2 experiments. The DHT concentrations are shown on the abscissa. +,*=p<.02.

Fig.2.Effects of DHT on fetal rat lung epithelial cell FPF response. The height of the bars represents the mean+SD incorporation of ^{3}H-SPC. The open bars represent cultures treated with DHT(1×10^{-7}M)at confluence; the shaded bars represent cultures grown to confluence in the presence of DHT(1×10^{-7}M). At the time of assay cultures were washed free of DHT and challenged with MEM containing 1uCi/ml ^{3}H-choline(=control) plus fibroblast-conditioned medium(=FCM,50% v/v),DHT(1×10^{-7}M),or fibroblast conditioned medium and DHT(=DHT+FCM).In the last two cases the cultures were washed free of DHT, cultivated in MEM/5% fetal bovine serum and then incubated in 1uCi ^{3}H-choline/ml MEM(=DHT control) or 1uCi ^{3}H-choline/ml + 50% FCM v/v(=DHT control FCM). *,p<.o1.

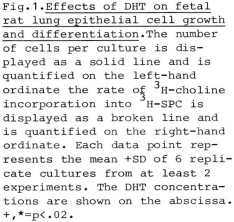

Based on these cell culture studies, there are marked effects of DHT on key steps in the maturation of both the lung mesenchyme and epithelium. These effects may explain the heterochronic development of the male and female lung. Furthermore, the observed effects of DHT on epithelial cell growth may lead to the elucidation of sexually dimorphic lung growth as well.

These studies were supported by NHLBI grant 28315.

REFERENCES

1. Smith B (1984). Pulmonary surfactant during fetal development and neonatal adaptation: hormonal control. In B. Robertson,et al (eds.): "Pulmonary Surfactant", Amsterdam: Elsevier, pp. 357-381.

2. Nielsen H, Zinman H, Torday J (1982). Dihydrotesto-sterone inhibits fetal rabbit pulmonary surfactant production. J Clin Invest 69:611-619.

3. Torday J (1985). Dihydrotestosterone inhibits fibro-blast-pneumonocyte factor-mediated synthesis of saturated phosphatidylcholine by fetal rat lung cells. Biochem Biophys Acta 835:23-28.

4. Torday J (1984). The sex difference in type II cell surfactant synthesis originates in the fibroblast in vitro. Exp Lung Res 7:187-194.

5. Nielsen H, Torday J (1985). Sex differences in avian embryo pulmonary surfactant production: evidence for sex chromosome involvement. Endocrinology 117:31-37.

6. Torday J (1984). Direct pharmocologic effects of DHT on the alveolar type II cell in vitro. Pediatr Res 18:146A.

7. Pagtakhan R, Bjelland J, Landau L, Loughin G, Kaltenborn W, Seeley G, Taussig L (1984). Sex differences in growth patterns of the airways and lung parenchyma in children. J Appl Physiol 56:1204-1210.

Progress in Developmental Biology, Part B, pages 429–432
© 1986 Alan R. Liss, Inc.

PATTERNING OF MYOGENIC CELLS IN THE EARLY CHICK LIMB BUD

Michael Solursh, Karen L. Jensen and
Rebecca S. Reiter

Department of Biology, University of Iowa,
Iowa City, Iowa 52242

It is widely believed that the voluntary muscles are derived from the somites. This idea is based on the observation that when quail somites are implanted into chick hosts the skeletal muscles are of quail origin (Chevallier et al., 1977; Christ et al., 1977). Presumably, the somite cells migrate to future myogenic sites. However, little is known about the distribution of myogenic cells between the time they leave the somites and the time they begin cytodifferentiation after stage 25 in the wing bud (Hilfer et al., 1973). Based on the distribution of somite-derived quail cells (Newman et al., 1981), or potential myogenic cells in small tissue isolates obtained from various regions of the limb bud, myogenic cells are clearly regionalized (Ahrens et al., 1979; Rutz et al., 1982). The present study was undertaken in order to localize more precisely myogenic cells in the developing limb bud.

Two independent markers were used. First, cryostat sections were prepared from chick limb buds at various stages and stained with a monoclonal antibody specific to desmin, the major muscle intermediate filament protein (Danto and Fischman, 1984). Immunofluorescence was carried out as described previously (Solursh et al., 1982). Alternatively, the distribution of somite-derived quail cells in the limb bud was examined by use of a quail-specific mouse monoclonal antibody, kindly provided by Dr. P.A. Kitos. Japanese quail somites were grafted in situ at the wing level of stage 12-13 chick embryos and the limbs frozen when the hosts had reached Hamburger and Hamilton stages 21 or 24.

Desmin-positive cells were first recognized in the wing

region at stage 16. From stage 21 through 24 the wing bud
was negative for sarcomere myosin but contained scattered
desmin-positive cells (Fig. 1a), which were restricted to an
elliptical region in the limb bud core, including the pre-
chondrogenic region. These cells were absent from the peripheral avascular zone that extends a relatively constant distance from the limb ectoderm (Caplan and Koutroupas, 1973).
This avascular region is also rich in hyaluronate (Singley
and Solursh, 1981), which is known to inhibit vasculogenesis
(Feinberg and Beebe, 1983). The desmin-positive cells appear
particularly concentrated in the venous-rich region just under the peripheral avascular zone. After stage 24 desmin-
positive cells begin to accumulate in dorsal and ventral myogenic regions which are now positive for sarcomere myosin, as
well. There are progressively fewer desmin-positive cells
outside of the dorsal and ventral muscle masses until stage
28 when they are largely restricted to these areas. At no
stage examined were desmin-positive cells associated with
the subclavian artery, making it unlikely that these cells
are smooth muscle precursor cells.

As an independent and established marker for myogenic
cells we examined the distribution of somite-derived quail
cells in the chick host wing bud. As can be seen in Figure
1b, the quail cells have a similar distribution to the desmin-positive cells. They are both restricted from the avascular peripheral region. Because of the co-distribution of
cells recognized by two independent markers, it is likely
that the myogenic cells are restricted from the avascular
periphery and concentrated in the venous-rich regions of the
limb bud. This distribution of putative myogenic cells supports the hypothesis that the vascular elements influence
the migratory pattern of myogenic precursors. As shown in the
chapter by Meier and Burton in this volume, the vascular pattern in the early wing bud region is established just before
the time of myoblast migration. Furthermore, myoblasts have
been shown to respond chemotactically in vitro to serum and
vascular endothelial cell products, such as platelet-derived
growth factor (Venkatasubramanian and Solursh, 1984).

The ectoderm might serve as a general determinant of
early tissue patterning. It has been suggested that it establishes the pattern of chondrogenic and non-chondrogenic tissue differentiation through a diffusible morphogen (see Solursh, 1984). The ectoderm also promotes the formation of
the peripheral avascular zone (Feinberg et al., 1983). Thus,
the ectoderm might influence the early myogenic pattern

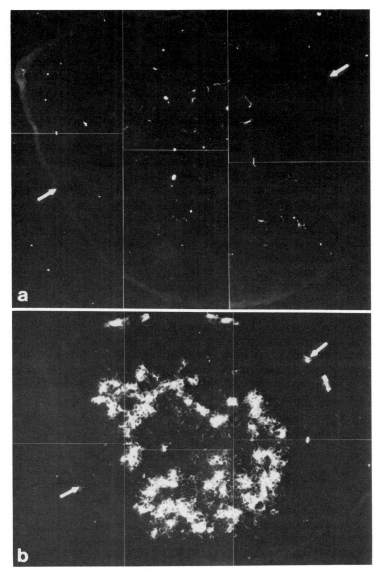

Figure 1. Adjacent frozen cross sections through an early
stage 24 chimeric chick wing bud prepared by implanting
quail somites at the wing level. The section in (a) was
stained with a monoclonal antibody directed against desmin.
The section in (b) was stained with a quail-specific monoclonal antibody to show the distribution of somite-derived
quail cells. A few quail ectoderm cells are present.
(arrows = ectoderm) (160X).

indirectly through effects on the vasculature. This hypothesis warrants further testing.

REFERENCES

Ahrens PB, Solursh M, Reiter RS, Singley CT (1979). Position-related capacity for differentiation of limb mesenchyme in cell culture. Dev Biol 69:436.

Caplan AI, Koutroupas S (1973). The control of muscle and cartilage development in the chick limb: the role of differential vascularization. J Embryol Exp Morph 29:571.

Chevallier A, Kieny M, Mauger A (1977). Limb-somite relationship: origin of the limb musculature. J Embryol Exp Morph 41:245.

Christ B, Jacob HJ, Jacob M (1977). Experimental analysis of the origin of the wing musculature in avian embryos. Anat Embryol 150:171.

Danto SI, Fischman DA (1984). Immunocytochemical analysis of intermediate filaments in embryonic heart cells with monoclonal antibodies to desmin. J Cell Biol 98:2179.

Feinberg RN, Beebe DC (1983). Hyaluronate in vasculogenesis. Science 220:1177.

Feinberg RN, Repo MA, Saunders JW (1983). Ectodermal control of the avascular zone of the peripheral mesoderm in the chick embryo. J Exp Zool 226:391.

Hilfer SR, Searls RL, Fonte VG (1973). An ultrastructural study of early myogenesis in the chick wing bud. Dev Biol 30:374.

Newman SA, Pautou M-P, Kieny M (1981). The distal boundary of myogenic primordia in chimeric avian limb buds and its relation to an accessible population of cartilage progenitor cells. Dev Biol 84:440.

Rutz R, Haney C, Hauschka S (1982). Spatial analysis of limb bud myogenesis: a proximodistal gradient of muscle colony-forming cells in chick embryo leg buds. Dev Biol 90:399.

Singley CT, Solursh M (1981). The spatial distribution of hyaluronic acid and mesenchymal condensation in embryonic chick wing. Dev Biol 84:102.

Solursh M (1984). Ectoderm as a determinant of early tissue pattern in the limb bud. Cell Differ 15:17.

Solursh M, Jensen KL, Linsenmayer TF (1982). Chondrogenesis from single limb mesenchyme cells. Dev Biol 94:259.

Venkatasubramanian K, Solursh M (1984). Chemotactic behavior of myoblasts. Dev Biol 104:428.

*This work was supported by NIH grants HD05505 and HD18577.

Progress in Developmental Biology, Part B, pages 433–436
© 1986 Alan R. Liss, Inc.

EXTRACELLULAR MATRIX MAINTAINS APICAL ECTODERMAL RIDGE IN CULTURE

James J. Tomasek and Jonathan A. Brier

Department of Anatomy, New York Medical College, Valhalla, New York 10595

INTRODUCTION

Limb outgrowth is dependent upon a reciprocal inter-action between the apical ectodermal ridge (AER) and underlying limb mesenchyme (Saunders, 1948). During the time of its inductive activity the avian AER has a con-figuration distinct from the adjacent dorsal or ventral ectoderm. It is a well-defined ridge, rimming the distal margin of the limb bud in the antero-posterior direction and consists of pseudostratified high columnar epithelial cells. The basal surfaces of these cells converge upon a central line running along the antero-posterior axis of the wing bud. The maintenance of the inductive activity of the AER as well as its configuration is dependent upon the underlying limb mesenchyme (Zwilling and Hansborough, 1956; Rubin and Saunders, 1972).

The means by which limb mesenchyme maintains the AER is not known. In order to study this interaction we have attempted to culture AER in the absence of limb mesen-chyme. Cultured epithelia require an extracellular matrix substratum for maintenance of their morphological and bio-chemical characteristics (Hay, 1984). In this study we have examined the fate of isolated AER and adjacent dorsal and ventral ectoderm cultured upon a hydrated type I collagen lattice.

METHODS AND MATERIALS

The AER and adjacent ectoderm of stage 21 duck wing buds (Koeche, 1958) was isolated as a sheet from the under-lying mesenchyme (Errick and Saunders, 1976). Ectodermal sheets were placed onto hydrated type I collagen lattices (Tomasek, et al, 1982). They were cultured for 4,18,24 or 48 hrs in Ham's F-12 media plus 10% fetal bovine serum, 1% antibiotic-antimycotic solution and 50 µg/ml ascorbic acid. Cultures were examined and photographed using dark field stereomicroscopy. For histological examination cultures were fixed and embedded in epon (Tomasek, et al, 1982).

RESULTS AND DISCUSSION

The maintenance of the AER and size of the cultured epithelial sheet could be easily monitored by dark field stereomicroscopy (Fig. 1). The AER is visible up to 24 hrs of incubation because it is thicker than the surround-ing ectoderm and will scatter more light. By 48 hr the AER is difficult to see, presumably because of the loss of its original thickness. This cultured ectodermal sheet increases in size over time on the collagen lattice.

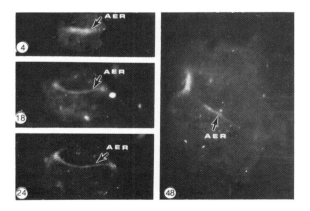

Figure 1. Dark field stereomicrographs of AER and adjacent ectoderm cultured for 4,18,24 or 48 hrs.

Histological examination of cultured ectodermal
sheets revealed similar results (Fig. 2). Note the absence
of any mesenchymal cells in these cultures. After 4 hrs
in culture the AER still appears thickened. The few
necrotic cells observed in such cultures are in the peri-
dermal layer. By 18 hrs the AER has lost its nipple-
shaped configuration, although it is still thicker then
the adjacent ectoderm. Only a few necrotic cells have
been observed in these cultures. The AER is still distinguishable from the adjacent ectoderm after 24 hrs, although
the sheet as a whole has become much thinner. This appears
to be due to the spreading of cells on the underlying
collagen substratum. Such spreading most likely accounts
for the increase in size of the ectoderm observed by dark
field stereomicroscopy. By 48 hrs the AER can no longer
be identified. The ectoderm has become very thin and
spread on the collagen.

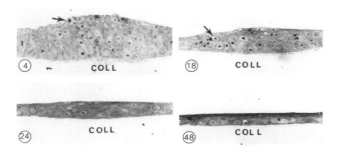

Figure 2. 1 μm-thick epon sections of AER and adjacent
ectoderm cultured for 4,18,24 or 48 hrs. Arrows point to
necrotic cells.

These results demonstrate that the AER and dorsal and
ventral ectoderm can survive in the absence of limb mesenchyme for at least 48 hr when provided with the proper in
vitro environment. In these experiments this includes the
presence of a hydrated type I collagen lattice that these
cells can use as a substratum. The inability of the AER
to remain morphologically distinctive from the adjacent
ectoderm for more than 24 hrs is consistent with previous

evidence suggesting the necessity of a mesenchymally derived ridge maintenance factor (Zwilling and Hansborough,
1956). The ability to culture AER and dorsal and ventral
wing ectoderm provides the opportunity to examine the
effect various types of extracellular matrices, growth
factors or mesenchymal factors have upon ridge configuration and aid in our understanding of this complex epithelial mesenchymal inductive interaction leading to limb
outgrowth.

REFERENCES

Errick, JE, Saunders, JW, Jr (1976). Limb outgrowth in
  the chick embryo induced by dissociated and reaggregated
  cells of the apical ectodermal ridge. Develop Biol
  501:26-34.
Hay, ED (1984). Cell-matrix interaction in the embryo:
  Cell shape, cell surface, cell skeletons, and their role
  in differentiation. In Trelstad, RL (ed): "The Role of
  Extracellular Matrix in Development," New York:Alan R.
  Liss, p 1.
Koecke, H-U (1958). Normalstadien der embryonal-entwicklung
  bei der hausente (Anas boschas domestica). Embryologia
  4:55-78.
Rubin, L, Saunders, JW, Jr (1972). Ectodermal-mesodermal
  interactions in the growth of limb buds in the chick
  embryo: constancy and temporal limits of the ectodermal
  induction. Develop Biol 28:94-112.
Saunders, JW, Jr (1948). The proximo-distal sequences of
  origin of the parts of the chick wing and the role of the
  ectoderm. J Exp Zool 108:363-404.
Tomasek, JJ, Hay, ED, Fujiwara, K (1982). Collagen modulates cell shape and cytoskeleton of embryonic corneal
  and fibroma fibroblasts: Distribution of actin, α-actinin,
  and myosin. Develop Biol 92:107-122.
Zwilling, E, Hansborough, L (1956). Interaction between
  limb bud ectoderm and mesoderm in the chick embryo. III.
  Experiments with polydactylous limbs. J Exp Zool
  132:219-239.

Progress in Developmental Biology, Part B, pages 437–440
© 1986 Alan R. Liss, Inc.

DEVELOPMENT OF THE APICAL ECTODERMAL RIDGE AND CHANGES IN
THE SUBEPIDERMAL MESENCHYME IN MOUSE LIMB BUDS

Abdul   Razak Datu,   Harukazu Nakamura and   Mineo
Yasuda
Department of Anatomy,   Hiroshima   university
School of Medicine, Kasumi 1-2-3, Minami-ku,
Hiroshima 734, Japan.

INTRODUCTION

It has been well documented that interaction between
the apical ectodermal ridge (AER) and the mesenchyme plays
an important role in limb development (reviewed by Fallon
et al., 1983). Searching for morphological changes in the
mesenchyme associated with the AER, Yasuda and Nakamura
(1983) described that the mesenchymal cell process meshwork
(CPM) beneath the AER was sparser than that beneath the
dorsal or ventral non-ridge epidermis. It has been reported
recently that, a smaller number of mesenchymal cell processes and a larger subepidermal extracellular space
(SEECS) were found beneath the AER than that beneath the
dorsal or ventral non-ridge epidermis (Datu et al., 1985).
However, quantitative study has not been done so far on the
CPM and SEECS in developing mouse limbs. The present study
mainly deals with the quantitative changes in CPM density
and SEECS width during the development of the AER in mouse
limb buds.

MATERIALS AND METHODS

Colony bred Jcl:ICR mice (Japan CLEA Ltd.) were used.
At half day intervals from embryonic day 9.5 to 12.5
(vaginal plug=day 0), the forelimb buds were dissected and
processed for transmission electron microscopy (TEM).   For
morphometric analyses, the apical, dorsal, and ventral
regions from at least five limb buds at each stage were
photographed, then were printed at a final magnification of

x5,860.   The space between the basal lamina and the first
row of mesenchymal cells which contained nuclei in TEM
photographs,   called SEECS,   was measured utilizing a
Mitablet digitizer (Watanabe) and an NEC PC-9801 computer.
The apical region was defined as an area including the most
distal mesenchyme of a limb bud.   When the AER was distinct, the region was always beneath the AER.   The measurement in the dorsal or ventral region was made at approximately the junction of the distal and middle thirds of the
whole limb bud from day 9.5 to 10.5 or of the hand plate
from day 11.0 to 12.5.   The SEECS width was calculated as
the ratio of total area of the SEECS (excluding the area of
mesenchymal cytoplasm larger than 0.4 μm in diameter)/
distance from the left to the right border of the measured
SEECS in TEM photographs.   The number of cell processes
(less than 0.4 μm in diameter) in the SEECS was counted.

RESULTS

     Quantification of the SEECS and the number of mes-
enchymal cell processes are summarized in Figures 1 and 2.
The average width of the SEECS (Fig. 1) and the number of
cell processes in the SEECS (Fig. 2) beneath the apical
epidermis at days 9.5 and 10.0 (pre-AER stage) are not
significantly different from that beneath the dorsal or
ventral epidermis.   However, at days 10.5, 11.0, and 11.5
(AER stage), the average width of SEECS beneath the AER is
significantly greater than that beneath the dorsal or ventral non-ridge epidermis.   The number of cell processes
beneath the AER is significantly smaller than that beneath

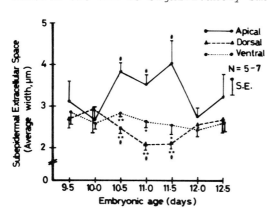

Fig. 1. Spatial and
temporal differences
in subepidermal extra-
cellular space (SEECS)
in mouse limb buds.
Significantly differ-
ent at *p<0.05   from
apical region;**p<0.01
from apical region;
#p<0.05 from pre- or
post-AER stage.

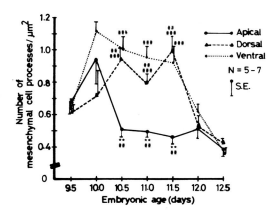

Fig. 2. Spatial and temporal differences in number of mesenchymal cell processes in mouse limb buds. Significantly different at **p<0.01 from dorsal or ventral region; ##p<0.01 from pre-AER stage; ###p<0.001 from post-AER stage.

the dorsal or ventral epidermis. At days 12.0 and 12.5 (post-AER stage), no significant differences in the width of the SEECS and in the number of cell processes are found among the apical, dorsal, and ventral regions.

Furthermore, at the AER stage, the SEECS width in the apical region is significantly larger than that at the pre- or post-AER stage, whereas the SEECS in the dorsal region is significantly narrower than that at the other two stages. The SEECS width in the ventral region remains constant through the observed stages (Fig. 1). The number of cell processes in the apical region at the AER stage is smaller than that at the pre-AER stage, but it does not differ from that at the post-AER stage. In the dorsal region, the number of cell processes at the AER stage is larger than that at the other two stages, and the number of cell processes in the ventral region at the post-AER stage is smaller than that at the AER stage (Fig. 2).

DISCUSSION

The results show that spatial and temporal differences in SEECS width and in CPM density exist at the epithelial-mesenchymal interface in mouse limb buds. TEM photographs of this study show a wide SEECS beneath the basal lamina of the AER, and a narrow space beneath the basal lamina of the dorsal or ventral non-ridge epidermis at the AER stage. These findings agree with previous descriptions made on normal and abnormal limb morphogenesis in chick embryos

(Sawyer, 1982). Sawyer reported that the normal limb bud had a well developed subepidermal space beneath the AER, and that this space was reduced beneath the hypoplastic AER in the wingless mutant chick embryos. Several experiments have dealt with the relation between CPM density and AER development in mouse limb buds following teratogenic insult (Yasuda and Nakamura, 1983; Datu et al., 1985). It was described that the CPM beneath the hypoplastic AER in acetazolamide-treated mouse limb buds was denser than that beneath the typical AER (Datu et al., 1985). In contrast, the limb bud of the talpid[3] embryos had a fewer cell processes beneath the hyperplastic AER than beneath the normal AER (Ede et al., 1974).

The present study shows a wider SEECS and a sparser CPM beneath the AER than those beneath the dorsal or ventral non-ridge epidermis at the AER stage. These indicate that spatial and temporal differences of SEECS width and CPM density exist in mouse limb buds, and that these differences are closely related to the AER development.

This work was supported in part by Grants-in-Aid for Scientific Research Nos. 5837003, 5937003, and 60570006 from the Ministry of Education, Science and Culture, Japan.

REFERENCES

Datu AR, Nakamura H, Yasuda M (1985). Pathogenesis of the mouse forelimb deformity induced by acetazolamide: An electron microscopic study. Teratology 31:253-263.
Ede DA, Bellairs R, Bancroft M (1974). A scanning electron microscope study of early limb-bud in normal and talpid[3] mutant chick embryos. J Embryol Exp Morphol 31:761-785.
Fallon JF, Rowe DA, Frederick JM, Simandl BK (1983). Studies on epithelial-mesenchymal interactions during limb development. In Sawyer RH, Fallon JF (eds): "Epithelial-Mesenchymal Interactions in Development," New York: Praeger Publisher, pp 3-25.
Sawyer LM (1982). Fine structural analysis of limb development in the wingless mutant chick embryo. J Embryol Exp Morphol 68:69-86.
Yasuda M, Nakamura H (1983). Pathogenesis of limb malformations in mice: An electron microscopic study. In Fallon JF, Caplan AI (eds): "Limb Development and Regeneration," New York: Alan R. Liss, part A pp 301-310.

Progress in Developmental Biology, Part B, pages 441–444
© 1986 Alan R. Liss, Inc.

DOES PANCREATIC MESODERM ELICIT THE APPEARANCE OF
ENDOCRINE CELLS IN GASTRIC EPITHELIUM?

Ann Andrew, Beverley Kramer and B.B. Rawdon

Department of Anatomy, Medical School (A.A.)
and Department of General Anatomy, School of
Dentistry (B.K., B.B.R.), University of the
Witwatersrand, Johannesburg 2001, South Africa

INTRODUCTION

Epithelio-mesenchymal interaction has been shown to be
concerned in the morphogenesis of the avian gastro-intestinal
tract and in the cytodifferentiation of its epithelium
(Gumpel-Pinot et al., 1978; Yasugi and Mizuno, 1978). The
possibility that the mesoderm may have a role in the differentiation of the regulatory peptide-containing "endocrine"
cell types in the epithelium is examined here.

MATERIALS AND METHODS

Mesoderm from the dorsal pancreatic bud of 4- to 5-day
chick embryos (stages 21 - 27 of Hamburger and Hamilton,
1951) was combined with proventricular endoderm from chick
and quail embryos of the same stages. Separation of the
layers was aided by treatment with 0,04% collagenase. For
control purposes, separated mesoderm and endoderm of the
proventriculus of each species were re-associated; pancreatic
controls were prepared in like manner. After two days in
vitro on a nutrient agar-based medium to allow adherence of
the layers, the explants were grown as chorio-allantoic
grafts until they had reached a total incubation age of 21
days. The grafts were freeze-dried, fixed in parabenzo-
quinone vapour, embedded in resin and sectioned at 1 μ.
Endocrine cell types were sought in differentiated gut and
pancreas in the grafts by means of an immunocytochemical
procedure. Each antiserum was applied to equally spaced
sections in every block analysed.

RESULTS

In accordance with the types of endocrine cells known to be present in the proventriculus of chicks at hatching i.e. at 21 days of incubation (Rawdon and Andrew, 1981), cells with insulin-, glucagon-, somatostatin- and pancreatic polypeptide-like immunoreactivity were found in both chick and quail pancreatic control grafts, and cells with glucagon-, somatostatin-, pancreatic polypeptide-, neurotensin- and bombesin-like immunoreactivity were demonstrated in glandular tubules of chick and quail proventricular controls. Similar glands differentiated in experimental grafts whether the endoderm was chick or quail; all five proventricular endocrine cell types were present, but no insulin cells. The proportions of the various endocrine cell types resembled the proportions in proventricular controls much more closely than those in pancreatic controls.

In a number of grafts, the presence of simple columnar epithelium with a striated border and goblet cells was noticed. In sections of these grafts immunostained for intestinal-type endocrine cells, motilin-, secretin-, gastrin/cholecystokinin- and serotonin-like immunoreactive cells (Fig. 1a-c) were revealed. This state of affairs was encountered in grafts of each type: in pancreatic control grafts, only pancreatic endoderm could have been responsible, and in proventricular controls, only pro- ventricular endoderm; in experimental grafts, proventricular endoderm - or inadvertently included pancreatic epithelium, as illustrated by one chimaeric graft, - must have been the source of the intestinal epithelium and endocrine cells.

DISCUSSION

Although proventricular endoderm of 4-day chick embryos already has a tendency to differentiate in a proventricular direction (Ishizuya-Oka, 1983), 5- or 5½-day chick or quail proventricular endoderm associated with heterologous gut mesoderm can undergo heterotypic differentiation in accor- dance with the source of the mesoderm (Yasugi and Mizuno, 1978; Gumpel-Pinot et al., 1978). The influence of mesoderm is further illustrated by the appearance of endocrine cells in endoderm of the gizzard (which is normally deficient in endocrine cells) when it is associated with rat duodenal fibroblasts (Haffen et al., 1983). Under the conditions of

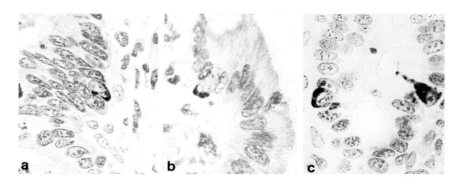

Figure 1. Cells with (a) motilin-, (b) gastrin/cholecystokin and (c) serotonin-like immunoreactivity in a proventricular (a, b) and a pancreatic (c) control graft. Indirect peroxidase. x 1000

the present experiment, pancreatic mesoderm, however, does not elicit endocrine cell differentiation in a pancreatic direction in proventricular endoderm; it does, though, permit fulfilment of the potential of proventricular endoderm for differentiation of its normal endocrine cell complement.

The ability of proventricular endoderm of 4-day chick embryos to differentiate into typical intestinal epithelium has been demonstrated by Ishizuya-Oka and Mizuno (1984). This ability was revealed when the endoderm was associated with 6-day duodenal mesenchyme, but not with other foregut mesenchyme. In the present study, the appearance of intestinal epithelium containing intestinal-type endocrine cells has been elicited in proventricular and in pancreatic endoderm associated not only with heterologous (pancreatic or proventricular) mesoderm, but, surprisingly, with homologous mesoderm. The factor(s) at play here cannot be attributed to the mesoderm per se: they may be related to the isolation of the grafts from the donor embryos.

This work was supported by grants from the South African Medical Research Council and the Council Research Committee of the University of the Witwatersrand, Johannesburg.

REFERENCES

Gumpel-Pinot M, Yasugi S, Mizuno T (1978). Differentiation of endodermic epitheliums associated with splanchnic mesoderm. C R Hebd Seanc Acad Sci Paris 286D:117-120.

Haffen K, Lacroix B, Kedinger M, Simon-Assman PM (1983). Inductive properties of fibroblastic cell cultures derived from rat intestinal mucosa on epithelial differentiation. Differentiation 23:226-233.

Hamburger V, Hamilton HL (1951). A series of normal stages in the development of the chick embryo. J Morph 88:49-92.

Ishizuya-Oka A (1983). Electron microscopic study of self-differentiation potency in the chick embryonic endoderm cultured in vitro. Roux Arch Devel Biol 192:171-178.

Ishizuya-Oka A, Mizuno T (1984). Intestinal cytodifferen-tiation in vitro of chick stomach endoderm induced by the duodenal mesenchyme. J Embryol exp Morph 82:163-176.

Rawdon BB, Andrew A (1981). An immunocytochemical survey of endocrine cells in the gastrointestinal tract of chicks at hatching. Cell Tiss Res 220:279-292.

Yasugi S, Mizuno T (1978). Differentiation of the digestive tract epithelium under the influence of the heterologous mesenchyme of the digestive tract in bird embryos. Develop Growth Differ 20:261-267.

Progress in Developmental Biology, Part B, pages 445–448

LIGATING THE EMBRYONIC URETER FACILITATES THE INDUCTION OF RENAL DYSPLASIA

Max Maizels, M.D. and Sidney B. Simpson, Ph.D.

Division of Urology, Children's Memorial Hospital Chicago, Illinois; and Department of Biochemistry, Molecular and Cell Biology, Northwestern University, Evanston, Illinois

The mechanisms which lead to renal dysplasia, a malformation common in children with congenital renal disease, are poorly understood. It has been shown that when the complement of condensed metanephrogenic mesenchyme is reduced by prolonged tissue culture, renal dysplasia is likely to result (Maizels & Simpson, 1983). Ligation of the embryonic ureter alone appears insufficient to induce renal dysplasia (Berman & Maizels, 1982). However, because children with renal dysplasia commonly also have renal obstruction, we hypothesized that obstruction of urine drainage of the embryonic kidney modifies the expression of dysplasia. This hypothesis was tested by determining if ligating the ureter increases the likelihood of the development of dysplasia in embryonic renal blastemas.

MATERIALS AND METHODS

The developments of 2 groups of isolated renal blastemas were compared. In one group of blastemas, the ureters were ligated, the blastemas were placed in tissue culture for 2-4 days, and then permitted to develop as grafts upon the chorio-allantoic membrane (CAM). The second group of blastemas were placed in tissue culture for 2-4 days without ligation of the ureter, and then permitted to develop as grafts upon the CAM. After 10 days of incubation the developments of both groups of blastemas was examined histologically. The impact of ligating the ureter of the

embryonic blastema upon the subsequent development of dysplasia was evaluated.

Tissue culture
    Renal blastemas were isolated from White Leghorn
chicken embryos (8 days incubation). The blastemas were
transferred onto a Millipore support and placed in organ
culture dishes containing CMRL medium 1066 (GIBCO), 5% heat
inactivated fetal calf serum (GIBCO), and 3% chick embryo
extract derived from homogenization of 10 day old chick
embryos. The blastemas incubated at standard conditions.

Ligation of ureter of renal blastemas
    The ureter was ligated under vision aided by optical
magnification with 9-0 Ti-cron^R surgical suture (Davis &
Geck, American Cyanamid Co., Danbury, CT).

Development of grafts upon the CAM
    After the blastemas completed incubation in tissue
culture, they were grafted onto host embryonated White
Leghorn chicken eggs (8 days incubation). AFter 8 days of
development in ovo the grafts were fixed in 10% formalin,
sectioned at 8u, stained with hemotoxylin and eosin, and
examined by light microscopy.

Definitions
    Dysplasia in chick kidneys was diagnosed when there
was a predominance of "primitive ducts". These structures
are epithelial lined ducts which may or may not be surrounded by whorled fibromuscular cells and which do not
appear to communicate with renal tubules (Bernstein, 1971).
Hydronephrosis was diagnosed when there was a generalized
appreciable distention of the lumen of the ureter, tubules,
and/or glomeruli (Berman & Maizels, 1982).

RESULTS

Appearances of renal blastemas prior to CAM grafting

    The appearances of 18 renal blastemas (8 days incu-
bation) placed in tissue culture for 0,2,3, and 4 days
was noted.

    In blastemas with ligation of the ureter, after 2 days

in tissue culture, the blastema demonstrates dilation of the ureteral bud branches. The condensed mesenchyme around the ureteral bud branches is sparse or not apparent. After 4 days in tissue culture the condensed metanephrogenic mesenchyme is not apparent and the ureteral bud branches show further enlargement. Blastemas without ligation of the ureter retained a regular branched appearance.

Development of renal blastemas as CAM grafts

Blastemas with ligation (35) and without ligation (23) of the ureter were placed in tissue culture for 2-3 or 4 days and were then permitted to develop further as CAM grafts. The surviving grafts (41) developed further and displayed normal architecture, hydronephrosis, or dysplasia.

Comparison of the developments of renal blastemas with and without ligation of the ureter as CAM grafts
Blastemas placed in tissue culture for 2-3 days showed dysplasia more often when the ureter was ligated than those without ligation of the ureter. Of 22 blastemas placed in tissue culture for 2-3 days, 14 (82%) with ligation of the ureter later showed dysplasia, while only 1 (20%) without ligation of the ureter later showed dysplasia ($X^2=4.34$, p .04) (Table).
Blastemas placed in tissue culture for 4 days did not show dysplasia statistically more often when the ureter was ligated than those without ligation of the ureter (p>NS).

TABLE

MODIFYING EFFECT OF LIGATING OF URETER UPON DEVELOPMENT OF 41 RENAL BLASTEMAS PLACED IN TISSUE CULTURE AND THEN GRAFTED

GRAFT HISTOLOGY	DURATION BLASTEMA IS IN TISSUE CULTURE			
	2-3 DAYS		4 DAYS	
	LIG	NO LIG	LIG	NO LIG
NORMAL	3	1	3	4
HYDRONEPHROSIS	0	3	1	0
DYSPLASIA	14*(82%)	1+(20%)	8(67%)	3(43%)
TOTALS	17	5	12	7

DISCUSSION

In this model, it appears that ligation of the ureter facilitates the development of primitive ducts consistent with renal dysplasia in blastemas which are already deficient of metanephrogenic mesenchyme. That renal dysplasia has not been noted in blastemas grafted directly after isolation or after ligation of the ureter, is consistent with the view that the development of dysplasia requires a defective renal mesenchyme.

Normal renal development requires ampullae of the normally branched ureteral bud to be adjacent to an ample complement of condensed metanephrogenic mesenchyme. From the data we postulate the view that primitive ducts of renal dysplasia develop when the embryonic renal blastema is exposed to insults which disperse or reduce the complement of condensed metanephrogenic mesenchyme is made deficient by prolonged tissue culture, primitive ducts result. When the ureter is ligated, the branches of the ureteral bud distend; this distention would reduce the density of condensed metanephrogenic mesenchyme adjacent to the ureteral bud ampullae. Consequently, the ureteral bud branches would not induce renal tubules, and would develop into primitive ducts.

REFERENCES

Berman, D.J., Maizels, M.(1982). The role of urinary obstruction in the genesis of renal dysplasia - A model in the chick embryo. J. Urol. 128:1091.
Bernstein, J. (1971). The morphogenesis of renal parenchymal maldevelopment (renal dysplasia). Ped. Clin. N.A. 18:395.
Mackie, G.G., Stephens, F.D.(1975). Duplex Kidneys: A correlation of renal dysplasia with position of the ureteral orifice. J. Urol. 114:274.
Maizels, M., Simpson, S.B., Jr. (1983). Primitive ducts of renal dysplasia induced by culturing ureteral buds denuded of condensed renal mesenchyme. Science, 219:509.

Index

Accessory gland complex of *Tenebrio molitor*, cell type-specific antigens in, 325–328

Acetylcholine receptors, colocalized distribution in muscles with basal lamina proteoglycan, 219–222

β-N-Acetylglucosaminidase, role in sea urchin sperm-egg interaction, 79–82

Acrosome reaction
  and sperm activation, 69–72
  protein sulfhydryl reactivity and, 70–72
  and sperm-egg interaction and fusion, 61–65

Actin filaments and cytoskeleton in odontoblasts of rat incisors, 329–330

Actinomycin D, and effect of fibroblast pneumonocyte factor on fetal lung development, 333–336

Adherons, chick neural retina, properties of, 5–6; *see also* Antibodies, anti-adheron

Adipocytes, interactions with epithelium, and hormone-dependent mammary epithelium differentiation, 417–423

Adrenergic neurons, neural crest cell differentiation in vitro and expression of, 267–271

Alkaline phosphatase
  activity in neural tube of mouse embryo, 145–148
  determinants in *Styela plicata* eggs, 341–344

Ambystoma mexicanum larva, pigment pattern formation in, 191–194

Amino acids, in preimplantation mouse embryos, 103–106

Ammonia treatment, and *Ambystoma mexicanum* larva pigment pattern formation, 191–194

Amphibians, ooplasmic determinants in, 357–360; *see also Ambystoma mexicanum* larva; *Xenopus* tadpoles

Androgens, and sex difference in fetal lung development, 426

Anthocidaris crassispina. See Sea urchins

Antibodies
  anti-adheron, 5
  anti-collagenase, degradation of collagen by carcinoma cells, 205–206
  anti-creatin kinase, in thymic myoid cell origins study, 257–258
  anti-dimer, and RNA determinants of UV-induced effects on *Smittia* development, 366–368
  anti-purpurin and heparan sulfate proteoglycan, disruption of neural retina histogenesis by, 7–10
  anti-substance P, and localization of substance P in human spinal cords, 149–151
  anti-vasoactive intestinal polypeptide, and differentiation of quail sensory neurons from neural crest cells, 245
  and arrest of neural crest cell migration, 235–237
  in chick myoblast fusion study, 43–46
  and tissue-specific expression of short-chain collagens, 169–171
  see also Monoclonal antibodies; Polyclonal antibodies

Antigens. *See* Cell surface, antigens

Anurans. *See Discoglossus pictus; Xenopus laevis*

Apical ectodermal ridge
  maintenance in culture, extracellular matrix, and, 433–436
  role in limb development, 437–440

Ascidians, and sperm-egg interaction and fusion in, 57–65; *see also Phallusia mamillata; Styela plicata* eggs

Ascorbate, and extracellular metabolism in human skin fibroblasts, 382–383